Elementary Mathematics:

*Its Structure
and Concepts*

Elementary Mathematics:

Its Structure and Concepts

Margaret F. Willerding

Professor of Mathematics
San Diego State College

John Wiley & Sons, Inc.
New York   London   Sydney

To Herman, with deep affection

Preface

This textbook is a result of five years of experimenting with mathematics training for teachers of elementary school mathematics and in-service classes for elementary school teachers. Its primary objective is to provide them with the mathematics background necessary to teach the material of the elementary school curriculum both as it is today and as it may change in the future.

I feel that a primary feature of this text is that in content and spirit it is consistent with the recent recommendations of national committees and groups concerned with teaching mathematics in the elementary schools; the materials included have been successfully used in preparing teachers to teach in "new programs" in arithmetic. The book is written in a language and style designed to appeal to the student with little mathematical maturity and background, and the simplicity of the language has proved it an effective teaching instrument. On the one hand the book provides the necessary background for the teaching of elementary mathematics because it treats sets, logic, numeration systems, number systems and operations, informal geometry, and topics in number theory; on the other hand, the material is presented in sufficient detail that it can be taught to students who have one year of high school algebra.

The book is recommended for a one-semester three-unit course or as a sequence of two one-semester courses of two units each semester, taught in the traditional fashion. I have used the material for a sequence of two one-semester courses of three units each in a team-teaching situation; under this type of arrangement I lectured to a large class of students (150–200) two periods a week. During a third period each week the students met in a small, twenty-student conference section with a conference instructor for discussion, problem solving, and reviewing topics found difficult.

I should like to take this opportunity to apologize for all the anticipated shortcomings of the book and to state that the following persons deserve much credit for their help in the production of the text: Dr. Marguerite Brydegaard, Dr. Richard Madden, and Dr. Harry Huls, who have worked as conference instructors in the course I have presented; Dr. Roy Dubisch who made suggestions for improvements in the presentations; Mrs. Ruth Hayward, who proofread the manuscript; and the many students at San Diego State College who have taken the course. A special note of appreciation must go to Dr. Brydegaard for her unfailing confidence in me, for her belief in the material and its presentation, and for her unfaltering friendship.

San Diego, California
January, 1966

Margaret F. Willerding
San Diego State College

Contents

Chapter 1 SETS, 1

1.1 What Is a Set? **1**. **1.2** Symbols, **1**. **1.3** The Empty Set, **2**. **1.4** Equality of Sets, **3**. **1.5** One-to-One Correspondence, **3**. **1.6** Subsets, **6**. **1.7** Number of Subsets, **7**. **1.8** Universal Set, **9**. **1.9** Venn Diagrams, **10**. **1.10** Ordered Sets, **13**. **1.11** Number and Numeral, **13**. **1.12** Standard Sets, **14**. **1.13** Cardinality, **15**. **1.14** Finite and Infinite Sets, **15**. **1.15** Union of Sets, **17**. **1.16** Intersection of Sets, **19**. **1.17** Relative Complement, **21**. **1.18** Ordered Pairs, **23**. **1.19** Cartesian Products, **24**. **1.20** Combining Set Operations, **27**.

Chapter 2 LOGIC, 29

2.1 Undefined Words, **29**. **2.2** Statements, **30**. **2.3** Compound Statements, **30**. **2.4** Implication, **32**. **2.5** Negation, **33**. **2.6** Equivalence Relations, **35**. **2.7** Tautology, **36**. **2.8** Derived Implications, **40**. **2.9** Proof, **43**. **2.10** Direct Proof, **43**. **2.11** Indirect Proof, **44**.

Chapter 3 WHOLE NUMBERS, 46

3.1 The Whole Numbers, **46**. **3.2** Order Property, **46**. **3.3** The Number Line, **48**. **3.4** Operations, **48**. **3.5** Addition, **50**. **3.6** Properties of Addition, **50**. **3.7** Multiplication, **54**. **3.8** Properties of Multiplication, **56**. **3.9** The Distributive Property, **59**. **3.10** Proving Theorems about Whole Numbers, **62**. **3.11** Inverse Operations, **62**. **3.12** Subtraction, **64**. **3.13** Division, **64**. **3.14** Properties of Subtraction and Division, **66**.

Chapter 4   SYSTEMS OF NUMERATIONS, 70

4.1 Ancient Systems of Numeration, **70**. **4.2** The Hindu-Arabic System, **73**. **4.3** Exponents, **75**. **4.4** Expanded Notation, **76**. **4.5** Bases Other than Ten, **78**. **4.6** The Duodecimal System, **82**. **4.7** The Binary System, **86**. **4.8** Binary-Octal Relation, **88**. **4.9** Summary, **90**.

Chapter 5   THE ALGORITHMS, 93

5.1 Definitions, **93**. **5.2** The Addition Algorithm, **94**. **5.3** The Subtraction Algorithm, **97**. **5.4** The Multiplication Algorithm, **99**. **5.5** The Division Algorithm, **102**.

Chapter 6   INFORMAL GEOMETRY, 108

6.1 Informal and Formal Geometry, **108**. **6.2** Undefined Terms, **108**. **6.3** Points, **109**. **6.4** Space, **109**. **6.5** Lines, **109**. **6.6** Planes, **111**. **6.7** Properties of Lines and Planes, **111**. **6.8** Separation of Space, **114**. **6.9** Rays, **120**. **6.10** Angles, **120**. **6.11** Triangles, **122**. **6.12** Simple Closed Curves, **126**. **6.13** Polygons, **127**. **6.14** Congruence, **130**. **6.15** Congruent Angles, **131**. **6.16** Circles, **132**. **6.17** Congruent Triangles, **134**. **6.18** Constructing Congruent Angles, **135**. **6.19** Constructing Congruent Triangles, **136**. **6.20** Classification of Triangles, **138**. **6.21** Classification of Quadrilaterals, **138**.

Chapter 7   NUMBER SENTENCES, 141

7.1 Mathematical Sentences, **141**. **7.2** Open Sentences, **142**. **7.3** Solution Sets, **142**. **7.4** Equivalent Open Sentences, **144**. **7.5** Compound Open Sentences, **146**. **7.6** Graphing Solution Sets, **148**. **7.7** Sentences with Two Variables, **150**. **7.8** Graphing Ordered Pairs, **151**.

Chapter 8   TOPICS IN NUMBER THEORY, 155

8.1 Figurate Numbers, **155**. **8.2** Subsets of the Whole Numbers, **158**. **8.3** Properties of Even and Odd Numbers, **159**. **8.4** Prime Numbers and Composite Numbers, **161**. **8.5** The Sieve of Eratosthenes, **162**. **8.6** Factors **163**. **8.7** The Fundamental Theorem of Arithmetic, **166**. **8.8** Divisibility Tests, **168**. **8.9** Complete Factorization, **171**. **8.10** Greatest Common Factor, **173**. **8.11** Euclid's Algorithm, **174**. **8.12** Least Common Multiple, **176**.

Chapter 9   FRACTIONS, 180

9.1 The Word "Fraction", **180**. **9.2** Definition of Fractions, **180**. **9.3** Fractions and the Number Line, **188**. **9.4** Ordering Fractions, **190**. **9.5** Addition of Fractional Numbers, **192**. **9.6** Subtraction of Fractional Numbers, **194**. **9.7** Properties of Addition of Fractional Numbers, **196**. **9.8** Multiplication of Fractional Numbers, **198**. **9.9** Properties of Multiplication of Fractional Numbers, **202**. **9.10** Division of Fractional Numbers, **204**. **9.11** Subsets of the Fractional Numbers, **207**. **9.12** Fractions as Symbols for Division, **208**. **9.13** Mixed Numerals, **209**.

9.14 Decimal Numbers, **211**. **9.15** Decimal Fractions, **212**. **9.16** Changing Common Fractions to Decimal Fractions, **214**.

Chapter 10   THE NON-NEGATIVE RATIONAL NUMBERS, 217

10.1 A Different Viewpoint, **217**. **10.2** Definitions, **218**. **10.3** Equality of Rational Numbers, **219**. **10.4** The Rational Numbers between Zero and One, **221**. **10.5** The Whole Numbers and the Rational Numbers, **223**. **10.6** Summary, **223**.

Chapter 11   THE INTEGERS, 226

11.1 Definition, **226**. **11.2** Integers and the Number Line, **227**. **11.3** Ordering the Integers, **228**. **11.4** Addition of Integers, **230**. **11.5** Properties of Addition of Integers, **232**. **11.6** Subtraction of Integers, **233**. **11.7** Multiplication of Integers, **235**. **11.8** Division of Integers, **238**. **11.9** The Integers and the Whole Numbers, **239**.

Chapter 12   THE RATIONAL NUMBERS, 241

12.1 Defining the Rational Numbers, **241**. **12.2** Operations with Rational Numbers, **242**. **12.3** Properties of the Rational Numbers, **244**. **12.4** Order of the Rational Numbers, **246**. **12.5** Subtraction and Division of Rational Numbers, **249**. **12.6** The Rational Number Line, **249**. **12.7** The Properties of the Rational Numbers, **251**. **12.8** Subsystems of the Rational Numbers, **252**. **12.9** The Number Field, **253**.

Chapter 13   REAL NUMBERS, 254

13.1 Further Extension of the Number System, **254**. **13.2** The Real Number Line, **255**. **13.3** Irrational Numbers, **256**. **13.4** The Real Numbers, **256**.

Chapter 14   MATHEMATICAL SYSTEMS, 258

14.1 Finite Systems, **258**. **14.2** Systems without Numbers, **263**. **14.3** A Mathematical Group, **267**. **14.4** A Noncommutative Group, **270**.

ANSWERS TO SELECTED EXERCISES, 277

SOME COMMON MATHEMATICAL SYMBOLS AND THEIR MEANINGS, 289

INDEX, 291

CHAPTER 1

Sets

1.1. WHAT IS A SET?

A set is simply a collection of things or objects. Familiar examples of sets are the following:

1. A set of dishes.
2. A flock of geese (another way of saying a set of geese).
3. A herd of cattle (another way of saying a set of cattle).
4. An army (another way of saying a set of soldiers).

You met the idea of set in your first formal experience with arithmetic. You were probably shown various sets of objects and asked to name the number associated with each set. The objects in a set are called the *members* or *elements* of the set. In a set of dishes the individual cups, saucers, plates, and so on, are elements of the set. The members of the set are said to be *belong* to the set.

A mathematical set must be well defined. By this we mean that there is a method or rule whereby set membership or nonmembership can be determined. Some well defined sets are

1. The set of letters of the Greek Alphabet.
2. The set of months of the year.
3. The set of even numbers.

1.2. SYMBOLS

If a set consists of John, Joe, and Alice we may use the symbol

$$\{\text{John, Joe, Alice}\}.$$

The members of the set are enclosed in braces, { }, with a comma separating the members. This symbol is read: "The set whose members are John, Joe, and Alice." We customarily use capital letters as names of sets. Thus

$$A = \{\text{John, Joe, Alice}\}.$$

When each member of a set is tabulated, as in set A, we say we have *listed* its members. Another way to designate the members of a set is to *describe* them. Thus

$$R = \{\text{Alaska, Hawaii}\}$$

may be designated as

$$R = \{\text{49th and 50th states of the United States of America}\}.$$

Symbols to denote individual members of a set are usually lower case letters of the alphabet: a, b, c, d, and so forth. We use the symbol ε to mean "is a member of" or "belongs to." Thus

$$B = \{a, b, c, d\}$$

and

$$c \,\varepsilon\, B.$$

1.3. THE EMPTY SET

It is very useful to have a set that contains no elements. Consider the set consisting of all the four-dollar bills in circulation in the United States. This set contains no elements. A set that contains no elements is called the *empty set* or the *null set*. It is represented by the symbol ϕ or the symbol { }.

Other examples of the empty set are the following:

1. The set of all rectangles with five sides.
2. The set of all odd numbers divisible by 2.

3. The set of all women who have been president of the United States before the year 1964.

1.4. EQUALITY OF SETS

Two sets with exactly the same elements are called *equal sets*. Sets

$$C = \{a, b, c, d\}$$

and

$$D = \{b, d, a, c\}$$

are equal because they contain exactly the same elements. The order in which the elements are listed is immaterial. We write

$$C = D.$$

Just as a committee consisting of Hayward, Rhodes, and Black is the same committee as one consisting of Rhodes, Hayward, and Black, a set having elements a, b, c, and d is the same as a set having elements b, d, a, and c.

1.5. ONE-TO-ONE CORRESPONDENCE

If the elements of the two sets can be matched in some manner so that each element of each set is associated with a single element of the other, then the elements of the sets are said to be in *one-to-one correspondence*. The elements of sets A and B in Figure 1.1 are matched and a one-to-one correspondence is exhibited.

$$A = \{\text{Ruth, Doris, Nellie}\},$$
$$\updownarrow \quad \updownarrow \quad \updownarrow$$
$$B = \{\text{Atlas, Gai, Suzie}\}.$$

Figure 1.1

Other pairings are possible as shown in Figure 1.2.

Figure 1.2

Regardless of how the correspondence is established, each member of each set is matched with one and only one member of the other set.

This very important concept is used every day. If a professor enters his class and finds that every student has a chair and that there are no empty chairs, he knows immediately that there is a one-to-one correspondence between the students in the class and the chairs in the room.

Two sets whose elements can be put into one-to-one correspondence are called *equivalent sets*.

The equivalence relationship between sets is not the same as the equality relationship. Equal sets are equivalent, but equivalent sets are not necessarily equal. The symbol $\sim$ (read "is equivalent to") is used to denote equivalence. Thus, if

$$A = \{a, b, c, d\} \quad \text{and} \quad B = \{f, g, h, i\},$$

then

$$A \sim B.$$

Observe that if $A \sim B$ and $B \sim C$, then $A \sim C$.

Questions involving "more" and "fewer" can be resolved by a one-to-one pairing of the elements of two sets and the observation of the existence of unpaired elements in one of the sets when the other is exhausted. For example, if we compare sets P and Q, where

$$P = \{a, b, c\},$$
$$Q = \{x, y, z, t, w\},$$

it is apparent that they are not equivalent. Since the elements of P are exhausted before those of Q we say that P has fewer elements than Q or that Q has *more* elements than P.

EXERCISE 1.1

Each of the following describes a set. Write the names of the members of each set within braces.

1. The set of all months of the year whose names begin with A.
2. The set of all months of the year which have exactly 30 days.
3. The set of all states in the United States whose names begin with N.
4. The set of all Presidents of the United States after Herbert Hoover but before Lyndon Johnson.

5. The set of all states of the United States which border Mexico.
6. The set of all letters of our alphabet.
7. The set of all days of the week.
8. The set of all months of the year.
9. The set of all consonants in our alphabet.
10. The set of all days of the week beginning with T.
11. The set of all states of the United States bordering the Atlantic Ocean.
12. The set of the first five days of the week.
13. The set of states of the United States bordering Canada.

Describe the elements of each of the following sets in Problems 14–17.

14. {a, e, i, o, u}
15. {Washington, Oregon, California, Alaska, Hawaii}
16. {Sunday, Saturday}
17. {January, March, May, July, August, October, December}
18. What are the individual objects of a set called?
19. Give the set of the following:

    a. days of the week beginning with D.
    b. triangles with four sides.
    c. people with three heads.

20. Which of the following sets are well defined?

    a. all months of the year that have exactly 31 days.
    b. all healthy men in San Diego County.
    c. all good girls.
    d. all integers greater than 69.

21. What symbols are used for the empty set?
Put the members of each of the following pairs of sets in Problems 22–25 into one-to-one correspondence.
22. {0, 5, 10, 15}   and   {1, 2, 3, 4}
23. {☆ △ ▱}   and   {▽ ⬦ ⊖}
24. {a} and {x}
25. {1, −, \, ╱}   and   {Joe, Charles, Walter, Oscar}
26. Put the members of sets G and H into one-to-one correspondence in three different ways.

      $G = \{3, 4, 5, 6, 7\}$ $H = \{a, b, c, d, e\}$
27. Pair the equal sets.

      $A = \{a, b, c, d\}$. $B = \{9, h, i, j\}$.
      $C = \{a, c, e, f\}$. $D = \{d, c, a, b\}$.
      $E = \{4, 8, 16, 9\}$. $F = \{16, 9, 4, 8\}$.
28. Pair the equivalent sets.

      $A = \{1, 2, 3, 4\}$. $B = \{2, 3, 4, 5, 6\}$.
      $C = \{2, 3, 4, 5\}$. $D = \{a, b, c, d, e\}$.
      $E = \{4, 8, 16\}$. $F = \{9, 12\}$.

29. Determine which of the following sets can be placed into one-to-one correspondence with each other.

    a. $A = \{a, b, c\}$.
    b. $B = \{\#, \oplus, \boxtimes, -\bigcirc-\}$.
    c. $C = \{1, 2, 3\}$.
    d. $D = \{10, 11, 12, 13\}$.
    e. $E = \{0, 3, 6, 9\}$.
    f. $F = \{\text{Arthur, Charles, Henry}\}$.

30. Let $A = \{1, 2, 3, 4\}$, $B = \{5, 6, 7, 8\}$, and $C = \{3, 6, 9, 12\}$. Insert the correct symbol ε or $\not\varepsilon$ in the following ($\not\varepsilon$ means "is not a member of").

    a. 1__A.   b. 1__B.   c. 1__C.
    d. 6__A.   e. 6__B.   f. 6__C.
    g. 3__A.   h. 3__B.   i. 3__C.

31. Which of the following pairs of sets are equal? Which of the following pairs of sets are equivalent? Which of the following pairs of sets are neither equal nor equivalent?

    a. $\{a, b, c\}$, $\{c, b, a\}$.
    b. ϕ, $\{0\}$.
    c. $\{2, 4, 6, 8\}$, $\{1, 3, 5, 7\}$.
    d. $\{1, 3, 5, 9, 11\}$, $\{a, b, c, d\}$.
    e. $\{3, 6, 9, 12, 15\}$, $\{2, 4, 6, 8\}$.

32. If $A \sim B$, is A necessarily equal to B?
33. If $A \sim B$ and $B \sim C$, what relation exists between A and C?
34. Define equality of two sets.
35. A classroom is "full" of boys and girls.

State two ways a teacher could determine whether or not there are more boys than girls.

1.6. SUBSETS

Any set B, all of whose elements are also elements of another set A, is called a subset of A. If

$$A = \{1, 2, 3, 4, 5\}$$

and

$$B = \{2, 4\},$$

then B is a *subset* of A. We write

$$B \subseteq A,$$

and read this, "*B* is a subset of *A*." Notice that the set $\{4, 5, 3, 2, 1\}$ is a subset of *A* since every one of its elements is an element of *A*. However, this set is equal to *A*. As a consequence of the definition of a subset, we agree that every set is a subset of itself. The empty set is also a subset of *A*. If it were not it would contain at least one element which is not an element of *A*. But the empty set contains no such member. Hence the empty set is a subset of *A*. In fact, the empty set is a subset of every set.

The set itself and the empty set are called *improper subsets* of a set. All other sets are called *proper subsets* of the set. The symbol $\subseteq$ denotes a subset whether proper or improper. The symbol $\subset$ denotes a proper subset.

Observe that if $A \subseteq B$ and $B \subseteq A$, then $A = B$. If *A* and *B* were not equal *A* would contain some element that was not an element of *B*, which is not possible since $A \subseteq B$, or *B* would contain some element that was not an element of *A*, which is not possible since $B \subseteq A$. Hence $A = B$.

1.7. NUMBER OF SUBSETS

A given set has many subsets. How many? Perhaps we can determine this number by considering a few specific cases. Let us consider the set $A_1 = \{1\}$. (The symbol A_1 is read "*A* sub-one." The "1" is called a subscript.) This set has two subsets, $\{1\}$ and ϕ.

Next let us consider the set

$$A_2 = \{1, 2\}.$$

Its subsets are

$$\{1, 2\}, \quad \phi, \quad \{1\}, \quad \{2\}.$$

We see that a set of two elements has four subsets or two times as many as a set of one element.

A set of three elements, $A_3 = \{1, 2, 3\}$, has eight subsets:

$$\phi, \{1\}, \{2\}, \{3\}, \{1, 2\}, \{2, 3\}, \{1, 3\}, \{1, 2, 3\}.$$

A set of three elements has twice as many subsets as a set of two elements. Examine Table 1.1.

Table 1.1

Set	Subsets	No. of Subsets
$\{1\}$	$\{1\}$ ϕ	$2 = 2^1$
$\{1, 2\}$	$\{1, 2\}$ $\{1\}$ $\{2\}$ ϕ	$4 = 2 \times 2 = 2^2$
$\{1, 2, 3\}$	$\{1, 2, 3\}$ $\{1\}$ $\{2\}$ $\{3\}$ ϕ $\{1, 2\}$ $\{1, 3\}$ $\{2, 3\}$	$8 = 2 \times 2 \times 2 = 2^{3*}$
$\{1, 2, 3, 4\}$	$\{1, 2, 3, 4\}$ $\{1\}$ $\{2\}$ $\{3\}$ $\{4\}$ $\{1, 2\}$ $\{1, 3\}$ $\{1, 4\}$ $\{2, 3\}$ $\{2, 4\}$ $\{3, 4\}$ $\{1, 2, 3\}$ $\{1, 2, 4\}$ $\{1, 3, 4\}$ $\{2, 3, 4\}$ ϕ	$16 = 2 \times 2 \times 2 \times 2 = 2^4$
$\{1, 2, 3, 4, 5\}$	$\{1, 2, 3, 4, 5\}$ $\{1\}$ $\{2\}$ $\{3\}$ $\{4\}$ $\{5\}$ $\{1, 2\}$ $\{1, 3\}$ $\{1, 4\}$ $\{1, 5\}$ $\{2, 3\}$ $\{2, 4\}$ $\{2, 5\}$ $\{3, 4\}$ $\{3, 5\}$ $\{4, 5\}$ $\{1, 2, 3\}$ $\{1, 2, 4\}$ $\{1, 2, 5\}$ $\{1, 3, 4\}$ $\{1, 4, 5\}$ $\{1, 3, 5\}$ $\{2, 3, 4\}$ $\{2, 3, 5\}$ $\{3, 4, 5\}$ $\{2, 4, 5\}$ $\{1, 2, 3, 4\}$ $\{1, 2, 3, 5\}$ $\{1, 2, 4, 5\}$ $\{1, 3, 4, 5\}$ $\{2, 3, 4, 5\}$ ϕ	$32 = 2 \times 2 \times 2 \times 2 \times 2 = 2^5$

*The superscript, 3 in this case, is called an exponent. Exponents will be discussed in Chapter 4.

Although we shall not prove it here, these examples should intuitively convince us that if a set has n elements then it has 2^n (that is, the product of n factors each of which is 2) subsets. Thus a set containing eight elements has precisely $2^8 = 256$ subsets; a set containing ten elements has precisely $2^{10} = 1024$ subsets.

EXERCISE 1.2

1. Write three subsets of $\{11, 12, 13\}$.
2. Write four subsets of $\{$red, blue, green, yellow$\}$.
3. Write six proper subsets of $\{$Marilyn, Sharon, Joan, Ruth$\}$.
4. For each set in the left column, choose the sets from the right column which are subsets of it.

a. $\{d, i, n\}$.
b. Set of letters in the word "dream."
c. $\{1, 2, 3, 4, 5\}$.
d. $\{2, 4, 6, 8, 10, 12\}$.
e. $\{5, 10, 15, 20\}$.
f. The numbers whose symbols are used on a clock face.
g. Set of letters in the word "reading."
h. $\{0, 3, 6, 9, 12, 15, 18, 21\}$.

1. ϕ
2. $\{e, d\}$
3. $\{2, 4\}$
4. $\{d, m\}$
5. $\{10\}$
6. $\{m, a, d, e\}$
7. $\{d, n\}$
8. $\{10, 12\}$

5. If $B = \{0, 2, 4, 6, 8, 10, 12, 14\}$,
   a. give the subset that contains all the odd numbers.
   b. give the subset that contains all the multiples of 3.
   c. give the subset that contains all numbers greater than 7.
6. If $A = \{1, 2, 3, 4, 5, 6, 7, 8, 9\}$,
   a. give the subset that contains all the even numbers.
   b. give the subset that contains no elements.
   c. $B = \{9, 8, 7, 6, 5, 4, 3, 2, 1\}$. Is B a subset of A?
   Is B a proper or an improper subset of A? Does $A = B$?
   Is $A \sim B$?
7. Find all the subsets of B when
   a. $B = \{1, 2, 3, 4\}$.
   b. $B = \{a, b, c\}$.
   c. $B = \{5, 7, 9, 11, 13\}$.
8. Give the number of subsets of B when
   a. $B = \{\star, 0\}$.
   b. $B = \{-, 1, \times \, \boxslash\}$.
   c. $B = \{5, 7, 9, 11, 13\}$.
   d. $B = \{1, 2, \cdots, 300\}$.
9. Given $A = \{a, b, c, d, e, f, g, h\}$, $B = \{a, c, e\}$, and $C = \{a, c, e, f, g, h\}$, which of the following are true statements?
   a. $A \subset C$.
   b. $C \subset A$.
   c. $B \subseteq A$.
   d. $B \subseteq C$.
10. Which of the following are subsets of the set of letters in the word "matching"?
   a. $\{t, a, m\}$.
   b. $\{m, a, t, c, h\}$.
   c. $\{t, h, i, n, g\}$.
   d. ϕ.
   e. $\{t, a, m, i, n, h\}$.

1.8. UNIVERSAL SET

It is useful when thinking about sets to have the members of a given set come from some specified "population." For example, if we are talking about sets of committees of a club, we must know the general population or membership of the club whom we consider as possible and eligible members of our sets (committees). The specified club from which we are drawing our sets (committees in this case) is called the *universal set* or simply the *universe*. In any particular discussion involving sets, every set in the discussion is a subset of the universe. The universe is usually denoted by the capital letter U.

1.9. VENN DIAGRAMS

There is a schematic representation which is used to depict set concepts. These representations are called *Venn* or *Euler diagrams*. In a Venn diagram a rectangular region is usually used to represent the universal set. The elements of U are represented as points inside the rectangle. The size of the rectangular region has nothing to do with the number of elements of U. Venn diagrams are used to picture relationships between sets rather than their comparative sizes. A subset of U is usually represented by a circular region inside of the rectangular region.

Figure 1.3 shows two subsets, A and B, of U which have no members in common. Two sets which have no common members are called *disjoint sets*.

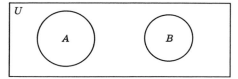

Figure 1.3

Examples of disjoint sets:
1. $X = \{$all dogs$\}$, $Y = \{$all cats$\}$;
2. $A = \{$all girls$\}$, $B = \{$all boys$\}$;
3. $E = \{$all odd numbers$\}$, $F = \{$all even numbers$\}$.
Figure 1.4 shows $E \subseteq D$.

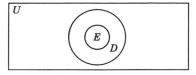

Figure 1.4

Figure 1.5 shows two sets which have some elements in common. These sets are called *overlapping sets*.

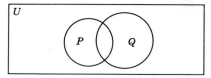

Figure 1.5

Examples of overlapping sets:

1. P = {all poodles}, $\quad\quad$ Q = {all white dogs};
2. R = {all multiples of 5}, $\quad$ S = {all multiples of 3};
3. T = {all sail boats}, $\quad\quad$ V = {all boats with motors}.

When more than two sets are related, their relationship may be shown in a Venn diagram. Examples of such relationships are shown in Figure 1.6.

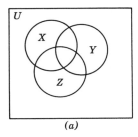
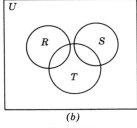
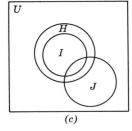

$\quad\quad\quad$ (a) $\quad\quad\quad\quad\quad\quad\quad\quad$ (b) $\quad\quad\quad\quad\quad\quad\quad\quad$ (c)

Figure 1.6

Figure 1.6a shows a Venn diagram representing three overlapping sets, X, Y, and Z. Each set represented in Figure 1.6a contains some elements in both of the other sets. Figure 1.6b represents three sets, R, S, and T. Sets R and T are overlapping sets; that is, they have elements in common. S and T are also overlapping sets. Sets R and S are disjoint sets. Figure 1.6c represents sets H, I, and J where $I \subseteq H$ and J overlaps both H and I.

EXERCISE 1.3

1. What is a suitable universal set for each of the following pairs of sets?

$\quad$ a. A = {horse, dog, cat, lion},
$\quad\quad$ B = {poodle, boxer, terrier}.
$\quad$ b. A = {lily, rose, jonquil},
$\quad\quad$ B = {cherry, apple, peach, lemon}.

2. Let U = {all college students}. Use Venn diagrams to illustrate the following pairs of sets.

$\quad$ a. A = {all college students taking mathematics},
$\quad\quad$ B = {all college students taking education}.
$\quad$ b. A = {all college football players},
$\quad\quad$ B = {all college basketball players}.
$\quad$ c. A = {all college students over twenty-one years of age},
$\quad\quad$ B = {all college students under twenty years of age}.
$\quad$ d. A = {all male college students},

$B = \{$all college students who play in a band$\}$,
$C = \{$all college students who play in an orchestra$\}$.

3. Draw a Venn diagram illustrating

    a. $U = \{$all counting numbers$\}$,
       $A = \{$all even numbers$\}$,
       $B = \{$all multiples of 4$\}$.
    b. $U = \{$all parallelograms$\}$,
       $A = \{$all rectangles$\}$,
       $B = \{$all squares$\}$.
    c. $U = \{$all boats anchored at San Diego Yacht Club$\}$,
       $A = \{$all sailboats$\}$,
       $B = \{$all motorboats$\}$.

4. Draw a Venn diagram of the following:

    a. Two disjoint sets A and B,
    b. $C \subseteq D$,
    c. Sets E, F, and G which are overlapping.

5. What is a universal set for each of the following sets?

    a. Set of honor students at San Diego State College.
    b. Set of Chevrolet cars.
    c. Set of coffee cups.
    d. Set of ski sweaters.

6. Draw a Venn diagram to show the relation between the following subsets of the students of a university:

    a. Freshman class.
    b. Senior class.
    c. Male students.
    d. Female students with blonde hair.
    e. Honor students.

Draw a Venn diagram which illustrates the proper relationship between the given sets in Problems 7–9.

7. U is the set of all animals.
    A is the set of all four-legged animals.
    B is the set of all two-legged animals.
8. U is the set of all countries of the world.
    A is the set of all European countries.
    B is the set of all North American countries.
    C is the set of all countries which are members of the United Nations.
9. U is the set of all living Americans.
    A is the set of all present members of the Senate.

B is the set of all living Americans over twenty-one years of age.

C is the set of all living Americans living in the state of Montana.

1.10. ORDERED SETS

Frequently the objects of a set present themselves in a definite order. For example, the set of numbers used in counting is usually thought of in order of magnitude: 1, 2, 3, 4, 5, . . . (the three dots mean "and so on in the same manner and continues indefinitely".) Up to this point the order in which elements of our sets appeared was immaterial. Now we wish to consider certain sets in which the order in which elements are arranged is important.

We shall approach this idea of "order" intuitively. Essentially, to "order" things is to list or arrange them in some particular fashion; one can then say of each element which of the other elements it "precedes". We do this by comparing pairs of elements in the list and deciding which precedes the other. The word "precedes" may be replaced by "shorter than," "above," "below," "less than," and so on, depending on the elements to be ordered.

For example, consider the set of temperatures on a particular day:

$$A = \{40°, 70°, 13°, 52°, 60°\}.$$

If we order these elements from the coldest temperature to the warmest, we have

$$13°, 40°, 52°, 60°, 70°.$$

That is, 13° is colder than 40°, 40° is colder than 52°, and so on. If we ask that the set A be ordered according to this criteria, we then have:

$$A_{\text{ordered}} = \{13°, 40°, 52°, 60°, 70°\},$$

Where A_{ordered} is used to denote the set whose elements are those of A, but considered in a specified order from left to right. The A_{ordered} is an *ordered set*.

1.11. NUMBER AND NUMERAL

A number is a mathematical abstraction. There is a distinction between a number and the symbol used to represent it. Numerals are names for numbers. Thus the symbol "4" is a numeral used to name the number four. This same idea is used when we write the name "Ruth." The symbol names a girl, but is not the girl herself.

In ordinary language there is usually little difficulty in distinguishing between the object and its name or symbol. In writing, since it is sometimes more difficult to make the distinction, this is usually done by enclosing the symbol in quotation marks, (either double or single). For example,

"Ruth" has four letters.

Here we do not mean that the girl, Ruth, received four letters in the mail, but that there are four letters of the alphabet in the word "Ruth."

In mathematics we handle comparable situations similarly.

Write "4" on the board.
The sum of 2 and 3 is 5.
He said 3, but he wrote "8" on the board.

When the context is clear, quotation marks are usually omitted.

1.12. STANDARD SETS

Let us establish some ordered sets of symbols beginning with the set {"1"}. The symbol {"1"} is read, "the set whose element is the numeral one." We continue

$$\{\text{"1"}, \text{"2"}\},$$
$$\{\text{"1"}, \text{"2"}, \text{"3"}\},$$
$$\{\text{"1"}, \text{"2"}, \text{"3"}, \text{"4"}\}, \text{ and so forth.}$$

We see that

$$\{\text{"1"}\} \subset \{\text{"1"}, \text{"2"}\} \subset \{\text{"1"}, \text{"2"}, \text{"3"}\} \subset \{\text{"1"}, \text{"2"}, \text{"3"}, \text{"4"}\} \subset \ldots$$

By comparing these sets, called *standard sets*, we can determine which belongs before the others in this sequence of subsets. For example, we recognize immediately that {"1", "2", "3", "4", "5"} belongs before {"1", "2", "3", "4", "5", "6", "7", "8"} in the sequence.

1.13. CARDINALITY

We now ask ourselves "How many elements are in a particular set?" Consider the sets

$$A = \{a, b\},$$
$$B = \{ \star, \bigcirc \},$$
$$C = \{\text{Ruth, Doris}\},$$
$$D = \{\text{Gai, Suzie}\}.$$

Each of these sets is equivalent to any other, since the elements of any two of the sets can be placed into one-to-one correspondence. Let us consider all of the sets equivalent to any one of these given sets, for example, {Ruth, Doris}. Among these sets is the standard set {"1", "2"}. These sets all possess a common property: their equivalence to the standard set {"1", "2"}. This property is independent of the elements in the set. This common property we shall call the number two. We say the number property of the set $C = \{\text{Ruth, Doris}\}$ is 2 and write $N(C) = 2$. This number property of a set is called the *cardinality* of the set.

Similarly the number property of {"1"} is 1; of {"1", "2", "3"}, 3; and so on. For any set A, $N(A)$ is called a *cardinal number*. The empty set ϕ is assigned the cardinality of zero, that is, $N(\phi) = 0$.

1.14. FINITE AND INFINITE SETS

The set of cardinal numbers, when arranged in order, is endless. Given any standard set, it is always possible to find another set with larger cardinality. We say that the set of cardinal numbers is *infinite*.

Any nonempty set, A, whose elements can be put into one-to-one correspondence with a standard set is called a *finite set*. In other words, if a set A is a finite set, its elements can be counted, and such a counting would terminate.

Examples of finite sets are

$A = \{\text{all the men who have been president of the United States}\}$,
$B = \{\text{population of India}\}$,
$C = \{\text{letters of the English alphabet}\}$,
$D = \{\text{grains of sand on the beach at La Jolla}\}$.

Examples of infinite sets are

$E = \{\text{cardinal numbers}\} = \{0, 1, 2, 3, \cdots\}$,

$F = \{$even cardinal numbers$\} = \{0, 2, 4, 6, \cdots\}$,
$G = \{$odd cardinal numbers$\} = \{1, 3, 5, 7, \cdots\}$.

Consider sets E and F. We can put the elements of these sets into one-to-one correspondence.

$$E = \{0 \quad 1 \quad 2 \quad 3 \quad 4 \quad \cdots\}$$
$$\updownarrow \quad \updownarrow \quad \updownarrow \quad \updownarrow \quad \updownarrow$$
$$F = \{0 \quad 2 \quad 4 \quad 6 \quad 8 \quad \cdots\}$$

A rule for this correspondence is $n \leftrightarrow 2n^*$, where n is any cardinal number; for example, $2 \leftrightarrow 2 \cdot 2 = 4$; $3 \leftrightarrow 2 \cdot 3 = 6$; $12 \leftrightarrow 2 \cdot 12 = 24$.

According to our definition of equivalence, $E \sim F$, but $F \subset E$. We see then that an infinite set may be put into one-to-one correspondence with a proper subset of itself. This is never possible with finite sets.

EXERCISE 1.4

1. Given $A = \{1, 2, 3, 4\}$, $B = \{a, b, c, d, e\}$, $C = \{a, b, c, d, e, f, k, l\}$,
   find a. $N(A)$.
        b. $N(B)$.
        c. $N(C)$.

2. Which of the following sets are infinite sets? Which are finite sets?

   a. Set of letters of our alphabet.
   b. Set of all counting numbers.
   c. Set of all people on earth.
   d. Set of all vowels.
   e. Set of all grains of sand on Jones Beach.
   f. Set of all cities in Europe.
   g. Set of all countries in Africa.
   h. Set of monkeys in the St. Louis Zoo.
   i. Set of numbers greater than 287.

3. Show a one-to-one correspondence between the set of counting numbers and the set of odd numbers.
4. Define an ordered set.
5. Given $A = \{1, 2, 3, 4, 5, 6, 7\}$, write the following:

   a. A subset B of A, such that $N(B) = 3$.
   b. The standard set which is equivalent to A.
   c. A subset C of A, such that $N(C) = 5$.

---

*$2n$ means the product of 2 and n; that is, $2 \times n$.

1.15. UNION OF SETS

Suppose we consider the following sets:

$$A = \{ \text{☆}, \bigcirc, \square \},$$
$$B = \{ \bigcirc, \#, \text{⊠}, \infty \}.$$

Let us join the elements of sets A and B to form a new set. This new set consists of all the elements belonging to A or B or both and is called the *union* of A and B. We write

$$A \cup B = \{ \text{☆}, \bigcirc, \square, \bigcirc, \#, \text{⊠}, \infty \},$$

and read "$A \cup B$" as "A union B."

This process of forming the union of two sets is called an *operation* on sets. Since it applies to just two sets at a time it is called a *binary operation*. Just as we perform a binary operation on two numbers and obtain another number (for example, $3 + 4 = 7$ or $3 \cdot 4 = 12$) we perform a binary operation on sets and obtain another set. Since the union of two sets is again a set in the same universe as the given sets, we say the universe is *closed* under the operation of union.

Consider the sets

$$A = \{ a, b, c, d \},$$
$$B = \{ a, c, d, e, f \},$$
$$C = \{ d, e, a, f \},$$
$$D = \{ i \}.$$

We see that $A \cup B = \{ a, b, c, d, e, f \}$. Notice that $A \cup B$ is not written $\{ a, b, c, d, a, c, d, e, f \}$, since there is no point of naming a, c, and d, which are elements of both sets, twice.

Notice that

$$A \cup D = \{ a, b, c, d, i \},$$

and

$$D \cup A = \{ i, a, b, c, d \}.$$

Thus $A \cup D = D \cup A$. The order in which the sets are considered in forming a union is of no consequence. In general, $A \cup B = B \cup A$ for all sets A and B. When the order in which we operate on two things does not affect the result, we say the operation is *commutative*. Therefore the process of forming the union of two sets is a *commutative operation*.

The operation of putting on a pair of socks and a pair of shoes is not commutative. The result of putting on a pair of shoes followed by putting on a pair of socks is quite different from the result of putting on a pair of socks followed by putting on a pair of shoes.

The Venn diagram in Figure 1.7 shows by the shading, $A \cup B$.

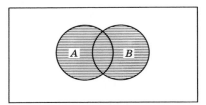

Figure 1.7

Let us see if we can find the union of three sets, A, B, and C. Since we can only find the union of two sets at a time we agree that the symbol $(A \cup B) \cup C$ means that we find $A \cup B$ and then join this newly found set with C. Let us also agree that the symbol $A \cup (B \cup C)$ means that we find $B \cup C$ and then join this set to A. In other words, the parentheses indicate which operation is to be performed first. Let

$$A = \{1, 2, 3\},$$
$$B = \{2, 4\},$$
$$C = \{1, 3, 5\}.$$

Then

$$(A \cup B) \cup C = \{1, 2, 3, 4\} \cup \{1, 3, 5\} = \{1, 2, 3, 4, 5\}$$

and

$$A \cup (B \cup C) = \{1, 2, 3\} \cup \{1, 2, 3, 4, 5\} = \{1, 2, 3, 4, 5\}.$$

Notice that $(A \cup B) \cup C = A \cup (B \cup C)$.

This example illustrates another property of the operation of union of sets. If A, B, and C are any three sets, then

$$(A \cup B) \cup C = A \cup (B \cup C).$$

This property is called the *associative property*. Since $(A \cup B) \cup C = A \cup (B \cup C)$, we usually omit the parentheses and write simply $A \cup B \cup C$.

The Venn diagram in Figure 1.8 shows by the shading, $A \cup B \cup C$.

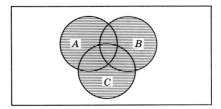

Figure 1.8

1.16. INTERSECTION OF SETS

Another operation on sets is the *intersection* of two sets. Suppose that

$$A = \{ ☆, ○, □, ⊕ \}$$

and

$$B = \{ ○, ⊕, ◌, ★ \}.$$

Sets A and B have some common elements. The set of those elements which are common to both A and B is called the *intersection set*. We write:

$$A \cap B = \{ ○, ⊕ \}$$

and read, "$A \cap B$" as "the intersection of A and B."

In Figure 1.9, $A \cap B$ is shown by the shading.

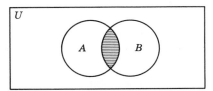

Figure 1.9

If A is the set given above and $C = \{$ $\}$, what is $A \cap C$? Since A and C have no common elements

$$A \cap C = \phi.$$

Notice that $A \cap B$ and $B \cap A$ have exactly the same elements. This is true in general. Hence the operation of forming the intersection of two sets is *commutative*.

Although the operation of intersection is a binary operation, we can find the intersection of more than two sets. Let us agree that $(A \cap B) \cap C$ means finding the intersection of A and B and then the intersection of this set and C, and that $A \cap (B \cap C)$ means finding the intersection of B and C and then finding the intersection of this set with A. The parentheses indicate which operation is to be performed first.

If

$$A = \{1, 2, 3, 4, 5, 6, 7, 8\},$$
$$B = \{2, 4, 6, 8, 10\},$$

and

$$C = \{3, 6, 9\},$$

then

$$A \cap B = \{2, 4, 6, 8\},$$
$$B \cap C = \{6\},$$
$$(A \cap B) \cap C = \{2, 4, 6, 8\} \cap \{3, 6, 9\} = \{6\},$$
$$A \cap (B \cap C) = \{1, 2, 3, 4, 5, 6, 7, 8\} \cap \{6\} = \{6\}.$$

We see from this example that

$$(A \cap B) \cap C = A \cap (B \cap C).$$

This is true in general; that is, if A, B, and C are any three sets, then

$$(A \cap B) \cap C = A \cap (B \cap C).$$

and the operation of intersection of sets is *associative*.

In Figure 1.10*a* we see a Venn diagram with $A \cap B$ shaded; in Figure 1.10*b* we see $(A \cap B) \cap C$ shaded.

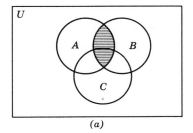
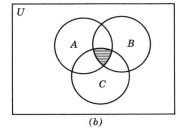

(a)   (b)

Figure 1.10

In Figure 1.11a we see $B \cap C$ shaded; in 1.11b we see $A \cap (B \cap C)$ shaded.

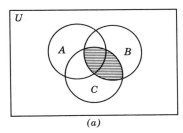
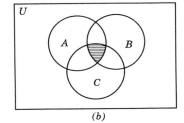

(a)   (b)

Figure 1.11

Figures 1.10 and 1.11 should convince us that $A \cap (B \cap C) = (A \cap B) \cap C$.

1.17.   RELATIVE COMPLEMENT

If B is a proper subset of A, then the set of elements of A which are not elements of B is called the *relative complement* of B to A. If

$$A = \{1, 2, 3, 4, 5\}$$

and

$$B = \{2, 4\},$$

then the relative complement of B to A is $\{1, 3, 5\}$. We write

$$A - B = \{1, 3, 5\}.$$

The relative complement is sometimes called the *difference* of A and B.

EXERCISE 1.5

1. Given $A = \{1, 2, 3, 4\}$, $B = \{a, b, c, d, e\}$, and $C = \{2, 4, 6, 8\}$ find

    a. $N(A)$.
    b. $N(A \cup B)$.
    c. $N(A \cap B)$.
    d. $N(A \cup C)$.
    e. $N(A \cap C)$.

2. Given $A = \{1, 2, 3, 4, 5, 6\}$, $B = \{2, 4, 6, 8, 10\}$, and $C = \{3, 6, 9, 12\}$, find

    a. $A \cup B$.   b. $A \cup C$.   c. $B \cup C$.
    d. $A \cap B$.   e. $A \cap C$.   f. $B \cap C$.
    g. $(A \cup B) \cup C$.   h. $A \cup (B \cup C)$.   i. $A \cup (B \cap C)$.

3. What does $P \cap (Q \cup R)$ equal if

    a. P and $Q \cup R$ are disjoint sets?
    b. $P \subset R$?
    c. $R = \phi$?
    d. $Q = R$?

4. Let $U = \{a, b, c, d, e\}$ and $C = \{a, c\}$. Suppose that A and B are nonempty sets. Find A in each of the following:

    a. $A \cup B = U, A \cap B = \phi$, and $B = \{a\}$.
    b. $A \subset B$ and $A \cup B = \{d, e\}$.
    c. $A \cap B = \{c\}$, $A \cup B = \{b, c, d\}$, and $B \cup C = \{a, b, c\}$.

5. What is $A \cup B$ if

    a. A and B are disjoint sets?
    b. $A \subset B$?
    c. A and B are overlapping sets?
    d. $A = B$?

6. What is $A \cap B$ if

    a. A and B are disjoint sets?
    b. $A \subset B$?
    c. A and B are overlapping sets?
    d. $A = B$?

7. Given

$U = \{$all elementary school teachers$\}$,
$A = \{$all elementary school teachers who have visited Mexico$\}$,
$B = \{$all elementary school teachers who have visited Canada$\}$,

describe in words
    a. $A \cup B$.   b. $A \cap B$.

8. Let $U = \{$cities in California$\}$.

   $A = \{$Los Angeles, San Francisco, San Diego$\}$.

   $B = \{$Fresno, Chico, San Diego, San Bernardino$\}$.

   $C = \{$Eureka, Sacramento, Los Angeles$\}$.

   $D = \{$San Diego, Cardiff, Oceanside, Riverside$\}$.

List the members of

   a. $A \cup B$,   b. $A \cap C$,   c. $(A \cap B) \cup D$,   d. $(B \cup D) \cap (C \cup A)$.

9. Give the set represented by

   a. $U \cup A$,   b. $U \cup \phi$,   c. $A \cup \phi$,

   d. $A \cup B$ if $B \subseteq A$,   e. $U \cap A$,   f. $U \cap \phi$,

   g. $A \cap \phi$,   h. $A \cap B$ if $B \subseteq A$.

10. Using the sets given in Exercise 8 find

   a. $A \cap B$;   b. $(A \cap B) \cap C$;   c. $(A \cap B) \cap (C \cap D)$.

11. Given $U = \{$all human beings$\}$, give the relative complement of the following sets of U.

   a. $\{$all females$\}$.

   b. $\{$all human beings less than twenty-one years of age$\}$.

   c. $\{$all married persons$\}$.

   d. $\{$all single persons$\}$.

12. Given $A = \{a, b, c, d, e\}$ and $B = \{a, e\}$, what is the relative complement of B to A?

13. Given $A = \{2, 4, 5, 6\}$,

   $B = \{1, 2, 3, 4, 5, 6\}$,

   $C = \{1, 3\}$,

   $D = \{1, 2, 3, 5\}$,

   $E = \{4, 6\}$,

which of the following are true statements?

   a. $A \cup C = B$.   b. $A \cup B = C$.

   c. $C \cup B = C$.   d. $D \subset B$.

   e. $C \subset B$.   f. $E \subset E$.

   g. $C \cup D = D$.

1.18.   ORDERED PAIRS

In everyday language when we speak of a "pair" we simply mean two objects, usually distinct, although similar. In mathematics, an *ordered pair* is a set of two objects, not necessarily different, one of which is designated as the first object of the pair. If a is the first element of an ordered pair and b the second, we commonly write (a, b) for the ordered pair. Examples of ordered pairs are (cat, dog), (5, 10), (knife, fork). The first element of the ordered pair, (cat, dog), is cat, the second element is dog. The two elements of an ordered pair may be the same; for example, the two elements in the ordered pair (9, 9). The ordered pair (2, 6) is not the same as the ordered pair (6, 2).

We define two ordered pairs to be equal if and only if they have identical first members and identical second members. Thus

$$(3, 5) = (3, 5),$$

and

$$(a, b) = (a, b),$$

but

$$(a, b) \neq (b, a) \quad \text{unless } a = b.$$

In general, $(a, b) = (c, d)$ if and only if $a = c$ and $b = d$.

1.19. CARTESIAN PRODUCTS

Suppose at the cafeteria we have the following choices of meat: roast beef and pork chops; and the following choices of vegetables: potatoes, corn, asparagus, and beets. You may have a choice of meat and one vegetable on the plate lunch. How many choices do you have? The choices are

> roast beef and potatoes
> roast beef and corn
> roast beef and asparagus
> roast beef and beets
>
> pork chops and potatoes
> pork chops and corn
> pork chops and asparagus
> pork chops and beets

From this list we see that there are eight choices. In this example we have two sets:

$$M = \{\text{roast beef, pork chops}\},$$
$$V = \{\text{potatoes, corn, asparagus, beets}\}.$$

The combinations of meat and vegetable form a set of all possible ordered pairs in which the first member of the ordered pair is an element of *M* and the second member of the ordered pair is a member of *V*. All these ordered pairs form a set called the *cartesian product** of the two sets.

A convenient way to represent the formation of a cartesian product is by means of an *array* or *lattice*. Figure 1.12 shows an array of the eight possible plate lunches.

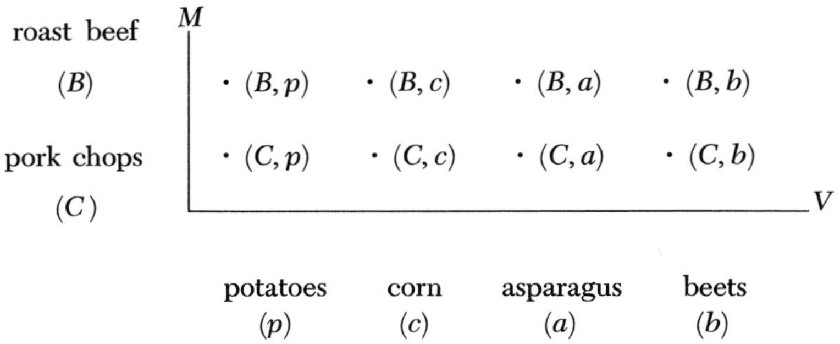

roast beef   **M**

(*B*)   · (*B, p*)   · (*B, c*)   · (*B, a*)   · (*B, b*)

pork chops   · (*C, p*)   · (*C, c*)   · (*C, a*)   · (*C, b*)

(*C*)   └─────────────────────────────────────── *V*

            potatoes   corn   asparagus   beets
              (*p*)   (*c*)   (*a*)   (*b*)

Figure 1.12

Each ordered pair consists of one kind of meat and one vegetable. In the array in Figure 1.12 a dot represents each ordered pair.

The cartesian product of *M* and *V* is represented by the symbol $M \times V$ and is read "*M* cross *V*."

In a cartesian product we have a set whose elements are not single elements but ordered pairs.

Consider

$$A = \{1, 2, 3\},$$
$$B = \{2, 3\}.$$

Then $A \times B$ is the set

$$A \times B = \left\{ \begin{matrix} (1, 2) & (1, 3) \\ (2, 2) & (2, 3) \\ (3, 2) & (3, 3) \end{matrix} \right\}.$$

*A cartesian product is sometimes called a product set.

Now let us form $B \times A$:

$$B \times A = \begin{cases} (2,1) & (2,2) & (2,3) \\ (3,1) & (3,2) & (3,3) \end{cases}.$$

By comparing $A \times B$ and $B \times A$ we see that $A \times B \neq B \times A$; hence the formation of cartesian products of sets is not commutative.

Arrays of $A \times B$ and $B \times A$ are shown in Figure 1.13.

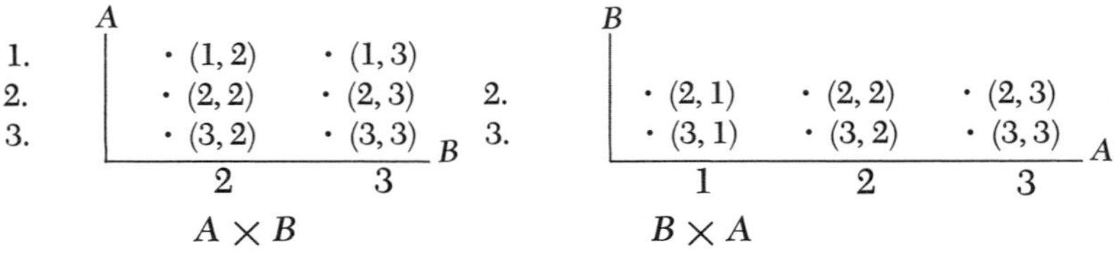

Figure 1.13

Notice that, although $A \times B \neq B \times A$, $N(A \times B) = N(B \times A)$.

EXERCISE 1.6

1. List all the ordered pairs possible from matching the elements of set $A = \{d, o, g\}$ with itself.

2. Define cartesian product.

3. Which of the following pairs of ordered pairs are equal?

    a. (a, b), (b, a).
    b. $(3, 2)$, $(1 + 2, 1 + 1)$.
    c. $(7, 6)$, $(7, 3 + 2)$.
    d. $(9, 0)$, $(5 + 4, 5 - 5)$.
    e. $(14, 7)$, $(7, 14)$.

4. Given $A = \{x, y, z, w\}$, $B = \{1, 2\}$, what is $A \times B$?

5. Given $A = \{\text{Chevrolet, Ford, Plymouth, Rambler}\}$,
        $B = \{\text{Coupe, Convertible, Sedan}\}$,

    a. List the ordered pairs in $A \times B$.
    b. List the ordered pairs in $B \times A$.
    c. Is $A \times B$ equal to $B \times A$?
    d. Is $N(A \times B)$ equal to $N(B \times A)$?

6. List the ordered pairs of $A \times B$ for each of the following pairs of sets.

    a. $A = \{a\}$, $B = \{1\}$.
    b. $A = \{1, 2\}$, $B = \{c, d, e\}$.
    c. $A = \{\text{red, blue, green}\}$, $B = \{\text{orange, white, yellow}\}$.
    d. $A = \{a, b, c\}$, $B = \phi$.

7. If set A has three elements and set B has two elements, how many ordered pairs are in the set $A \times B$?

8. If set A has n elements and set B has five elements, how many ordered pairs are in the set $A \times B$?

9. If set A has n elements and set B has m elements, how many ordered pairs are in the set $A \times B$?

10. In general is $A \times B$ equal to $B \times A$?

11. Is $N(A \times B)$ equal to $N(B \times A)$?

1.20.   COMBINING SET OPERATIONS

The combination of the operations of union and intersection offer many possibilities for the formation of new sets from given sets. Venn diagrams are very useful aids for visualizing the resulting sets when set operations are combined.

For example, consider

$$A \cap (B \cup C).$$

In Figures 1.14 we have a sequence of Venn diagrams showing $A \cap (B \cup C)$. In Figure 1.14a, $B \cup C$ is shown by shading. In Figure 1.14b $A \cap (B \cup C)$ is shown by shading.

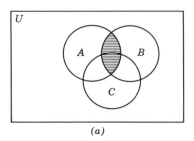
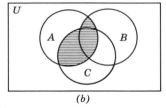

(a)   (b)

Figure 1.14

ow let us consider $(A \cap B) \cup (A \cap C)$. In Figure 1.15a we have a ɪn diagram which shows $A \cap B$ by shading. Figures 1.15b and 1.15c show $A \cap C$ and $(A \cap B) \cup (A \cap C)$.

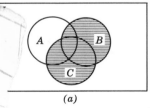
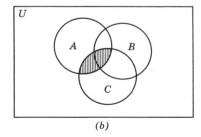

(a)   (b)

Figure 1.15

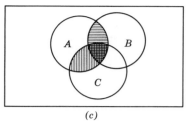

(c)

Figure 1.15

In Figures 1.14*b* and 1.15*c* we see that the same area is shaded in both cases. This leads us to state that

$$A \cap (B \cup C) = (A \cap B) \cup (A \cap C).$$

This is known as the *distributive property*.

EXERCISE 1.7

1. Make a sequence of Venn diagrams (see Figures 1.14 and 1.15) to illustrate that the following statements are true.

  a. $(A \cup B) \cup C = A \cup (B \cup C)$.
  b. $(A \cup B) \cap (A \cup C) = A \cup (B \cap C)$.
  c. $(A \cap B) \cap C = A \cap (B \cap C)$.
  d. $(A \cap B) \cup (A \cap C) = A \cap (B \cup C)$.

2. Let $A = \{1, 2, 3, 4, 5, 6, 7\}$, $B = \{1, 3, 5, 7, 9, 11\}$, $C = \{2, 4, 6, 8\}$. List the members in each set.

  a. $(A \cap B) \cup C$.
  b. $(B \cup C) \cap (A \cup C)$.
  c. $(A \cap B) \cup (C \cap \phi)$.

3. Let $A = \{0, 1, 2, 3, 4, 5, 6, 7, 8, 9\}$, $B = \{0, 2, 4, 6\}$, $C = \{3, 6, 9\}$, $D = \{1, 3, 5, 7, 9, 11, 13\}$, and $E = \{4, 8, 12, 16\}$. Compute each of the following:

  a. $(A - B) \cup (C \cap D)$,
  b. $(A - C) \cup (A - B)$,
  c. $A \cap (B \cup C)$,
  d. $(E \cap D) \cup (B \cap C)$,
  e. $C \times E$,
  f. $E \cap (D \cup A)$,
  g. $D \cap (E \cup B)$.

CHAPTER **2**

Logic

2.1. UNDEFINED WORDS

The first requirement for an understanding of any subject, be it mathematics or tennis, is to know the meanings of the words that are used. We early acquire the habit of looking up the definitions of unfamiliar words in the dictionary. A little experience using the dictionary will convince us that some words must be undefined. Without our knowing the meaning of some words our use of the dictionary will lead us around in a circle. For example, suppose we look up the verb "to desire." We may find that as we look up each definition given, we are ultimately led back to "to desire."

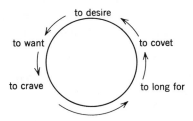

We must make a beginning somewhere, and in mathematics we do this by choosing a small number of words which we accept as *undefined*. The choice of these undefined words depends upon the subject, as we shall see when we study geometry.

With these basic undefined words or terms we now define other words in terms of them. Of course, we must assume that we have some ordinary English words at our disposal.

For example, if we accept *point, line,* and *betweenness* as our undefined terms we may define the line segment *AB,* where *A* and *B* are two points on a line, as the set consisting of the points *A* and *B* and all the points of the line that lie between *A* and *B.*

2.2. STATEMENTS

With our undefined and defined words we form sentences called *statements.* These statements must have *truth value,* that is, they must be either true or false, but not both. The following sentences are statements.

1. Abraham Lincoln was president in 1862.
2. Chicago is west of New York.
3. A dog has four legs.
4. A cow purrs.
5. Snakes can fly.

The following sentences are not statements by our definition because, as they stand, they have no truth value. That is, we cannot tell whether or not they are true or false.

6. He is the best student in the class.
7. That city has a population of 40,000.
8. That number is a factor of 8.

In a deductive system such as mathematics we accept a set of statements that are assumed to be true. These statements are called *axioms* or *postulates.* Once our axioms are stated, we use them and a process called *logical reasoning* to prove other statements called *theorems.*

2.3. COMPOUND STATEMENTS

There are several ways in which we can combine two statements to form a third statement. Those to be discussed are (1) conjunction, (2) disjunction, (3) implication, and (4) negation.

In a *conjunction* we combine two given statements by placing an "and" between them. Thus the conjunction of the two statements,

1. It is raining,
2. The streets are flooded,

is "It is raining and the streets are flooded."

We say that a conjunction is true if both of the statements, called *components,* used to form it are true and that it is false otherwise. If "It is raining" is true, and "The streets are flooded" is true, then the conjunction, "It is raining and the streets are flooded," is true. If "It is raining" is true, and "The streets are flooded" is false, the conjunction is false. If "It is raining" is false and "The streets are flooded" is true, the conjunction is false. If "It is raining" is false and "The streets are flooded" is false, the conjunction is false.

We usually denote statements by lower case letters of the alphabet such as p, q, r, and s. If p and q are the components used to form a conjunction we write

$$p \wedge q$$

and read this "p and q." Table 2.1 shows the truth values of the conjunction $p \wedge q$. Such a table is called a *truth table.* The T and F in the table mean true and false, respectively.

Table 2.1

p	q	$p \wedge q$
T	T	T
T	F	F
F	T	F
F	F	F

In a *disjunction* we combine two statements by placing "or" between them. The disjunction of the statements (1) and (2) above is "It is raining or the streets are flooded." The disjunction is true if either one, or the other, or both of its components are true, and false otherwise. If "It is raining" is true, and "The streets are flooded" is true, then the disjunction "It is raining or the streets are flooded" is true. If either "It is raining" or "The streets are flooded" is true, the disjunction is true. If both "It is raining" and "The streets are flooded" are false, the disjunction is false.

If p and q are the components used to form the disjunction, we write

$$p \vee q$$

and read this "p or q." Table 2.2 shows the truth value of $p \vee q$.

Table 2.2

p	q	$p \vee q$
T	T	T
T	F	T
F	T	T
F	F	F

Note carefully that the connective "or," when used in a disjunction, is used in the *inclusive* sense; that is, "or" means p or q or *both*. In everyday language we often use "or" in the *exclusive* sense; that is, "or" means p or q but not both. For example, we say "I shall buy a coat or I shall buy a suit." This means, of course, that either a coat or a suit will be purchased, but not both. Hereafter, the word "or" will always be used in this text in the inclusive sense.

2.4. IMPLICATION

A very important compound statement in mathematics is the *implication*. It takes the form of an "if – then" sentence. Examples of implications are the following:

1. If it is raining, then the streets are flooded.
2. If $2 + 2 = 4$, then 5 is greater than 2.
3. If a polygon has three sides, then it is a triangle.

From any two statements we can form two implications; from "It is raining" and "The streets are flooded" we can form the implications:

a. If it is raining, then the streets are flooded.
b. If the streets are flooded, then it is raining.

In implication (a), the statement "It is raining" is called the *hypotheses* and the statement "The streets are flooded" is called the *conclusion*. In implication (b), the statement "The streets are flooded" is the hypotheses and "It is raining" is the conclusion. The two implications that can be formed from two given statements are related to each other as we shall see later.

If p and q are symbols denoting two statements, we use the symbol

$$p \to q$$

to denote the implication "If p, then q." The symbol $p \to q$ may also be read "p implies q." Table 2.3 shows the truth values of the implication $p \to q$. Table 2.4 shows the truth values of the implication $q \to p$.

Table 2.3		
p	q	$p \to q$
T	T	T
T	F	F
F	T	T
F	F	T

Table 2.4		
p	q	$q \to p$
T	T	T
T	F	T
F	T	F
F	F	T

The first lines of the tables are easily accepted. The second line of Table 2.3 and the third of Table 2.4 are also intuitively easy to accept: it is easily accepted that our reasoning must be false if it leads from a true hypotheses to a false conclusion. The third and fourth lines of Table 2.3 and the second and fourth lines of Table 2.4 are less familiar and harder to accept.

We shall accept these truth tables as definitions of the truth values of the implications $p \to q$ and $q \to p$. In other words, *we define the implication* p $\to$ q *as true unless* p *is true and* q *is false, in which case it is false.*

2.5. NEGATION

If p is any statement, the statement "p is false" is called the *negation* of p and is denoted by the symbol $\sim p$. For example, if p denotes the statement "3 is greater than 2," then $\sim p$ denotes the statement "It is false that 3 is greater than 2" or "3 is not greater than 2."

EXERCISE 2.1

Which of the following are statements? Give the truth value of each statement.

1. Black coffee contains no calories.
2. General Eisenhower was a Republican president.
3. Her birthday is February 29.
4. June is the sixth month of the year.
5. The year 1935 was a presidental election year.
6. All cats eat lettuce.
7. That number is the sum of 6 and 7.
8. He is twenty-one years old.
9. All cows have lavender eyes.
10. Poodles are people.

Form the (a) conjunction and (b) disjunction of the following four pairs of statements.

11. The sky is blue.   The grass is green.
12. Today is Monday.   Yesterday was Sunday.
13. The train is late.   We shall be late to work.
14. All birds have wings.   Cats purr.

15. Form the implication $p \to q$ of the statements in Problems 11–14. Use the first statement as the hypotheses and the second statement as the conclusion.

Form the negation of the following statements.

16. It is raining.
17. Dogs have four legs.
18. People work hard.
19. Water is wet.
20. Ice is cold.

Give the hypotheses and the conclusion in each of the following implications.

21. If I go skiing, I shall have fun.
22. If he cooperates with his boss, he shall be promoted.
23. If we go fishing, I shall catch a bass.
24. If a number is even, it is divisible by 2.
25. You were born in leap year, if you were born in 1952.
26. Choose an ordinary, nontechnical word and build a circular chain of definitions from this word back to itself. Use a standard dictionary for your definitions. Do not put simple connectives such as "the," "and," "is," and so forth in your chain.

27. Take the following symbolic translations:

p: Chicago is the Windy City.

q: New York is the Empire State.

Write each of the following in symbolic notation.
a. Chicago is not the Windy City.
b. Chicago is the Windy City or New York is not the Empire State.
c. If New York is the Empire State, then Chicago is not the Windy City.
d. New York is the Empire State and Chicago is the Windy City.

28. Given p: all rectangles are quadrilaterals,

q: all squares are rectangles,

write the English statement for the following:
a. $p \wedge q$.
b. $p \vee q$.
c. $(\sim p) \wedge (\sim q)$.
d. $p \to q$.
e. $q \to p$.
f. $\sim q \to p$.

2.6. EQUIVALENCE RELATIONS

We are familiar with many kinds of relations. For example,

> Tom *is older than* Larry.
> Mary *is the sister of* Alice.
> New York *is east of* Chicago.

"Is older than," "is the sister of," and "is east of" are relations. These relations are *binary relations* because they relate two elements of a set. Some mathematical relations are described by such phrases as "is equal to," "is greater than," "is less than," and "is a factor of."

Symbolically, we shall denote a relation with the capital letter R, and if the relation R relates two elements a and b, in that order, where a and b are elements of set S, we shall express this by the symbol aRb. We read aRb as "a is related to b." For example, "Tom is older than Larry" may be written aRb, where a stands for Tom, b stands for Larry, and R for the relation "is older than."

If we have a given relation R on a set S we require that for every a and b in S, either aRb is true or $a\cancel{R}b$ is true. The symbol $a\cancel{R}b$ is the negation of aRb.

If a relation satisfies the following properties it is called an *equivalence relation.*

Reflexive Property

We say that a relation R is reflexive if each element a in S in which the relation R is defined is related to itself. That is, aRa is true for all a in S. For example, if S is the set of all people and R is the relation "lives in the same house as," then aRa is true, since every person lives in the same house as himself.

Symmetric Property

We say that a relation R is symmetric if, for every element a and b in S in which the relation R is defined, aRb implies bRa. For example, if S is the set of all people and R is the relation "lives in the same house as," then if a lives in the same house as b $(a\,R\,b)$ then it is true that b lives in the same house as a $(b\,R\,a)$.

Transitive Property

A relation R is transitive if, for every element a and b in S in which the relation R is defined, aRb and bRc implies aRc. For example, if S is the set of all people and R is the relation "lives in the same house as," then if a lives in the same house as b $(a\,R\,b)$ and b lives in the same house as c $(b\,R\,c)$, then it is true that a lives in the same house as c $(a\,R\,c)$.

The relation "lives in the same house as" for the set of all people is an equivalence relation since it satisfies the reflexive, symmetric, and transitive properties.

Other equivalence relations are "is equal to" for the set of all numbers, "is the same age as" for the set of all men, and "is the same height as" for the set of all children.

Another important property of the equality relation is the *substitution principle*. The substitution principle states that if a and b are symbols for the same element of a set, that is, if $a = b$, then any true (or false) statement involving a will remain true (or false) if a, anywhere it appears in the statement, is replaced by b in the statement in which it appears.

Consider the following examples which illustrate the substitution principle:

1. $7 + 3 = 10$ is a true statement. Since $6 + 4 = 10$, we may, by the substitution principle, replace 10 by $6 + 4$ to obtain the true statement $7 + 3 = 6 + 4$.

2. $3 \times 4 = 16$ is a false statement. Since $8 \times 2 = 16$, we may, by the substitution principle, replace 16 by 8×2 to obtain the false statement $3 \times 4 = 8 \times 2$.

2.7. TAUTOLOGY

A *tautology* is a statement formed by combining other statements which is true regardless of the truth values of the statements used to form it. That is, a tautology is true regardless of the truth or falsity of the statements used to form it.

For example, the statement:

$$\sim [p \wedge (\sim p)]$$

is a tautology. This is demonstrated in the truth table (Table 2.5).

Table 2.5

p	$\sim p$	$p \wedge (\sim p)$	$\sim [p \wedge (\sim p)]$
T	F	F	T
F	T	F	T

In making a truth table to show that $\sim [p \wedge (\sim p)]$ is a tautology, we write the headings

$$p, \sim p, \quad p \wedge (\sim p), \quad \sim [p \wedge (\sim p)].$$

Under p we enter the possible truth values, T and F, and carry each line across to the right. If p is true, $\sim p$ is false, $p \wedge (\sim p)$ is false, and the negation of $p \wedge (\sim p)$, that is, $\sim [p \wedge (\sim p)]$ is true. We find that the statement $\sim [p \wedge (\sim p)]$ is true in all cases, and hence is a tautology. This statement is called *the law of the excluded middle.*

For example, if p is the statement "John is here," the statement "It is false that John is here and John is not here" is true regardless of whether p is true or false.

Now let us show that the statement

$$p \vee (\sim p)$$

is a tautology. We again form a truth table as shown in Table 2.6. Since $p \vee (\sim p)$ is true regardless of the truth or falsity of p, it is a tautology.

Table 2.6

p	$\sim p$	$p \vee (\sim p)$
T	F	T
F	T	T

For example, if p is the statement "John is here," the statement "John is here or John is not here" is true regardless of whether p is true or false. We shall now construct a truth table to show that the statement

$$[(p \to q) \wedge (q \to r)] \longrightarrow (p \to r),$$

called the *law of syllogism,* is a tautology.

A more complicated truth table is required to exhibit the fact that the law of syllogism is a tautology. We begin with three columns as shown below because three statements are used to form the law of syllogism. The eight lines show the possible combinations of truth values for p, q, and r.

p	q	r
T	T	T
T	T	F
T	F	T
T	F	F
F	T	T
F	T	F
F	F	T
F	F	F

On the basis of the truth values of p, q, and r we find the truth values of $p \to q$, $q \to r$, $(p \to q) \land (q \to r)$, and $p \to r$ as shown in Table 2.7.

Table 2.7

p	q	r	$p \to q$	$q \to r$	$(p \to q) \land (q \to r)$	$p \to$ r	$[(p \to q) \land (q \to r)] \to (p \to r)$
T	T	T	T	T	T	T	T
T	T	F	T	F	F	F	T
T	F	T	F	T	F	T	T
T	F	F	F	T	F	F	T
F	T	T	T	T	T	T	T
F	T	F	T	F	F	T	T
F	F	T	T	T	T	T	T
F	F	F	T	T	T	T	T

Since $[(p \to q) \land (q \to r)] \to (p \to r)$ is always true regardless of the truth or falsity of p, q, and r, it is a tautology.

The Law of Syllogism is also called the *chain rule*. Successive application of the rule permits a chain of implications of any desired length. If $p \to q$, $q \to r$, and $r \to s$, then $p \to s$.

Anyone who has taken a course in plane geometry is familiar with the application of the chain rule. In proving a theorem we start with a hypotheses, establish a sequence of implications, and end with the desired conclusion. Each step in the theorem must be justified in terms of axioms, definitions, previously proved theorems, or principles of logic.

Another rule necessary in proving theorems is the *law of detachment.* This rule states that if p is true and $p \to q$ is true, then q is true.

For example, if we know that "Perkins has a 3.0 grade point average" and we are given the true implication, "If Perkins has a 3.0 grade point average, then he will graduate cum laude," the law of detachment assures us that "Perkins will graduate cum laude."

The proof of the law of detachment follows immediately in Table 2.8 where the statement is shown to be a tautology.

Table 2.8

p	q	$p \to q$
T	T	T
T	F	F
F	T	T
F	F	T

Since $p \to q$ is given true, we are given the conditions in lines 1, 3, or 4 of Table 2.8. Since p is also given true, we base our conclusions about q on lines 1 or 2. Since line 1 is the only line that satisfies the hypotheses that p and $p \to q$ are true, we see that q must be true.

EXERCISE 2.2

Using truth tables determine whether or not the following are tautologies.

1. $(p \wedge q) \to p$
2. $(p \vee q) \to p$
3. $[(p \to q) \wedge (r \to s) \wedge (p \vee r)] \to (q \vee s)$
4. $(p \vee q) \to \{ \sim [(\sim p) \wedge (\sim q)] \}$
5. $q \to p$
6. $(\sim p) \to (\sim q)$
7. $(\sim p) \to (\sim p)$
8. $p \to (\sim q)$
9. $(\sim p) \to q$

If the implication and the statement given in each problem below is true, what conclusion can be drawn by using the law of detachment?

10. If the sun is shining on Friday, we shall go to the beach. The sun is shining on Friday.

11. If we complete our work on Tuesday, we shall have a test on Friday. We complete our work on Tuesday.

12. If John is a graduate student, he is eligible for an assistantship. John is a graduate student.

For each of the following sets, decide whether the indicated relations are (a) reflexive; (b) symmetric; (c) transitive; or (d) equivalence relations.

13. The relation "is as intelligent as" for all people.
14. The relation "is the cousin of" for all persons.
15. The relation "is greater than" for $\{1, 2, 3, \ldots\}$.
16. The relation "is the brother of" for all males.
17. The relation "is the brother of" for all persons.
18. State in symbols
    a. the law of the excluded middle,
    b. the law of detachment,
    c. the law of syllogisms.

Construct a truth table for each of the following:

19. $p \to (p \lor q)$,
20. $(p \land q) \to p$,
21. $(p \to q) \to (\sim q \to \sim p)$,
22. $(p \land \sim p) \to q$,
23. $(q \land r) \to (q \lor r)$,
24. $\sim (p \lor q) \to (\sim p) \land (\sim q)$,
25. $(p \land q) \lor r$.

2.8.   DERIVED IMPLICATIONS

From an implication, $p \to q$, we can form several related implications which may or may not be true if the given implication is true. The most important are

Converse:	$q \to p$
Inverse:	$(\sim p) \to (\sim q)$
Contrapositive:	$(\sim q) \to (\sim p)$.

By comparing Tables 2.3 and 2.4 we see that the converse $q \to p$ may be false when the implication $p \to q$ is true. For example, the implication

"If a quadrilateral is a square, then it is a rectangle"

is true, but its converse

"If a quadrilateral is a rectangle, then it is a square"

is false.

Of course, in some cases, the converse of a true implication may be true. For example, the following implication and its converse are both true.

Implication: If it is ten o'clock C.S.T. in St. Louis, then it is eleven o'clock in New York.

Converse: If it is eleven o'clock E.S.T. in New York, then it is ten o'clock in St. Louis.

Let us construct a truth table and investigate whether the inverse is true when a given implication is true and false when it is false.

Table 2.9

p	q	$\sim p$	$\sim q$	$p \to q$	$(\sim p) \to (\sim q)$
T	T	F	F	T	T
T	F	F	T	F	T
F	T	T	F	T	F
F	F	T	T	T	T

The last two columns in Table 2.9 differ, hence the inverse of a true implication is not always true.

Now let us construct a truth table (Table 2.10) and discover whether the contrapositive of a true implication is always true, and false when the implication is false.

Table 2.10

p	q	$\sim p$	$\sim q$	$p \to q$	$(\sim q) \to (\sim p)$
T	T	F	F	T	T
T	F	F	T	F	F
F	T	T	F	T	T
F	F	T	T	T	T

Since the last two columns of Table 10 are identical, we assert that an implication and its contrapositive are simultaneously true or false, that is, they are *logically equivalent.*

We use the fact that an implication and its contrapositive are logically equivalent in two ways:

1. If we know a given implication is true, we can infer that its contrapositive is true and vice versa.

2. Proving (or disproving) the contrapositive of an implication is equivalent to proving (or disproving) the implication.

Many errors in reasoning are caused by assuming that the converse of a true implication is also true. The statement "If Smith is preparing for medical school, then he takes chemistry" may be true, but even if it is true, the converse, "If Smith takes chemistry, he is preparing for medical school" may not be true.

Sometimes statements are made that assume that the inverse is true. When a candidate for a political office says, "If I am elected, then the budget will be balanced," he wishes the voters to believe that the inverse of his statement is true. That is, he wishes the voters to assume that if he is not elected the budget will not be balanced. If the voters make the error in assuming that the inverse of his statement is true, their reasoning is faulty.

The contrapositive of a true statement is always true. Advertisers frequently suggest the contrapositive in their advertisements. When an ad reads, "If you drive a Hexo car, you are driving the best," it wants the reader to think that if he is not driving the best car on the market, then he doesn't drive a Hexo car. Politicians also sometimes may resort to the fact that the contrapositive of a true statement is true. When a politician declares, "If you desire lower taxes, then you should vote for me," he wants the people to conclude that if they do not vote for him then they do not want lower tax rates, and, of course, it is assumed that everyone wants lower taxes.

EXERCISE 2.3

Form the (a) converse, (b) inverse, and (c) contrapositive of the implications below.

1. If Peggy and Patty are twins, then Peggy and Patty have the same birthday.
2. If Alice is Tim's sister, then Tim is Alice's brother.
3. If a triangle has two congruent sides, then the triangle is isosceles.
4. If Christmas falls on Friday, then New Year's falls on Friday.
5. If 2 divides 8, then 8 divides 16.
6. If the alarm does not go off, then Jack will oversleep.
7. If a rectangle is a square, then the rectangle has four congruent sides.
8. If a pentagon has five congruent sides, then the pentagon is a regular polygon.

Using truth tables show that the following pairs of statements are logically equivalent.

9. $\sim(p \wedge q)$ and $(\sim p) \vee (\sim q)$
10. $\sim(p \rightarrow q)$ and $p \wedge (\sim q)$
11. $\sim(p \vee q)$ and $(\sim p) \wedge (\sim q)$

12. Is the inverse of the converse of an implication the same as the converse of the inverse of an implication?

2.9. PROOF

Mathematics is a deductive science. It is based on a method of reasoning called deduction. Each branch of mathematics such as arithmetic, algebra, and geometry has been developed and organized according to the rules of logic. A branch of mathematics which is organized logically is called a *logical system,* or since the proofs in mathematics are based on deduction, a *deductive system.*

The essentials of a deductive system are the following:

1. Undefined words.
2. Words defined in terms of the undefined words.
3. An initial set of statements about the defined and undefined words which are assumed to be true (the axioms).
4. The laws of logic for combining these axioms to form new statements called theorems.

We now have the machinery we need to prove theorems. We will not discuss here how mathematicians conjecture theorems which they wish to prove true. This process of guessing statements about the terms in our system (and it is educated guessing) requires a high degree of intellectual ability and mathematical experience. We are interested here in the process of proving that certain conjectured statements are true theorems.

Proofs usually fall into two classes:

1. Direct.
2. Indirect.

In a direct proof a chain of syllogisms are arranged from the given statements to the desired conclusion.

In an indirect proof we assume that the statement, which we wish to prove, is false, that is, that its negation is true. We then use our laws of logic and finally reach a contradiction. When we reach this contradiction we know that our assumption is false; hence the given statement is true.

There is no given technique for proving a theorem. Cleverness, innate ability, and experience are helpful. We learn a great deal about this technique by reading proofs that others have made and by understanding the types of proof used in a deductive system.

2.10. DIRECT PROOF

Study the following examples. In each case the given theorem is proved by means of a direct proof.

THEOREM 1.   If $p, q \rightarrow (\sim p)$, and $(\sim q) \rightarrow s$ are true, then s is true.

PROOF.   We desire a chain of syllogisms from p to s. The statement $q \rightarrow (\sim p)$ involves the statement $(\sim p)$ rather than p. Fortunately we may substitute the contrapositive of $q \rightarrow (\sim p)$ and have as true

$$p \rightarrow (\sim q).$$

Now we have

p	is true by hypotheses,
$p \rightarrow (\sim q)$	is true since $q \rightarrow (\sim p)$ is true,
$(\sim q) \rightarrow s$	is true by hypotheses.

We can now conclude that $p \rightarrow s$ by the law of syllogisms and by the law of detachment, s is true.

THEOREM 2.   Given   1. $(\sim p)$ is true,
                         2. q is true,
                         3. $[(\sim p) \lor q] \rightarrow r$ is true.
        Prove: r is true.

PROOF.

$(\sim p)$	is true by hypotheses,
q	is true by hypotheses,
$[(\sim p) \lor q] \rightarrow r$	is true by hypotheses.

However, since $(\sim p)$ and q are both true, $(\sim p) \lor q$ is true by definition of a disjunction. Since $[(\sim p) \lor q] \rightarrow r$ is true, we know that r is true by the law of detachment.

2.11. INDIRECT PROOF

The indirect method of proof is often called proof by contradiction. By contradiction we mean a statement of the form "p and not p" which is false because a statement cannot be true and false at the same time.

For example, suppose a boy told his mother that he had run all the way home from baseball practice so that he would not be late for dinner. His mother said, "No, you did not! If you had run all the way you would be out of breath. You are not out of breath. Therefore, you did not run all the way home." The mother is using an indirect proof.

Study the following indirect proof.

THEOREM.   Given p is true, $q \rightarrow (\sim p)$ is true, and $(\sim q) \rightarrow r$ is true. Prove that r is true.

PROOF.   Assume $(\sim r)$ is true. Since $(\sim q) \rightarrow r$ is true, the contrapositive $(\sim r) \rightarrow q$ is true. Hence,

$(\sim r)$	is true by assumption,
$(\sim r) \rightarrow q$	is true; contrapositive of true statement,
$q \rightarrow (\sim p)$	is true by hypotheses.

We conclude that $(\sim r) \rightarrow (\sim p)$ by the law of syllogism. Then $(\sim p)$ is true by the law of detachment; but p is true by hypotheses. Hence our assumption that $(\sim r)$ is true is false, and r is true.

EXERCISE 2.4

1. Given: (1) p is true,
   (2) q is true,
   (3) $(\sim p) \rightarrow s$ is true,
   (4) $q \rightarrow (\sim s)$ is true.
   Prove: s is false.
2. Given: (1) p is true,
   (2) $p \rightarrow q$ is false.
   Prove: q is false.
3. Given: (1) $p \vee q$ is true,
   (2) $\sim p$ is true.
   Prove: q is true.
4. Given: (1) $p \rightarrow q$ is true,
   (2) $q \rightarrow \sim p$ is true.
   Prove: $\sim p$ is true.
5. Given: (1) $p \rightarrow q$ is true,
   (2) $q \rightarrow p$ is true,
   (3) $p \rightarrow r$ is true,
   (4) p is true.
   Prove: r is true.
6. Given: If John graduates with honors, his father will give him a trip to Europe. If John gets a trip to Europe, he will visit Germany. If John does not visit France, he will not visit Germany. John graduates with honors.
   Prove: John will visit France.
7. Given: If $ABCD$ is a square, then it is a rectangle. $ABCD$ is a square or $ABCD$ is a rhombus. $ABCD$ is not a rhombus.
   Prove: $ABCD$ is a rectangle.
8. Given: If a number is divisible by 4, then it is divisible by 2. If a number is divisible by 2, then it is even. If a number is even, then it has a factor 2. A number does not have a factor 2.
   Prove: The number is not divisible by 4.
9. Given: Geometric figure $ABCD$, is a rectangle and a parallelogram. If $ABCD$ is a rectangle, then it is a parallelogram. If $ABCD$ is a parallelogram, then it is a quadrilateral.
   Prove: $ABCD$ is a parallelogram or a quadrilateral.

CHAPTER 3

Whole Numbers

3.1. THE WHOLE NUMBERS

The numbers represented by the set of numerals

$$\{0, 1, 2, 3, \ldots, 99, 100, \ldots\}$$

are called the *whole numbers*. If zero is omitted from the set, we have the set of *natural numbers* or *counting numbers* since they are the only numbers we need to count how many. When we use zero to denote the fact that there aren't any, zero is not a counting number, since in counting the members of a set, there is no element before the first element.

Through experience, we observe certain properties of the whole numbers. The first property which we observe is that the set has a first element, zero, but that it has no last element. There is no largest or greatest whole number. If you name the largest whole number you can think of, someone else can add one to it and have a larger whole number. Hence we see that there is no last member of the set of whole numbers. We characterize this property by saying that the set of whole numbers is an *infinite set*.

3.2. ORDER PROPERTY

Adults object when little children count by saying, "One, two, seven, nine, three, five." They object because the *order* in which the number names are said is incorrect. Everyone readily agrees that there is a correct

46

and an incorrect way to order the whole numbers. This property is called the *order property* of the whole numbers.

Whole numbers can be ordered by means of standard sets. (See Chapter 1, Sections 1.10 and 1.12.) Two sets such as

$$A = \{a, b, c, d, e,\}$$

and

$$B = \{\bigcirc, \star, *, \square, \triangle\}$$

are equivalent since their members can be placed in a one-to-one correspondence. The standard set $\{"1", "2", "3", "4", "5"\}$ is equivalent to sets A and B. Hence, the cardinal number for these sets is 5.

If a standard set, S, is a proper subset of a standard set, T, then the cardinal number of S is defined to be less than the cardinal number of T. For example, $\{"1", "2"\}$ is a proper subset of $\{"1", "2", "3"\}$ and hence $2 < 3$. The number zero, the cardinal number of the empty set, is the least of the cardinal numbers.

The elements of the set $\{3, 0, 4, 2\}$ can be ordered $0 < 2 < 3 < 4$ by observing that

$$\{\ \} \subset \{"1", "2"\} \subset \{"1", "2", "3"\} \subset \{"1", "2", "3", "4"\}.$$

Thus we have an ordering of the set of whole numbers.

When the set of whole numbers is written in order, $0, 1, 2, 3, 4, \ldots$, each number is less than any number that succeeds it in the sequence. Thus, $0 < 1 < 2 < 3 < 4 < \ldots$. The statement $2 < 5$, which is read "2 is less than 5," may also be written $5 > 2$, which is read "5 is greater than 2." The symbols $<$ and $>$ mean "is less than" and "is greater than," respectively.

If we choose an ordered pair of whole numbers (a, b), then exactly one of the following statements is true:

1. $a < b$,
2. $a = b$,
3. $a > b$.

This is called the *trichotomy principle*.

3.3. THE NUMBER LINE

The number line gives a model for visualizing the order of the whole numbers. The whole numbers may be represented as shown in Figure 3.1. A line is drawn with a sequence of equally spaced dots. A dot is chosen to correspond to zero and labeled "0". The dots (called points) to the right of 0 are labeled successively 1, 2, 3, 4, and so on. Thus, we have

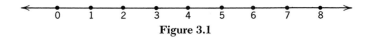

Figure 3.1

a matching of the whole numbers with the equally spaced dots. Each point is the *graph* of the whole number to which it corresponds and each whole number is the *coordinate* of the point to which it corresponds.

Observation of the number line shows the following:

1. To each whole number there corresponds one and only one point on the number line.

2. A whole number a is less than a whole number b if the point corresponding to a is to the left of the point corresponding to b.

3. A whole number a is greater than a whole number b if the point corresponding to a is to the right of the point corresponding to b.

4. There is no greatest whole number; the sequence of points chosen to correspond to whole numbers continues indefinitely to the right.

5. Zero is the least whole number.

3.4. OPERATIONS

An operation in mathematics is a way of associating an ordered pair of numbers with a unique third number. When we associate 9 with the ordered pair $(6, 3)$ we are performing the operation of addition. When we associate 18 with the same ordered pair, we are performing the operation of multiplication. Subtraction and division are also arithmetical operations.

Addition, subtraction, multiplication and division are called the four *basic operations* of arithmetic. Addition and multiplication are called *primary* operations; subtraction and division are called *secondary* operations.

EXERCISE 3.1

1. Rewrite each of the following sets as ordered sets.
    a. $\{3, 4, 1, 2, 8\}$,
    b. $\{b, g, a, c\}$,

c. $\{8, 4, 2, 6, 10\}$,
d. $\{5, 9, 1, 7, 3\}$,
e. $\{m, a, r, c, h\}$,
f. $\{p, l, a, c, e\}$.

2. Consider the ordered pairs below and the number associated with each ordered pair. What operation has been performed on the members of the ordered pair to give the result associated with the ordered pair?

  a. $(7, 9)$,   16,
  b. $(18, 4)$,   14,
  c. $(27, 9)$,   3,
  d. $(576, 9)$,   64,
  e. $(4, 28)$,   32,
  f. $(186, 97)$,   89,
  g. $(17, 25)$,   425.

3. What is the least element in the set of whole numbers? What is the greatest element?

4. Given the number line below. What are the coordinates for the points marked with an x?

5. Define a binary operation.
6. What are the four basic operations of arithmetic?
7. What are the primary operations of arithmetic?
8. What are the secondary operations of arithmetic?
9. What is another name for the set of counting numbers?
10. How many whole numbers are between each of the following pairs of whole numbers?

  a. 16 and 27   b. 17 and 18
  c. 37 and 92   d. 0 and 18.

11. What is the Trichotomy Principle?
12. Place the appropriate symbol ("=", "<", ">") in each of the following blanks to make the statements true.

  a. 3×4 _____ 4×3.
  b. $7 + 9$ _____ $8 + 6$.
  c. $5 + (9 + 6)$ _____ 6×42.

13. Operation $*$ (read "star"), which may be performed on two whole numbers, is described as doubling the first number and adding the second. Thus

$$5 * 3 = (2 \times 5) + 3 = 13,$$
$$3 * 2 = (2 \times 3) + 2 = 8,$$
$$a * b = (2 \times a) + b.$$

Perform this operation on the following pairs of whole numbers.

  a. $a = 2, b = 6$.   b. $a = 4, b = 5$.
  c. $a = 3, b = 9$.   d. $a = 8, b = 4$.

3.5. ADDITION

The union of disjoint sets is the basis for the concept of adding numbers. If $A = \{ \star, \bigcirc, \square \}$
and

$$B = \{ \text{🐱} \quad \text{🐕} \}$$

then

$$A \cup B \{ \star, \bigcirc, \square, \text{🐱} \quad \text{🐕} \}.$$

We know that $N(A) = 3$, $N(B) = 2$, and $N(A \cup B) = 5$.

The sum of the cardinal numbers of two disjoint sets is defined as the cardinal number of the union of the two sets. We say that $2 + 3 = 5$.

When we start with two disjoint sets and form their union, we are operating on sets. When we start with two numbers and get a third, we are operating on numbers. Addition is a *binary operation* on the cardinal numbers associated with two disjoint sets. Addition, then, is an operation on numbers representing the cardinality of the two sets, not on the numbers of the sets themselves.

There are special names for the numbers operated on in addition. The numbers operated on are *addends*, and the result of an addition is called the *sum*. The symbol for the operation is $+$.

Addition may be shown as

$$6 + 7 = 13 \quad \text{or} \quad \begin{array}{r} 6 \\ +7 \\ \hline 13 \end{array}$$

The 6 and 7 are addends; their sum is 13.

3.6. PROPERTIES OF ADDITION

Addition is an operation on an ordered pair of numbers called *addends*, to produce a unique third number called the *sum*. The addends may be thought of as the cardinal numbers of each of two disjoint sets. The sum of these numbers can be defined as the cardinal number of the union of these two disjoint sets.

Addition is called a *binary operation* because it is performed on just two numbers. If we add the following pairs of whole numbers, their sum in each case is a whole number.

$$3 + 4 = 7,$$
$$9 + 6 = 15,$$
$$18 + 9 = 27,$$
$$236 + 154 = 390.$$

Experience with other pairs of whole numbers and our intuition assures us that the sum of any ordered pair of whole numbers is a whole number. We generalize this by saying that the set of whole numbers is *closed* under the operation of addition. This property of addition of whole numbers is called the *closure property of addition*.

If we consider two disjoint sets

$$A = \{|, \setminus, /, -\},$$

and

$$B = \{\bigcirc, \phi, \ominus\},$$

we see that

$$A \cup B = \{|, \setminus, /, -, \bigcirc, \phi, \ominus\},$$

and

$$B \cup A = \{\bigcirc, \phi, \ominus, |, \setminus, /, -\}.$$

Thus

$$A \cup B = B \cup A, \text{ and } N(A \cup B) = N(B \cup A).$$

Since addition of whole numbers is associated with the union of two disjoint sets, we see that

$$7 + 6 = 6 + 7,$$
$$9 + 4 = 4 + 9,$$
$$10 + 14 = 14 + 10.$$

In general, if a and b are whole numbers, then $a + b = b + a$. This property of addition of whole numbers is called the *commutative property of addition*. It states that the order of the addends may be changed without changing the sum.

Addition is a binary operation, that is, it can be performed on just two numbers at one time. If we are asked to add three numbers, for example, 4, 5, and 6, we must operate on just two numbers at a time. There is a natural way of associating the three numbers to find their sum. We may add 4 and 5 first, to produce the sum, 9. To this sum we may add 6 to get the sum, 15. We write this

$$(4 + 5) + 6 = 9 + 6$$
$$= 15.$$

On the other hand, we may add 5 and 6 first to produce the sum, 11. We may add this sum to 4 to get 15. We write this

$$4 + (5 + 6) = 4 + 11$$
$$= 15.$$

Whatever way we associate the addends, the sum is 15; that is,

$$(4 + 5) + 6 = 4 + (5 + 6).$$

This is true for any set of three whole numbers, as illustrated by the following examples:

$$(1 + 2) + 3 = 1 + (2 + 3),$$
$$(5 + 7) + 12 = 5 + (7 + 12),$$
$$(8 + 6) + 7 = 8 + (6 + 7).$$

In general, if a, b, and c are any whole numbers, then $(a + b) + c = a + (b + c)$. This property is called the *associative property of addition*.

Because $(a + b) + c = a + (b + c)$, it is not necessary to use parentheses in writing the sum of three addends. We write $(a + b) + c$ and $a + (b + c)$ as simply $a + b + c$. The associative property of addition may be generalized to hold for four or more addends.

The number zero plays a special role with respect to addition. Notice that

$$0 + 16 = 16 + 0 = 16,$$
$$0 + 9 = 9 + 0 = 9,$$
$$0 + 3 = 3 + 0 = 3.$$

In fact, if a is any whole number, then $0 + a = a + 0 = a$; that is, the sum of zero and any whole number is that whole number. Since zero is the only whole number satisfying this property, it is called the *identity element for addition*, or the *additive identity*.

The operation of addition of whole numbers possesses still another property called the *cancellation property of addition*. Notice that

$$3 + (2 + 2) = 3 + 4 \rightarrow 2 + 2 = 4,$$
$$5 + (6 + 3) = 5 + 9 \rightarrow 6 + 3 = 9,$$
$$8 + (7 + 6) = 8 + 13 \rightarrow 7 + 6 = 13.$$

In general, if a, b, and c are whole numbers, then $a + b = a + c \rightarrow b = c$.

EXERCISE 3.2

What properties of the operation of addition of whole numbers are illustrated by each of the following statements?

1. $3 + 4 = 4 + 3$.
2. $8 + 0 = 8$.
3. $3 + (9 + 6) = (3 + 9) + 6$.
4. $0 + 17 = 17$.
5. $3 + m = m + 3$.
6. $k + 9 = t + 9 \rightarrow k = t$.
7. What sum is associated with each of the ordered pairs of whole numbers below?

    a. (178, 193).   b. (342, 76).
    c. (786, 97).   d. (193, 178).
    e. (76, 342).   f. (99, 107).

8. Which ordered pairs in Problem 7 give the same sum? Why?
9. What is the additive identity for the set of whole numbers?
10. If $2 < 6$, how is $2 + n$ related to $6 + n$ if n is any whole number?
11. Which of the following activities are commutative?

    a. To put on a hat and a coat.
    b. To mix equal parts of blue paint and red paint.
    c. To put on shoes and socks.
    d. To cook dinner and eat it.
    e. To put on a swimming suit and jump into the pool.

12. Which of the following statements are true for any whole numbers a and b?

    a. $(a + b) + 0 = a + b$.
    b. $(a + b) + 6 = a + (b + 6)$.
    c. $5 + (a + b) = (a + 5) + b$.
    d. $12 + (a + b) = (8 + a) + (4 + b)$.

13. Tell which properties of addition of whole numbers make statements (a), (b), and (c) in Problem 12 true.
14. By inspection, determine whether there exists a whole number which may replace n in each of the statements below to make each statement true.

    a. $n + 7 = 9$.   b. $n + 5 = 5 + n$.
    c. $n + 6 = 6$.   d. $(n + 3) + 4 = n + 7$.
    e. $n + 8 = 0$.   f. $n + 4 = 2 + 1$.

15. Group the numbers 4, 9, 7, and 7 as a sum in as many different ways as you can. Carry out the additions and compare the final sums.
16. What properties of addition are used when you add a column of figures starting at the top and ending at the bottom and checking the answer by starting at the bottom and ending at the top?

17. Which of the following sets are closed under the operation of addition?

    a. $\{0\}$.

    b. $\{0, 2, 4, 6, \ldots\}$.

    c. $\{0, 1\}$.

    d. $\{1, 3, 5, 7, \ldots\}$.

18. Let $*$ (read "star") denote the operation of finding the average of two whole numbers. That is, $a * b = \frac{1}{2}(a + b)$. For example,

$$2 * 4 = \frac{1}{2}(2 + 4) = \frac{1}{2} \times 6 = 3,$$
$$3 * 11 = \frac{1}{2}(3 + 11) = \frac{1}{2} \times 14 = 7.$$

Compute

    a. $7 * 21$,   b. $8 * 16$,

    c. $9 * 33$,   d. $5 * 33$.

    e. Is this operation commutative over the set of whole numbers?

19. Give six pairs of actions from ordinary life which are commutative under the operation "followed by," and give six pairs of actions which are not commutative under the operation.

20. Applying the Cancellation Law of Addition involves more than physically striking out the same numeral from both sides of a statement of equality. In each of the following decide which "cancellations" are justified and which are not.

    a. $3a + 4 = 3a + n \rightarrow 4 = n$,

    b. $4(a + 2) = a + c \rightarrow 4(\cancel{a} + 2) = \cancel{a} + c$ and $4 \times 2 = c$,

    c. $6x + 2 = 6y + a \rightarrow \cancel{6}x + 2 = \cancel{6}y + a$ and $x + 2 = y + a$.

3.7. MULTIPLICATION

Multiplication of whole numbers is an operation which associates with two whole numbers, called *factors*, a unique whole number called the *product*. When the number 12 is associated with the ordered pair $(6, 2)$ by multiplication, the 6 and 2 are the factors, and 12 is the product.

Multiplication may be clarified by looking at the cartesian product of two sets. The cartesian product of two sets, A and B, is a process of matching or pairing each element of set A with each element of set B, (see Chapter 1, Section 1.19). For example, let

$$A = \{\star, \bigcirc, \oplus\},$$
$$B = \{\varhexagon, \square, \lozenge, \boxtimes\}.$$

We find the cartesian product, $A \times B$, by matching each element of A with each element of B as shown.

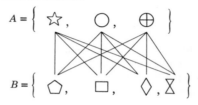

The orderly arrangement of these matchings, is called an *array*. There are 12 different pairs, three rows, and four columns in the array in Figure 3.2. The product, written 3 × 4 and read "three times four," is defined as

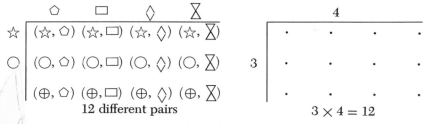

Figure 3.2

number of ordered pairs in the array. Each ordered pair may be rep-
ited by a dot, as shown on the right in Figure 3.2.

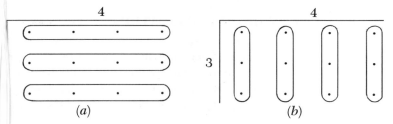

Figure 3.3

ice that a 3 × 4 array is the union of three disjoint sets each having
ements. In order words, 3 × 4 may be thought as the sum of three
Figure 3.3a),

$$3 \times 4 = 4 + 4 + 4.$$

product 3 × 4 may also be thought of as the union of four disjoint
·h having three elements (Figure 3.3b). Thus 3 × 4 may be thought
· sum of four threes,

$$3 \times 4 = 3 + 3 + 3 + 3.$$

product may be represented by an array. Examples are illus-
Figure 3.4.

$$2 \times 3 = 6 \qquad\qquad 3 \times 5 = 15 \qquad\qquad 5 \times 4 = 20$$

Figure 3.4

The number of rows is always written first and the number of columns second. Thus, 5×4 is represented by an array of five rows and four columns. In general, $a \times b$ is represented by an array of a rows and b columns; $b \times a$ is represented by an array of b rows and a columns.

3.8. PROPERTIES OF MULTIPLICATION

The product of every pair of whole numbers is a whole number. No matter what pair of whole numbers are chosen as factors, their product is always a unique whole number. This property of multiplication is described by saying the set of whole numbers is closed under multiplication and is called the *closure property of multiplication*. Study the illustrations in Figure 3.5.

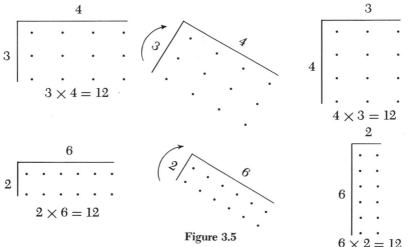

$$3 \times 4 = 12 \qquad\qquad\qquad\qquad 4 \times 3 = 12$$

$$2 \times 6 = 12 \qquad\qquad\qquad\qquad 6 \times 2 = 12$$

Figure 3.5

Notice that $3 \times 4 = 4 \times 3$, and $2 \times 6 = 6 \times 2$. This is true in general.

..at is, if a and b are any whole numbers, $a \times b = b \times a$. This is called the *commutative property of multiplication*.

Figure 3.5 demonstrates the truth of this property for two particular sets of factors. A (3×4) array can be changed to a (4×3) array by simply turning the page $90°$ clockwise.

Multiplication is a binary operation, that is, it is an operation on two numbers at a time. To find the product of three numbers, for example, 4, 5, and 6, we may multiply 4 and 5 and get the product 20, and then multiply 20 and 6 and get the product 120. We write this

$$(4 \times 5) \times 6 = 20 \times 6$$
$$= 120.$$

We might have multiplied 5 and 6 and obtained the product 30, and then multiplied 4 and 30 and obtained the product 120. We write this

$$4 \times (5 \times 6) = 4 \times 30$$
$$= 120.$$

In either case, the product is the same; that is, $(4 \times 5) \times 6 = 4 \times (5 \times 6)$.

Observation of several examples, such as those below helps convince us that the order in which we associate the factors in multiplication does not affect the product.

1.
$$(3 \times 4) \times 2 = 3 \times (4 \times 2)$$
$$12 \times 2 = 3 \times 8$$
$$24 = 24$$

2.
$$(7 \times 5) \times 9 = 7 \times (5 \times 9)$$
$$35 \times 9 = 7 \times 45$$
$$315 = 315$$

3.
$$(2 \times 8) \times 5 = 2 \times (8 \times 5)$$
$$16 \times 5 = 2 \times 40$$
$$80 = 80.$$

In general, if a, b, and c are any whole numbers, then $(a \times b) \times c = a \times (b \times c)$. This is called the *associative property of multiplication*.

In the examples above we have used the familiar $\times$ as the sign of multiplication. Sometimes a raised dot is used to signify multiplication, as in

$$2 \cdot 3 = 6,$$
$$4 \cdot 8 = 32.$$

When two letters are used to stand for numbers, both the dot and the $\times$ are generally omitted and $a \times b$ is written ab.

We can illustrate the associative property of multiplication by considering a figure made up of cubical blocks. Let us use a box of dimensions 3 by 4 by 2. The number of blocks in both Figure 3.6a and Figure 3.6b

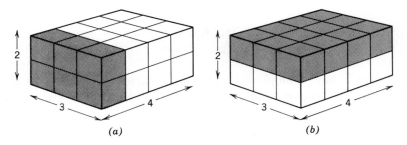

(a)   (b)

Figure 3.6

is 24. In Figure 3.6a the shading shows 2×3 blocks in each vertical slice and four vertical slices. Thus, Figure 3.6a shows $(2 \times 3) \times 4$.

Figure 3.6b shows, by shading, 3×4 blocks in each horizontal slice and two horizontal slices. Thus, Figure 3.6b shows $2 \times (3 \times 4)$.

Since the number of blocks is the same in each case, we see that $(2 \times 3) \times 4 = 2 \times (3 \times 4)$.

This same idea may be generalized with a box of dimensions a by b by c. Since $(a \times b) \times c = a \times (b \times c)$, it is not necessary to use parentheses in writing the product of three factors.

The associative property of multiplication may be generalized for any number of factors.

The number 1 plays the same role for multiplication as the number 0 plays with respect to addition. Observe that

$$1 \times 7 = \;\; 7 \times 1 = 7,$$
$$1 \times 9 = \;\; 9 \times 1 = 9,$$
$$1 \times 26 = 26 \times 1 = 26,$$

or in general, if a is any whole number, $1 \times a = a \times 1 = a$.

The number 1 is called the *identity element for multiplication* or the *multiplicative identity*.

The operation of multiplication of whole numbers possesses another property called the *cancellation property of multiplication*. Observe that

$$3 \times 4 = 3 \times (3 + 1) \longrightarrow 4 = 3 + 1,$$
$$5 \times 7 = 5 \times (4 + 3) \longrightarrow 7 = 4 + 3,$$
$$8 \times 6 = 8 \times (2 + 4) \longrightarrow 6 = 2 + 4.$$

In general, if a, b, and c are whole numbers and $c \neq 0$, then

$$ca = cb \longrightarrow a = b.$$

3.9. THE DISTRIBUTIVE PROPERTY

There is a very important property of whole numbers that ties together the operations of addition and multiplication. The property is called the *distributive property of multiplication with respect to addition* or, simply the *distributive property*. The easiest way to discover this property is to study some examples.

1. $(2 \times 3) + (2 \times 5) = 6 + 10$
   $$= 16$$
   $$= 2 \times 8$$
   $$= 2 \times (3 + 5).$$
2. $(5 \times 4) + (5 \times 9) = 20 + 45$
   $$= 65$$
   $$= 5 \times 13$$
   $$= 5 \times (4 + 9).$$
3. $(8 \times 7) + (8 \times 6) = 56 + 48$
   $$= 104$$
   $$= 8 \times 13$$
   $$= 8 \times (7 + 6).$$
4. $(9 \times 5) + (9 \times 12) = 45 + 108$
   $$= 153$$
   $$= 9 \times 17$$
   $$= 9 \times (5 + 12).$$

As we study these examples, we see that if a, b, and c are any whole numbers it is plausible that

    a. $(a \times b) + (a \times c) = a \times (b + c)$,
    b. $a \times (b + c) = (a \times b) + (a \times c)$,
    c. $(b \times a) + (c \times a) = (b + c) \times a$,
    d. $(b + c) \times a = (b \times a) + (c \times a)$.

Notice that we can distribute from left to right, as in (b) or from right to left as in (d). The two statements, (b) and (d), are equivalent because of the *commutative property of multiplication.*

It is important that we be able not only to "distribute multiplication over addition" as in (b) and (d) but also to "undistribute," as in statements (a) and (c).

We can convince ourselves of the truth of the distributive property by using arrays. For example, let us demonstrate that $2 \times (3 + 4) = (2 \times 3) + (2 \times 4)$. The (2×7) array in Figure 3.7a can be separated by a vertical

$2 \times 7 = 2 \times (3 + 4)$ $(2 \times 3) + (2 \times 4)$
      (a) (b)

Figure 3.7

line segment into a (2×3) array and a (2×4) array as shown in Figure 3.7b. This does not change the number of dots, hence

$$2 \times (3 + 4) = (2 \times 3) + (2 \times 4).$$

EXERCISE 3.3
    1. What product is associated with each of the following ordered pairs?

      a. $(8, 4)$,   b. $(9, 7)$,   c. $(3, 4)$,
      d. $(4, 8)$,   e. $(4, 3)$,   f. $(7, 18)$,
      g. $(19, 27)$,   h. $(242, 17)$,   i. $(306, 27)$.

    2. Which ordered pairs in Problem 1 give the same product? Why?
    3. Draw arrays illustrating the following products.

      a. 3×4,   b. 5×2,   c. 7×3,
      d. 1×6,   e. 8×1,   f. 8×4.

    4. Give the cartesian product, $A \times B$ when

$$A = \{ ☆, ○ \}$$
$$B = \{ △, □, ▱ \}.$$

5. Given. $C = \{$ $\}$, $D = \{$ $\}$,

what is $C \times D$? What is $D \times C$? Is $C \times D = D \times C$? What is $N(C \times D)$? What is $N(D \times C)$? Is $N(C \times D) = N(D \times C)$?

6. What properties of multiplication are illustrated by each of the following statements?

    a. $8 \times 4 = 4 \times 8$,
    b. $3 \times (4 \times 5) = (3 \times 4) \times 5$,
    c. $8 \times 14 = 14 \times (3 + 5)$,
    d. $9 \times 1 = 9$,
    e. $5 \times p = 5 \times q \rightarrow p = q$.

7. Use the distributive property to write the following products as the sum of two addends.

    a. $2 \times (5 + 8)$,   b. $7 \times (16 + 34)$,
    c. $14 \times (5 + 9)$,   d. $28 \times (7 + 16)$.

8. What is the multiplicative identity for the set of whole numbers?
9. If $2 < 6$, how is $2 \times n$ related to $6 \times n$, if n is any counting number?
10. Which of the following sets are closed under multiplication?

    a. $\{0, 1\}$,
    b. $\{1, 3, 5, 7, \ldots\}$,
    c. $\{0, 1, 2, 3, 4\}$,
    d. $\{3, 6, 9, 12, \ldots\}$.

11. Group the numbers 2, 3, 7, and 9 as a product in as many ways as possible. Carry out the multiplications and compare the products.

12. Write zero as a multiple of 5; of 7; of 9. Can you write 8 as a multiple of zero?

13. By inspection, determine whether there exists a whole number which may replace n in each of the statements below to make each statement true.

    a. $4 \times n = 0$.   b. $3 \times n = 15$.
    c. $1 \times n = n$.   d. $5 \times n = 4 \times 5$.
    e. $n \times (3 + 4) = n \times 7$.   f. $2 \times n + 0 = 0$.
    g. $5 \times n = 7$.   h. $4 \times n = 7$.

14. Draw an array to verify that $7 \times (2 + 3) = (7 \times 2) + (7 \times 3)$.

15. An ice cream shop advertises fifty-one different flavors of ice cream. They serve double-dip cones. How many different combinations of flavors (including two dips of the same flavor) must you choose from when you order a double-dip cone?

16. Why is $2 + 2 = (1 \times 2) + (1 \times 2)$?

17. Why is $(1 \times 5) + (1 \times 5) = (1 + 1) \times 5$?

18. Use an array to demonstrate that 3×5 may be thought of as $5 + 5 + 5$.

19. The number zero is unique among the set of whole numbers. List some ways in which it is unique.

20. Show by the distributive property that $30 + 60 = 90$.

3.10. PROVING THEOREMS ABOUT WHOLE NUMBERS

Up to this point we have listed statements, which we called properties of the set of whole numbers and the operations of addition and multiplication, which we accepted as true. By using these properties, called *axioms*, we can prove theorems about the system of whole numbers.

THEOREM 1.   If a is any whole number, then $a \times 0 = 0$.
PROOF.

$a \times 0$ is a whole number	Closure for multiplication
$(a \times 0) + 0 = a \times 0$	Identity for addition
$a \times 0 = (a \times 0) + 0$	Symmetric property of equality
$0 + 0 = 0$	Identity for addition
$a \times (0 + 0) = (a \times 0) + 0$	Substitution principle
$a \times (0 + 0) = (a \times 0) + (a \times 0)$	Distributive property
$(a \times 0) + 0 = (a \times 0) + (a \times 0)$	Transitive property of equality
$0 = a \times 0$	Cancellation for addition
$a \times 0 = 0$	Symmetric property of equality

THEOREM 2.   If a and b are whole numbers such that $a \neq 0$ and $a \times b = 0$, then $b = 0$.
PROOF.

$a \times b = 0$	Hypothesis
$a \times 0 = 0$	Theorem 1
$a \times b = a \times 0$	Transitive property of equality
$b = 0$	Cancellation law of multiplication

THEOREM 3.   If a, b, and c are whole numbers such that $a = b$, then $a + c = b + c$.
PROOF.

$a + c = a + c$	Reflexive property of equality
$a = b$	Hypothesis
$a + c = b + c$	Substitution principle

THEOREM 4.   If a, b, and c are whole numbers such that $a = b$, then $a \times c = b \times c$.
PROOF.

$a \times c = a \times c$	Reflexive property of equality
$a = b$	Hypothesis
$a \times c = b \times c$	Substitution principle

3.11. INVERSE OPERATIONS

We often do something and then undo what has been done. For example, we sit down and then stand up. We put on a pair of gloves and then take them off. We walk three blocks north and then walk three blocks south. These "undoing" activities are called the *inverses* of the doing activities.

Every activity does not have an inverse. For example, scrambling eggs has no inverse. There is no possible way to unscramble eggs and get them back to their original form.

Mathematical operations also have inverses. The inverse of adding 7 to a number is subtracting 7. The inverse of subtracting 6 from a number is adding 6. The operation of subtraction is the inverse of addition.

Addition is an operation on two known addends to produce a third number called a sum. Subtraction is an operation of finding an unknown addend when the sum and one of the addends are known.

The operation of division is the inverse of the operation of multiplication. In multiplication we multiply 4 by 5 to get the product 20. In order to get back to 4 we divide 20 by 5. Multiplication is the operation on two known factors to produce a third number called a product. Division is the operation of finding an unknown factor when the product and one factor are known.

EXERCISE 3.4

1. What is the inverse operation of each of the following activities?

   a. Walking five blocks south.
   b. Putting on a sweater.
   c. Writing "4" on the chalkboard.
   d. Dropping a deck of cards on the floor.
   e. Raising the left hand.
   f. Closing the door.

2. Which of the following activities have no inverse?

   a. Riding up three floors in an elevator.
   b. Reading a book.
   c. Cutting your hair.
   d. Stepping out of an airplane in flight.
   e. Sitting down.

3. What is the inverse operation of addition?
4. What is the inverse operation of multiplication?

In Problems 5–10, a, b, c, and d represent whole numbers.

5. Prove $(a + b) + c = (c + b) + a$.
6. Prove $a(bc) = c(ab)$.
7. Prove $ac + cb = c(b + a)$.
8. Prove $(a + b)(c + d) = ac + bc + ad + bd$.
9. Prove that if $a = b$ and $c = d$, then $a + c = b + d$.
10. Prove that if $a = b$ and $c = d$, than $ac = bd$.

3.12. SUBTRACTION

How do we define subtraction? Suppose we have the numbers 6 and 2. There are several ways of determining the number $6 - 2$.

1. If we think in terms of sets, we choose a set A with 6 members and a set B with 2 members. Then we hunt for a set C so that when we join B and C we get a set $B \cup C$ which equals set A.

There are four elements in set C.

$$B \cup C = \{a, b, c, d, e, f\} = A.$$

2. If we think in terms of subsets we choose a set A with 6 elements and remove from A a subset B with 2 elements. The remainder set, C, has $6 - 2 = 4$ elements.

3. Generally, in mathematics, we think of subtraction in terms of addition. We say $6 - 2$ is the answer to the question, "What number added to 2 gives 6?"

In general, if a and b are whole numbers, we define $a - b$ to be the whole number c if $b + c = a$. If a and b are whole numbers, $a - b$ is a whole number c if and only if $a \geq b$. This is read, "a is greater than or equal to b." The symbol $\geq$ is a combination of $>$ and $=$. If $a < b$ there is no whole number c such that $b + c = a$.

3.13. DIVISION

The operation of division applied to an ordered pair of numbers $(12, 2)$ means that we must determine an unknown factor (in this case, 6) such that the product of 2 and this unknown is 12.

If we go back to arrays, we see that in the case of the division $12 \div 2$

we are asking the question, if a set of 12 elements is arranged in two rows with the same number of elements in each row, how many elements will there be in each row? We may also ask, if a set containing 12 elements is arranged in two columns with the same number of elements in each column, how many elements will there be in each column? These arrays are shown in Figure 3.8.

Figure 3.8

In many cases of division there will be no answer. For example, for the ordered pair $(18, 5)$ there is no answer. There is no array with five rows with the same number of elements in each row that will contain 18 elements.

Division is the inverse operation of multiplication. The division $15 \div 3$ asks the question: "What number multiplied by 3 gives the product 15?" Division is described as finding an unknown factor in a product when the product and one factor are known. Thus,

$$6 \div 3 = 2 \rightarrow 2 \times 3 = 6,$$
$$15 \div 5 = 3 \rightarrow 3 \times 5 = 15.$$

In general if a and b are whole numbers, then $a \div b$ is the whole number c if $b \times c = a$.

Zero presents a problem in the operation of division. Observe that

$$0 \div 2 = n \rightarrow n \times 2 = 0,$$
$$0 \div 3 = n \rightarrow n \times 3 = 0,$$
$$0 \div 9 = n \rightarrow n \times 9 = 0.$$

Since these statements are true if and only if $n = 0$, we conclude that 0 divided by any counting number is zero. Let us look at the following examples:

$$2 \div 0 = n \rightarrow n \times 0 = 2,$$
$$3 \div 0 = n \rightarrow n \times 0 = 3,$$
$$5 \div 0 = n \rightarrow n \times 0 = 5.$$

Since zero times any number is zero, there is no whole number n to make the statements above true. Hence, division by zero is impossible. When we define $a \div b = c$ as $b \times c = a$ we must state that $b \neq 0$.

There is another special case that we must consider; that is, $0 \div 0$. In this particular case we are looking for an unknown factor, n, such that

$$n \times 0 = 0.$$

Since zero times any number is zero, the unknown factor, n, may be any number. Thus, $0 \div 0$ is called an *indeterminate* symbol because it may be the name for any number.

In fact, $a \div 0$ is impossible for all numbers, including $a = 0$.

3.14. PROPERTIES OF SUBTRACTION AND DIVISION

We now ask ourselves if the operations of subtraction and division possess any of the properties of addition and multiplication. Since $a - b$ names a whole number c if and only if $a \geq b$, we conclude that the set of whole numbers is not closed under subtraction.

That subtraction is neither commutative nor associative is demonstrated in the examples below:

$$6 - 4 \neq 4 - 6,$$
$$8 - 7 \neq 7 - 8,$$
$$9 - 3 \neq 3 - 9,$$
$$(9 - 7) - 3 \neq 9 - (7 - 3),$$
$$(12 - 8) - 2 \neq 12 - (8 - 2).$$

If $a - b = a$, it is clear that b must be equal to 0. But although $a - 0 = a$, $0 - a$ is not the name of a whole number, and we conclude that there is no identity for the operation of subtraction.

Is the set of whole numbers closed under division? Since $7 \div 3$ is not the name of a whole number, we can conclude that the operation of division does not possess the closure property.

Division is neither commutative nor associative, as is demonstrated by the examples below:

$$8 \div 2 \neq 2 \div 8,$$
$$12 \div 3 \neq 3 \div 12,$$
$$(24 \div 6) \div 2 \neq 24 \div (6 \div 2),$$
$$(18 \div 6) \div 3 \neq 18 \div (6 \div 3).$$

Since $6 \div 1 = 6$ but $1 \div 6$ is not a whole number, 1 is not the identity element for division.

Distributive Property of Multiplication over Subtraction

Division and subtraction have several important properties. Observe the following examples:

1.
$$6 \times (4 - 2) = (6 \times 4) - (6 \times 2),$$
$$6 \times 2 = 24 - 12,$$
$$12 = 12.$$
2.
$$4 \times (8 - 3) = (4 \times 8) - (4 \times 3),$$
$$4 \times 5 = 32 - 12,$$
$$20 = 20.$$
3.
$$5 \times (9 - 6) = (5 \times 9) - (5 \times 6),$$
$$5 \times 3 = 45 - 30,$$
$$15 = 15.$$

These examples illustrate the relationship of multiplication to subtraction. In general, if a, b, and c are whole numbers and $b \geq c$, then

$$a \times (b - c) = (a \times b) - (a \times c).$$

This property is called the *distributive property of multiplication over subtraction*.

Distributive Property of Division over Addition

Observe the following:

1.
$$(8 + 4) \div 2 = (8 \div 2) + (4 \div 2),$$
$$12 \div 2 = 4 + 2,$$
$$6 = 6.$$

2. $$(24 + 16) \div 4 = (24 \div 4) + (16 \div 4),$$
$$40 \div 4 = 6 + 4,$$
$$10 = 10.$$

These examples are illustrations of the *distributive property of division over addition*. In general, if a, b, and c are whole numbers, and $a \div c$, $b \div c$ and $(a + b) \div c$ are whole numbers, then $(a + b) \div c = (a \div c) + (b \div c)$.

Distributive Property of Division over Subtraction

The examples below are illustrations of a property called the *distributive property of division over subtraction*.

1. $$(12 - 4) \div 2 = (12 \div 2) - (4 \div 2),$$
$$8 \div 2 = 6 - 2,$$
$$4 = 4.$$

2. $$(24 - 12) \div 6 = (24 \div 6) - (12 \div 6),$$
$$12 \div 6 = 4 - 2,$$
$$2 = 2.$$

3. $$(15 - 9) \div 3 = (15 \div 3) - (9 \div 3),$$
$$6 \div 3 = 5 - 3,$$
$$2 = 2.$$

In general, if a, b, and c are whole numbers with $a \geq b$, and if $a \div c$, $b \div c$, and $(a - b) \div c$ are whole numbers, then

$$(a - b) \div c = (a \div c) - (b \div c).$$

EXERCISE 3.5

1. Which of the following are names for whole numbers?

   a. $3 + 18$.   b. $7 - 9$.
   c. $18 \div 9$.   d. $46 + 9$.
   e. $18 - 46$.   f. $17 \div 3$.
   g. $19 - 12$.   h. $17 - 86$.
   i. $112 \div 2$.   j. $136 \div 7$.

2. What property is illustrated by each of the following statements?

   a. $(2 \times 5) + (2 \times 8) = 2 \times (5 + 8)$.

    b. $4 \times (8 - 2) = (4 \times 8) - (4 \times 2)$.
    c. $(8 - 6) \div 2 = (8 \div 2) - (6 \div 2)$.
    d. $(12 + 8) \div 4 = (12 \div 4) + (8 \div 4)$.
    e. $5 \times 100 = (5 \times 40) + (5 \times 60)$.
    f. $(5 \times 3) - (5 \times 1) = 5 \times 2$.
    g. $[(2 + 3) \times 6] + [(2 + 3) \times 4] = (2 + 3) \times (6 + 4)$.

3. Which of the following symbols are meaningless?

    a. $6 \div 0$.   b. $0 \div 6$.
    c. $7 \div 0$.   d. $0 \div 9$.
    e. $18 \div 0$.   f. $0 \div 7$.

4. Complete the following table.

Known Addend	Sum	Number Sentence	Unknown Addend
a. 75	164	$164 = N + 75$	89
b. 69	230		
c. 56	340		
d. 92	176		
e. 99	127		

5. Use the numbers in each addition statement to write two true subtraction statements.

    a. $17 + 84 = 101$.   b. $36 + 54 = 90$.
    c. $19 + 20 = 39$.   d. $47 + 36 = 83$.

6. Write two division statements for each multiplication statement given.

    a. $7 \times 6 = 42$.   b. $16 \times 4 = 64$.
    c. $36 \times 5 = 180$.   d. $24 \times 7 = 168$.

7. Use the Distributive Property of Multiplication over Subtraction to find each product below. For example:

$$5 \times 49 = (5 \times 50) - (5 \times 1) = 250 - 5 = 245.$$

    a. 8×97 b. 7×89
    c. 7×69 d. 5×79.

CHAPTER **4**

Systems of Numeration

4.1. ANCIENT SYSTEMS OF NUMERATION

A *numeration system* is a means of naming numbers. It involves a set of symbols for representing numbers and some rules or *principles* for combining the symbols to form names for numbers. The earliest numeration system used by prehistoric man probably involved but a single symbol, the tally, | , marked on a stick or the wall of a cave.

Rather than dwelling on the history of man's development of a system of numeration, we shall study briefly two ancient systems of numeration, the Egyptian and the Roman, because they offer an opportunity to learn by contrast. The study of these systems, appraising their weaknesses as well as their strong points, and noticing their basic principles, furthers our ability to understand our own system of numeration.

In presenting these ancient systems of numeration, we shall consider their respective *principles*, for these contain the essence of the system. From these principles a system derives its structure and organization. The symbols used to name the numbers are of only passing interest. The symbols and the choice of compounding point, called the *base*, may be referred to as the *accidentals* of the system. Accidentals are those things about the system that are not fundamentally necessary to the system for it to function. If the accidentals are changed, the system itself remains unaffected. On the other hand, to change the principles is to change the system itself. We shall see this more clearly later when we introduce systems of numeration in bases other than ten.

70

The ancient Egyptians attained a high degree of civilization many thousands of years ago. Among their various accomplishments was a form of picture writing known as hieroglyphics. Included in this, to satisfy their number requirements, was a set of numerical symbols. The Egyptians did not use standard sets for each quantity as we do; instead, they evolved a system of repetition which permitted coverage of a wide range of values with a limited symbolism. As we study the Egyptian system, we note the systematic way in which new symbols were introduced.

In its operation this system followed a simple pattern. The symbol for one was a stroke, $/$; the symbol for two was one written twice, $//$; three, $///$; and so on to nine, $/////////$. Up to this point the system was hardly more than a tally method of one-to-one correspondence. At ten a compounding took place and the heel bone symbol $\cap$ replaced what would have been ten strokes. As the Egyptian continued to count, his notation grew by the principle of *addition*. Thus the symbol for what we call twelve was $\cap//$; eighteen, $\cap////////$; twenty, $\cap\cap$; forty-three, $\cap\cap\cap\cap///$; and so on. At one-hundred, or ten tens, a new symbol, the scroll 9 , was introduced for what otherwise would have been ten heel bones. Essentially, the value of any Egyptian number was precisely the sum of its parts. The Egyptian system of notation was governed by the principles of *addition* and *repetition*.

Repeating the basic symbols usually took care of cases of multiplicity for the Egyptians, except in those instances where a new symbol was substituted for ten of a lower order. Table 4.1 shows the symbols for numbers in both our Hindu-Arabic and the Egyptian systems of notation:

Table 4.1

Hindu-Arabic symbol	Egyptian Symbol	number name
1	$\mid$	one
10	$\cap$	ten
100	9	one-hundred
1000	⚱	one-thousand
10,000	$\int$	ten-thousand
100,000	⌒	one-hundred thousand
1,000,000	⚹	one-million

The second ancient system of notation that we shall study is the Roman System. Like the Egyptian, the Roman system of notation employed the principle of *addition*. That is, the value of any numeral is equal to the sum of its parts. It may be characterized as a *decimal* or base ten system.

Special symbols, represented certain powers of ten; I = units, X = ten, C = one hundred = ten × ten, M = one thousand = ten × ten × ten. An economy of symbolism was effected by the Roman system with the introduction of mid-values in each of these orders. Thus, V = five (mid-ten), L = fifty (mid-hundred), and D = five hundred (mid-thousand). The principle of *repetition* was utilized with respect to the basic symbols of I, X, C, and M to form other numerals. For example:

> III = three,
> XXXII = thirty-two,
> CCCXXIII = three hundred twenty-three,
> MMCCII = two thousand two hundred two.

To handle the larger numbers, a third principle, *multiplication*, was put to use. A bar drawn over portions of the numeral indicated that the number represented by those symbols covered was to be multiplied by one thousand, then added to the remaining symbols of the expression to effect its total values. Thus, the number represented by

> $\overline{\text{XXX}}$II = twenty thousand twelve (20,012),
> $\overline{\text{XXXV}}$ = thirty-five thousand (35,000),

and

> $\overline{\text{MMMD}}$ = three million, five hundred thousand (3,500,000).

Still a fourth principle, that of *subtraction*, came into being at a later date. It is claimed by some historians that this was an invention of the early clockmakers, who were hard pressed for space on the face of their clocks. Whatever the case, by substituting IV for IIII and IX for VIIII, a more economical notation was achieved. Had this contraction been restricted only to the specific values of four and nine, however, we would not have a principle but merely a special case. In today's version of Roman notation we do see in effect the principle of subtraction. It operates specifically with respect to the *fours and nines of each order*. Thus:

IV = four.	XL = forty.	CD = four hundred.
IX = nine.	XC = ninety.	CM = nine hundred.

However, this saving in symbolism produces a new problem. In the Egyptian system, the value of the number expressed was not materially effected by the order in which the symbols in the numeral were written. For example, the Egyptians could write twenty-three either as ∩∩∣∣∣ or as ∩∣∩∣∣. In the Roman system coupling I and V, could mean either six or four, depending upon whether the addition or subtraction principle was to operate. Thus, we see in the Roman System a rule of order. For the Roman system it is this: symbols are to be written from left to right in order of decreasing value, and the principle of addition applies. The only exceptions to this order are the pairs, I before V or X, X before L or C, and C before D or M, in which case the subtraction of the number represented by the left numeral from the right is indicated.

EXERCISE 4.1

1. Write the following Egyptian numerals in decimal notation.

   a.   ∩∩∣∣∣∣

   b.   99∩ ⁞⁞⁞⁞

   c.   𓍶 𓋹 99∣∣∣

   d.   𓆓 𓆓 ⌒ ∣∣∣ ∩∩∩∩ ∣∣∣∣∣

2. Write the following decimal numerals in Egyptian notation.

   a. 36.   b. 372.   c. 5,583.
   d. 1,000,750.   e. 14,341.   f. 128,339.

3. Write the following Roman numerals in decimal notation.

   a. MCMLVI.   b. MDX.
   c. MDCCLXXVI.   d. MCMLXIX.

4. Write the following decimal numerals in Roman notation.

   a. 1776.   b. 1952.
   c. 1969.   d. 1919.

5. Does the Egyptian system have a zero? Why or why not?
6. How many symbols are needed to write numerals in the Roman system? What are they?

4.2. THE HINDU-ARABIC SYSTEM

The Hindu-Arabic system is a place value system with symbols chosen for zero, one, two, three, four, five, six, seven, eight, and nine. The next number, ten, is the compounding point in the system and is called the *base* of the system. Because the base of the system is ten, it is called the *decimal* system from the Latin word "decem," meaning ten.

The symbols for zero, one, . . ., nine, that is, the symbols in the set $\{0, 1, 2, 3, 4, 5, 6, 7, 8, 9\}$ are called *digits*. To write numerals for all numbers greater than nine, we use a combination of these digits. These combinations are formed according to a pattern determined by our system of *place value*.

Let us observe a number written in the decimal system and analyze what is meant by a place value system. The number four hundred eighty-six is written

$$\textcircled{2}\,\textcircled{1}\,\textcircled{0}$$
$$4\ 8\ 6 = (\text{four} \times \text{one hundred}) + (\text{eight} \times \text{ten}) + (\text{six} \times \text{one}).$$

The numerals written in circles above the digits indicate that there are three positions involved in writing a numeral with three digits. Similarly, there are four positions involved in writing a numeral with four digits, and so on. In the numeral 486, the digit 6 occupies the 0 position; the digit 8, the 1 position; and the digit 4, the 2 position. To each position is assigned a number, which is the place value of the position. In the decimal system, the place values of the various positions are shown in Table 4.2.

Table 4.2
Place Value in Base Ten

6	5	4	3	2	1	0
one million	hundred thousand	ten thousand	one thousand	one hundred	ten	one
1,000,000	100,000	10,000	1000	100	10	1
$10 \times 100,000$	$10 \times 10,000$	10×1000	10×100	10×10	10×1	1

Place value is a number assigned to a position and is independent of the digit in the position. In any decimal numeral the number represented by a digit, such as the "4" in 486, is a product. This product is the number represented by the digit in the position and the place value assigned to the position. The numbers represented by the digits in 486 are as follows:

$$4 \text{ represents } 4 \times 100,$$
$$8 \text{ represents } 8 \times 10,$$
$$6 \text{ represents } 6 \times 1.$$

The entire number is the sum of the products. Thus, $486 = (4 \times 100) + (8 \times 10) + (6 \times 1) = 400 + 80 + 6$.

The basic principles of the Hindu-Arabic system are the *place value principle* and the *additive principle*. The principle of place value involves two basic ideas: (1) there is a number, called the place value, assigned to each position, and (2) each digit in a numeral represents the product of the number it names and the place value of its position.

4.3. EXPONENTS

In many systems of numeration, and particularly in our decimal system, ten, ten times ten, ten times ten times ten, and so forth, play an important role. The products, consisting of a specified number used as a factor one or more times, may be written in a shorthand form, such as in the following examples:

$$10 \times 10 = 10^2,$$
$$10 \times 10 \times 10 = 10^3,$$
$$10 \times 10 \times 10 \times 10 \times 10 = 10^5.$$

The number which is used as a factor is called the *base*. The superscript to the right of the base is called the *exponent*. The exponent tells how many times the base is to be used as a factor. Thus,

$$10^4 = 10 \times 10 \times 10 \times 10 = 10,000.$$

The base is 10 and the exponent is 4. We read "10^4" as "ten to the exponent four" or "ten to the fourth power." Similarly, we read 10^2 as "ten to the second power" or "ten squared," 10^3 as "ten to the third power" or "ten cubed," 10^5 as "ten to the fifth power," and so on. The numbers 10^2, 10^3, . . ., are called the *powers of ten*.

The base can be any counting number, and can be zero if the exponent is not zero. Thus:

$$2^3 = 2 \times 2 \times 2 = 8,$$
$$5^4 = 5 \times 5 \times 5 \times 5 = 625,$$
$$3^2 = 3 \times 3 = 9.$$

If the exponent is one, the power is defined as the base:

$$3^1 = 1,$$
$$5^1 = 5,$$
$$10^1 = 10.$$

If the exponent is zero, the power is defined as one:

$$2^0 = 1,$$
$$5^0 = 1,$$
$$10^0 = 1,$$
$$8^0 = 1.$$

The powers of ten present a very interesting pattern. Observe that

$$10^0 = 1,$$
$$10^1 = 10,$$
$$10^2 = 10 \times 10 = 100,$$
$$10^3 = 10 \times 10 \times 10 = 1000,$$
$$10^4 = 10 \times 10 \times 10 \times 10 = 10,000,$$
$$10^5 = 10 \times 10 \times 10 \times 10 \times 10 = 100,000.$$

Notice that 10^5 is another name for 100,000. This numeral consists of "1" followed by five "0s". Similarly,

$$10^6 = 10 \times 10 \times 10 \times 10 \times 10 \times 10 = 1,000,000.$$

Hence, the numeral naming 10^6 consists of "1" followed by six "0s".

This is true in general: The numeral naming 10^n consists of a "1" followed by n "0s".

4.4.   EXPANDED NOTATION

The decimal system of numeration has the number ten as the base. Starting at position 0, every place to the left of position 0 has a place value ten times as great as the position to its right. Thus,

position	number name	place value
0	one	$1 = 1 \ \ = 10^0$
1	ten	$10 = 10 = 10^1$
2	one hundred	$100 = 10 \times 10 = 10^2$
3	one thousand	$1000 = 10 \times 10 \times 10 = 10^3$
4	ten thousand	$10,000 = 10 \times 10 \times 10 \times 10 = 10^4$
.	.	.
.	.	.
.	.	.

Every decimal numeral may be written in a form involving exponents, thus

$$673 = (6 \times 100) + (7 \times 10) + (3 \times 1),$$
$$= (6 \times 10^2) + (7 \times 10^1) + (3 \times 10^0),$$
$$4387 = (4 \times 1000) + (3 \times 100) + (8 \times 10) + (7 \times 1),$$
$$= (4 \times 10^3) + (3 \times 10^2) + (8 \times 10^1) + (7 \times 10^0).$$

This form is called *expanded notation*.

EXERCISE 4.2

1. Define place value.
2. What is the base of the decimal system?
3. Write the following in expanded notation using exponents.

   a. 486.　　b. 307.　　c. 8765.
   d. 84,000.　　e. 437,168.　　f. 107,826.

4. Write the following using exponents.

   a. $2 \times 2 \times 2 \times 2$.　　b. $5 \times 5 \times 5$.
   c. $3 \times 3 \times 3 \times 3 \times 3$.　　d. $7 \times 7 \times 7 \times 7 \times 7 \times 7$.

5. Give a simple name for the following:

   a. 8^0.　　b. 9^0.　　c. 10^0.
   d. 14^0.　　e. 2^0.　　f. 12^0.

6. What does the "4" represent in each of the following numerals?

   a. 36,904.　　b. 234,162.
   c. 4,073,800.　　d. 50,341.
   e. 127,416.　　f. 10,487,000.

7. Give a standard numeral for:

   a. 10^7.　　b. 10^4.　　c. 10^8.
   d. 10^3.　　e. 10^6.　　f. 10^2.

8. Write in decimal notation

   a. $(3 \times 10^5) + (2 \times 10^4) + (1 \times 10^3) + (7 \times 10^2) + (6 \times 10^1) + (0 \times 10^0)$.
   b. $(4 \times 10^4) + (2 \times 10^2) + (1 \times 10^0)$.
   c. $(5 \times 10^5) + (3 \times 10^4)$.
   d. $(7 \times 10^3) + (1 \times 10^1)$.
   e. (8×10^5).

9. Write the decimal numeral for each of the following numbers.

    a. nine
    b. seventeen
    c. three hundred six
    d. four thousand sixty-four
    e. one million thirty-four thousand six

10. Write each of the following as a power of ten.

    a. one hundred
    b. one million
    c. ten million
    d. ten thousand
    e. one billion (1000 million)

4.5. BASES OTHER THAN TEN

The selection of ten as a base or compounding point of our system of notation was more a physiological accident of nature than a rational choice. Actually, the choice has little to commend it. Twelve would have made a better selection because of its greater divisibility. The choice of ten as a base is probably owing to the fact that man was born with ten fingers.

There are advantages to be gained from speculation on what might have been had man actually been born with, for example, eight, twelve, five, or two fingers instead of ten. Such conjectures lead to new scales of notation and offer an excellent opportunity to learn more about our own decimal system. In such instances, things which are essential to our system, the principles, are not changed, although those things which are only accidental to the system differ from scale to scale. Moreover, consideration of these new scales carries an additional value for teachers in that it points out many of the difficulties which a young child encounters as he attempts to gain control over what is for him an equally strange system, our decimal system.

Let us construct a few scales of notation involving a base other than ten. These scales will be designed in accordance with the principles of addition and place value characteristic of the Hindu-Arabic system of notation. Instead of ten distinct symbols, however, we shall sometimes need more, sometimes less, but the symbol for zero is always necessary. The compounding point will vary with the base selected. We could introduce a brand new set of symbols for each new scale, but that would only complicate matters unnecessarily. After all, the digits are merely symbols which represent certain concepts and are applicable in any scale. We shall continue to use the familiar Arabic numerals 0, 1, 2, 3, 4, 5, 6, 7, 8, 9, augmenting this set or eliminating from it when necessary.

In building systems of numeration with bases other than ten we shall probably encounter semantic difficulties. It is important here that we know the difference between a number word and its symbolic concept. Familiarity with the decimal system leads us to pair the number word and the symbol without distinction. Actually, they are independent of each other. We tend to think "ten" as always being expressed by the symbol 10. We are so familiar with the decimal system that we are not conscious of the fact that the 1 stands for one ten and the 0 for an absence of ones. If we were working in a system of numeration of base twelve, for example, the symbol "10" would stand for one dozen and no ones, or twelve.

In working with systems of numeration for bases other than ten, let us agree to read the symbol 16 as "one-six." This, of course, means one of the base and six more.

In the Hindu-Arabic system, it will be recalled, each digit contributes to the total value of the number in relation to the number it names and its place value. Since we shall continue to use the Arabic symbols, the number named by a digit will be immediately understood, except in cases where the base exceeds ten. Here additional symbols must be defined, which we shall do at the time they are needed. In the matter of place value it will be further recalled that there exists a relationship between the position and power of the base. In other scales of notation this relationship between position and power of the base will remain constant, an essential "principle" of the system; on the other hand, the choice of base, an accidental, will vary. This is, whereas in base ten the positions from right to left are successive powers of ten—units, tens, hundreds, thousands, and so forth—, in base five, for instance, they would be successive powers of five—units, fives, twenty-fives, one hundred twenty-fives, and so forth. Similarly in base eight they would be successive powers of eight—units, eights, sixty-fours, five hundred twelves, and so forth.

Now let us use the principles of our decimal system and build a system of notation with base eight called the *octal* system. Since the base of our system is eight, we need eight digits. Let us use the familiar digits of our base ten system, that is, the set of numerals {0, 1, 2, 3, 4, 5, 6, 7}.

In the decimal system (base ten) each succeeding position, reading from right to left, has a value ten times as great as the preceding position. In the base eight system, each succeeding position reading from right to left will have a value *eight* times as great as the preceding position. Thus, in base eight system, the 0 position will be the units place, position 1—the eights, position 2—eight times eight, or sixty-fours, and so forth, each position being eight times as great as the succeeding position.

The place values in base eight have position 0, 1, 2, and so forth, as in base ten, but the place value assigned to each position is a power of eight. Table 4.3 illustrates place value in base eight.

Table 4.3
Place Value in Base Eight

3	2	1	0
five hundred twelve	sixty-four	eight	one
eight × eight × eight	eight × eight	eight	one
eight^3	eight^2	eight^1	eight^0

Thus, in the scale of eight, the numeral 43 means $43 = (4 \times eight^1) + (3 \times eight^0)$. That is, 43 in base eight is the same as 35 in the base ten.

Similarly, 524 (base eight) $= (5 \times eight^2) + (2 \times eight^1) + (4 \times eight^0)$
$$= 340 \text{ (base ten)},$$
and
$$1037 \text{ (base eight)} = (1 \times eight^3) + (0 \times eight^2) + (3 \times eight^1)$$
$$+ (7 \times eight^0) = 543 \text{ (base ten)}.$$

From now on we shall use a subscript to denote the base to which a numeral is written. For example $543_{(eight)}$ means that the numeral is written in a base eight system. If no subscript is used, the numeral is in the decimal system.

It is quite simple to convert a numeral in base eight to a numeral naming the same number in base ten. We need only to apply the principle of place value in our system. The number represented by each digit in this numeral is a product as it was in a base ten numeral. The digit 7 is the product of seven and the place value assigned to its position. The digit 6 is the product of six and the place value assigned to its position, and so on. Finally, the number is the sum of the particular products as in the example:

$$234_{(eight)} = (2 \times eight^2) + (3 \times eight^1) + (4 \times eight^0).$$

In base ten numerals we write

$$(2 \times 8^2) + (3 \times 8^1) + (4 \times 8^0) = (2 \times 64) + (3 \times 8) + (4 \times 1),$$
$$= 128 + 24 + 4,$$
$$= 156.$$

Hence, $234_{(eight)} = 156$.

Similarly,

$$1023_{(eight)} = (1 \times eight^3) + (0 \times eight^2) + (2 \times eight^1) + (3 \times eight^0),$$
$$= (1 \times 8^3) + (0 \times 8^2) + (2 \times 8^1) + (3 \times 1),$$
$$= 512 + 0 + 16 + 3,$$
$$= 531.$$

The sets of x's in Figure 4.1 shows the number of elements as named by 23 and $27_{(eight)}$. That is,

$$23 = 27_{(eight)}$$

xxxxxxx xxxxxx
xxxxxxx

$$(2 \times eight^1) + (7 \times eight^0) = 27_{(eight)},$$

xxxxxxxxx xxx
xxxxxxxxx

$$(2 \times ten^1) + (3 \times ten^0) = 23.$$

Figure 4.1

To write a numeral in base ten as a corresponding numeral in base eight, think of the objects in standard sets regrouped in eights. If we have sixty-nine objects, can we make a set of sixty-four or eight^2 objects? We have *one* set of sixty-four, so we place a "1" in position 2. We have grouped sixty-four objects and have five left to be grouped. We cannot make a set of eight objects out of five objects, so we place a "0" in position 1. We have five objects left so we place a "5" in position 0. Thus

$$69 = 64 + 0 + 5,$$
$$= (1 \times 64) + (0 \times 8) + (5 \times 1),$$
$$= (1 \times eight^2) + (0 \times eight^1) + (5 \times eight^0),$$
$$= 105_{(eight)}.$$

Thus, 69 and $105_{(eight)}$ are names for the same number.
Similarly,

$$284 = 256 + 24 + 4,$$
$$= (4 \times 64) + (3 \times 8) + (4 \times 1),$$
$$= (4 \times eight^2) + (3 \times eight^1) + (4 \times eight^0),$$
$$= 434_{(eight)}.$$

and

$$1364 = 1024 + 320 + 16 + 4,$$
$$= (2 \times 512) + (5 \times 64) + (2 \times 8) + (4 \times 1),$$
$$= (2 \times eight^3) + (5 \times eight^2) + (2 \times eight^1) + (4 \times eight^0),$$
$$= 2524_{(eight)}.$$

We can also change a base ten numeral to a base eight numeral by division. Study the following illustration.

$$8\overline{)284}$$
$$8\overline{)35} \quad R \quad 4 \times 8^0$$
$$8\overline{)4} \quad R \quad 3 \times 8^1 \qquad 284 = 434_{(eight)}.$$
$$0 \quad R \quad 4 \times 8^2$$

$$8\overline{)1364}$$
$$8\overline{)170} \quad R \quad 4 \times 8^0$$
$$8\overline{)21} \quad R \quad 2 \times 8^1 \qquad 1364 = 2524_{(eight)}.$$
$$8\overline{)2} \quad R \quad 5 \times 8^2$$
$$0 \quad R \quad 2 \times 8^3$$

4.6.   THE DUODECIMAL SYSTEM

We shall now construct a system of numeration with a base greater than ten. The *duodecimal system,* with base twelve, is just such a system. In the duodecimal system, we need twelve symbols and form sets of twelves (dozens), twelve-twelves (gross), twelve-twelve-twelves (great gross), and so forth. If we use, as previously, the symbols 0, 1, 2, 3, 4, 5, 6, 7, 8, 9, we will need two new symbols to represent ten and eleven. Let us use χ^* (read dec) for ten and ε (read el) for eleven. Our set of digits for the duodecimal system is then $\{0, 1, 2, 3, 4, 5, 6, 7, 8, 9, \chi, \varepsilon\}$.

*Sometimes T is used for ten and E for eleven. It should be remembered that any symbol we like may be used to name a number.

In the duodecimal system we group in sets of one dozen. The numeral for the set

$$xxxxxxxxxxx \; xxxxx$$

is 15$_{(twelve)}$ (read, "one-five, base twelve" or "one dozen and five"). Table 4.4 shows numerals in the decimal and duodecimal systems.

Table 4.4
Numerals in Duodecimal and Decimal System

decimal notation	duodecimal grouping	duodecimal notation
0		0
1	*x*	1
2	*xx*	2
3	*xxx*	3
4	*xxxx*	4
5	*xxxxx*	5
6	*xxxxxx*	6
7	*xxxxxxx*	7
8	*xxxxxxxx*	8
9	*xxxxxxxxx*	9
10	*xxxxxxxxxx*	χ
11	*xxxxxxxxxxx*	ε
12	*xxxxxxxxxxxx*	10
13	*xxxxxxxxxxxx x*	11
14	*xxxxxxxxxxxx xx*	12
	· · ·	
25	*xxxxxxxxxxxx* *xxxxxxxxxxxx x*	21
26	*xxxxxxxxxxxx xx* *xxxxxxxxxxxx*	22
	· · ·	
35	*xxxxxxxxxxxx xxxxxxxxxxx* *xxxxxxxxxxxx*	2ε
36	*xxxxxxxxxxxx* *xxxxxxxxxxxx* *xxxxxxxxxxxx*	30

We use the same method as before to change from base twelve numerals to base ten numerals. For example,

$$34_{(twelve)} = (3 \times twelve^1) + (4 \times twelve^0),$$
$$= (3 \times 12) + (4 \times 1),$$
$$= 36 + 4,$$
$$= 40.$$

and

$$12\varepsilon_{(twelve)} = (1 \times twelve^2) + (2 \times twelve^1) + (\varepsilon \times twelve^0),$$
$$= (1 \times 144) + (2 \times 12) + (11 \times 1),$$
$$= 144 + 24 + 11,$$
$$= 179.$$

We use the same method previously explained to change from base ten to base twelve numerals. For example,

$$164 = 144 + 12 + 8,$$
$$= (1 \times 12^2) + (1 \times 12^1) + (8 \times 12^0),$$
$$= (1 \times twelve^2) + (1 \times twelve^1) + (8 \times twelve^0),$$
$$= 118_{(twelve)}.$$

or, using the method of dividing by the base,

$$
\begin{array}{rl}
12\overline{)164} & \\
12\overline{)13} & R \quad 8 \times 12^0 \\
12\overline{)1} & R \quad 1 \times 12^1 \\
0 & R \quad 1 \times 12^2.
\end{array}
\qquad 164 = 118_{(twelve)}.
$$

In another example

$$35 = 24 + 11,$$
$$= (2 \times 12^1) + (11 \times 12^0),$$
$$= (2 \times twelve^1) + (\varepsilon \times twelve^0),$$
$$= 2\varepsilon_{(twelve)}.$$

or

$$
\begin{array}{rl}
12\overline{)35} & \\
12\overline{)2} & R \quad 11 \times 12^0 \\
0 & R \quad 2 \times 12^1 \quad (\text{or } \varepsilon \times twelve^0)
\end{array}
\qquad 35 = 2\varepsilon_{(twelve)}.
$$

EXERCISE 4.3

1. Write the first twenty-five numerals in the base eight system.
2. Write the first twenty-five numerals in the base five system.
3. Write the numbers from 25 to 40 in the base eight system.
4. Write the numbers from 25 to 50 in the base five system.
5. Write the numeral from the base eight system that represents the number of *x*'s below.

$$x\ x\ x\ x\ x\ x\ x\ x\ x\ x\ x\ x\ x\ x$$

6. Write the numeral from the base five system that represents the number of *x*'s in Problem 5.
7. Write the number of fingers you have in the

    a. decimal system.
    b. octal system.
    c. base five system.

8. How many digits are needed in a base eight system of numeration; in a base two system; in a base five system; in a base twenty system?
9. Change the following to base ten numerals

    a. $22_{(eight)}$.   b. $71_{(eight)}$.
    c. $134_{(eight)}$.   d. $707_{(eight)}$.
    e. $2031_{(eight)}$.   f. $1464_{(eight)}$.

10. Change the following decimal numerals to base eight numerals.

    a. 34.   b. 76.   c. 89.
    d. 69.   e. 126.   f. 667.

11. Write the four-digit numeral that represents the largest possible number in the

    a. base eight system.
    b. base five system.
    c. base seven system.

12. Use the symbols "$<$" and "$>$" to compare numbers named by the pairs of numerals below.

    a. $164_{(eight)}$. $14_{(eight)}$.
    b. $707_{(eight)}$. $716_{(eight)}$.
    c. $4317_{(eight)}$. $4137_{(eight)}$.

13. Change the following to decimal numerals.

    a. $32_{(five)}$.   b. $214_{(five)}$.
    c. $100_{(five)}$.   d. $1344_{(five)}$.

14. Change the following decimal numerals to base five numerals.

a. 7.   b. 9.   c. 16.
d. 23.   e. 25.   f. 74.
g. 136.   h. 260.   i. 707.

15. Change the following numerals to decimal notation.

    a. $34_{(five)}$.   b. $130_{(four)}$.   c. $26_{(nine)}$.
    d. $301_{(seven)}$.   e. $42_{(twenty)}$.   f. $1111_{(three)}$.
    g. $111_{(two)}$.   h. $202_{(four)}$.   i. $2164_{(eight)}$.

16. Write the following duodecimal numerals as decimal numerals.

    a. $1\chi7_{(twelve)}$.   b. $\chi\varepsilon_{(twelve)}$.
    c. $\chi0\varepsilon_{(twelve)}$.   d. $96_{(twelve)}$.
    e. $107_{(twelve)}$.   f. $316_{(twelve)}$.

17. Change the following decimal numerals to duodecimal numerals.

    a. 34.   b. 179.   c. 285.   d. 275.

18. Use the symbols "$=$", "$<$", "$>$" to compare the pairs of numbers named by the numerals below.

    a. $26_{(eight)}$, $1011_{(eight)}$.
    b. $5_{(ten)}$, $11_{(four)}$.
    c. $100_{(eight)}$, $346_{(nine)}$.
    d. $\chi\varepsilon_{(twelve)}$, $1234_{(five)}$.

19. What does the "4" represent in each of the following numerals?

    a. 432.   b. $124_{(five)}$.   c. $304_{(seven)}$.
    d. $142_{(eight)}$.   e. $240_{(twelve)}$.   f. $403_{(six)}$.

20. What is the numeral for the next number after each of the following?

    a. $66_{(seven)}$.   b. $22_{(three)}$.
    c. $444_{(five)}$.   d. $\varepsilon\varepsilon\varepsilon_{(twelve)}$.

4.7. THE BINARY SYSTEM

Since the *binary system* is important in the computer field, it is important that special attention be given to it. The binary, or base two system, requires only two symbols, 0 and 1. The place values in this system are the powers of two.

$$\text{two}^0 = \text{one,}$$
$$\text{two}^1 = \text{two,}$$
$$\text{two}^2 = \text{four,}$$
$$\text{two}^3 = \text{eight, and so forth.}$$

The binary numeral for two is $10_{(two)} = (1 \times \text{two}^1) + (0 \times \text{two}^0)$.

Table 4.5
Numerals in Binary and Decimal System

decimal notation	binary grouping	binary notation
0		0
1	x	1
2	xx	10
3	xx x	11
4	xx	100
	xx	
5	xx x	101
	xx	
6	xx xx	110
	xx	
7	xx xx x	111
	xx	
8	xx	1000
	xx	
	xx	
	xx	
9	xx x	1001
	xx	
	xx	
	xx	
10	xx xx	1010
	xx	
	xx	
	xx	

Binary numerals are based on sets of two, just as the decimal system is based on sets of ten, the octal system on sets of eight, and the duo-decimal system on sets of twelve. Table 4.5 shows numerals in base two (binary) and base ten (decimal).

Let us examine some binary numerals:

$$1001_{(two)} = (1 \times two^3) + (0 \times two^2) + (0 \times two^1) + (1 \times two^0),$$
$$= (1 \times 2^3) + (0 \times 2^2) + (0 \times 2^1) + (1 \times 2^0),$$
$$= 8 + 0 + 0 + 1,$$
$$= 9.$$
$$11011_{(two)} = (1 \times two^4) + (1 \times two^3) + (0 \times two^2) + (1 \times two^1)$$
$$+ (1 \times two^0),$$
$$= (1 \times 16) + (1 \times 8) + (0 \times 4) + (1 \times 2) + (1 \times 1),$$
$$= 16 + 8 + 0 + 2 + 1,$$
$$= 27.$$

We convert base ten numerals to binary numerals using the same method as before. Study the following:

$18 = 16 + 2,$
$\quad = (1 \times 16) + (0 \times 8) + (0 \times 4) + (1 \times 2) + (0 \times 1),$
$\quad = (1 \times two^4) + (0 \times two^3) + (0 \times two^2) + (1 \times two^1) + (0 \times two^0),$
$\quad = 10010_{(two)}.$

or

$$
\begin{array}{ll}
2)\underline{18} & \qquad 18 = 10010_{(two)}. \\
\ 2)\underline{9} & \ R \ \ 0 \times 2^0 \\
\ 2)\underline{4} & \ R \ \ 1 \times 2^1 \\
\ 2)\underline{2} & \ R \ \ 0 \times 2^2 \\
\ 2)\underline{1} & \ R \ \ 0 \times 2^3 \\
\ \ \ 0 & \ R \ \ 1 \times 2^4
\end{array}
$$

4.8. BINARY-OCTAL RELATION

Writing binary numerals is cumbersome because they require many digits.

$$64 = 1{,}000{,}000_{(two)},$$
$$46 = 101{,}110_{(two)}.$$

Binary numerals convert easily to octal numerals, and octal numerals require fewer digits than the corresponding binary numerals. For example,

$$1000_{(two)} = 10_{(eight)},$$
$$101110_{(two)} = 56_{(eight)}.$$

Let us examine the method for converting a binary numeral to an octal numeral. First we insert commas in the binary numerals, starting from the right in the customary fashion in groups of three, thus: $1{,}101{,}111_{(two)}$. We then convert the numeral to the octal system as follows:

$$1{,}101{,}111_{(two)} = [1 \times two^6] + [(1 \times two^5) + (0 \times two^4) + (1 \times two^3)]$$
$$+ [(1 \times two^2) + (1 \times two^1) + (1 \times two^0)].$$

Notice that the first bracket [   ] encloses the number represented by "1", the second bracket the number represented by "101", and the third bracket the number represented by "111".

Observe the three expressions enclosed by brackets.

$$[1 \times \text{two}^6] = \text{sixty-four},$$
$$= 1 \times \text{eight}^2,$$
$$[1 \times \text{two}^5] + [0 \times \text{two}^4] + [1 \times \text{two}^3] = \text{thirty-two} + \text{zero} + \text{eight},$$
$$= 32 + 0 + 8,$$
$$= 40,$$
$$= 5 \times \text{eight},$$
$$[1 \times \text{two}^2] + [1 \times \text{two}^1] + [1 \times \text{two}^0] = \text{four} + \text{two} + \text{one},$$
$$= 4 + 2 + 1,$$
$$= 7 \times \text{one}.$$

Putting these together, we have $1{,}101{,}111_{(\text{two})} = 157_{(\text{eight})}$.

This example suggests a method for converting the numeral $1{,}101{,}111_{(\text{two})}$ to numeral $157_{(\text{eight})}$. It looks much more complicated than it really is. Notice the three groups of digits: 1, 101, 111. Let us consider each group alone as a binary numeral.

"1" names one in base two,
"101" names five in base two,
"111" names seven in base two.

However, we found that $1{,}101{,}111_{(\text{two})} = 157_{(\text{eight})}$. This demonstrates a pattern for converting binary numerals to octal numerals. Study the following examples:

$$11{,}101{,}111{,}001_{(\text{two})} = 3571_{(\text{eight})},$$
$$111{,}000{,}110{,}111_{(\text{two})} = 7067_{(\text{eight})}.$$

We can convert an octal numeral to a binary numeral in a similar fashion. In this case we consider each digit in the octal numeral separately and write it in binary notation thus:

octal numeral	4	6	7	3
	four	six	seven	three
binary numeral	100,	110,	111,	011.

Hence, $4673_{(\text{eight})} = 100{,}110{,}111{,}011_{(\text{two})}$.

4.9.   SUMMARY

We have studied place value systems of numeration using base ten (our own familiar decimal system), base eight, base twelve, and base two. Place value systems may be constructed using any base. All place value systems have some common features.

1. Every place value system of numeration has a base which may be any whole number greater than one.

2. The number of symbols necessary in any place value system is the same as the base.

3. Each position in a numeral is assigned a place value which is a power of the base.

Table 4.6 shows the place values in a base five system of numeration.

Table 4.6
Place Value in Base Five

position	3	2	1	0
	one hundred twenty-five	twenty-five	five	one
	five × five × five	five × five	five	one
	five^3	five^2	five^1	five^0

Table 4.7 shows the numeral sequence for several place value systems of numeration.

In examining Table 4.7 we make the following observations:

1. The base numeral always is written 10.

2. In writing a numeral for any number greater than the base, more than one digit must be used.

3. Each digit in a numeral represents a number. This number is the product of a number less than the base and the place value assigned to the position in which the digit is written.

4. The number named by any numeral is the sum of products defined in (3) above.

Table 4.7
Numeral Sequences for Selected Place Value Systems

twelve	ten	eight	Base five	four	three	two
1	1	1	1	1	1	1
2	2	2	2	2	2	10
3	3	3	3	3	10	11
4	4	4	4	10	11	100
5	5	5	10	11	12	101
6	6	6	11	12	20	110
7	7	7	12	13	21	111
8	8	10	13	20	22	1000
9	9	11	14	21	100	1001
χ	10	12	20	22	101	1010
ε	11	13	21	23	102	1011
10	12	14	22	30	110	1100
11	13	15	23	31	111	1101
12	14	16	24	32	112	1110
13	15	17	30	33	120	1111
14	16	20	31	100	121	10000
15	17	21	32	101	122	10001
16	18	22	33	102	200	10010
17	19	23	34	103	201	10011
18	20	24	40	110	202	10100
19	21	25	41	111	210	10101
1χ	22	26	42	112	211	10110
1ε	23	27	43	113	212	10111
20	24	30	44	120	220	11000

EXERCISE 4.4

1. Write the first twenty numerals in the binary system.
2. Write the numbers from 32 to 48 in binary notation.
3. Change the following binary numerals to decimal notation.

    a. $101,111_{(two)}$.   b. $1,111_{(two)}$.
    c. $110,101,100_{(two)}$.   d. $101,111,111,101_{(two)}$.

4. Change the following decimal numerals to binary numerals.

    a. 7.   b. 16.   c. 27.   d. 136.

5. Change the following binary numerals to octal numerals.

    a. $101,100_{(two)}$.   b. $100,001,010_{(two)}$.
    c. $111,111,111_{(two)}$.   d. $101,011,001_{(two)}$.

6. Change the following octal numerals to binary numerals.

    a. $73_{(eight)}$.   b. $64_{(eight)}$.
    c. $100_{(eight)}$.   d. $346_{(eight)}$.

7. Use the symbols "$=$", "$<$", and "$>$" to compare the pairs of numbers named by the numerals below.

    a. $101,111_{(two)}$, $57_{(eight)}$.
    b. $111,000_{(two)}$, $77_{(eight)}$.
    c. $101,001,110_{(two)}$, $500_{(eight)}$.
    d. $111,111,000_{(two)}$, $1364_{(eight)}$.

8. What disadvantages are there in the use of a system of numeration with a small base?

9. What is the numeral for the base in the binary system; in the octal system?

CHAPTER **5**

The Algorithms

5.1. DEFINITIONS

Just as our system of numeration evolved out of a desire for simplicity and compactness in recording numbers, the algorithms evolved from a desire for speed, accuracy, and efficiency in carrying out numerical calculations.

It is important to distinguish between an operation and the *algorithm* associated with that operation. A mathematical operation associates with each pair of numbers a unique number. An algorithm, on the other hand, is a pattern used to find this number.

An algorithm, such as the addition algorithm, has a particular pattern which everyone familiar with the algorithm uses. In addition, several addends are written in columns, the numbers in each column are added, and the sums recorded in a definite order. These patterns are important since they minimize the chances of error and shorten the work in computation. An algorithm depends upon two things: (1) the properties of a set of numbers and its operations, and (2) the properties of the system of notation used in recording the numbers.

Although the properties of the whole numbers and their operations are true regardless of how the numbers are recorded, the familiar algorithms work only when these numbers are recorded in a place value system of notation.

In discussing the algorithms we shall assume that we have at our disposal the following:

1. The set of whole numbers.

2. The sum of any pair of whole numbers from the set of digits in our system of numeration which we shall call the *addition facts* or *basic sums*.

3. The product of any pair of whole numbers from the set of digits on our system of numeration which we shall call the *multiplication facts* or *basic products*.

4. The properties of the whole numbers and their operations.

5. A place value system of numeration.

5.2. THE ADDITION ALGORITHM

Although the history of the evolution of the addition algorithm as we know it today is very interesting, it is not our purpose to discuss this evolution. We shall instead discuss the reasons why these patterns with which we are all familiar work, that is, provide a logical basis for the addition algorithm.

We usually record the addition of $18 + 27$ as

$$\begin{array}{r} 18 \\ +27 \\ \hline 45 \end{array}$$

or at the more elementary level as

$$\begin{array}{r} 18 = 10 + 8 \\ +\ 27 = 20 + 7 \\ \hline 30 + 15 = (30 + 10) + 5 \\ = 45. \end{array}$$

Let us consider this rather elementary addition problem and state the logical reasons, that is, the properties and principles that justify adding ones and ones, tens and tens, and so forth, and the process of "carrying." The reason for each step in the addition example below is stated at the right of each step.

$18 + 27 = [(1 \times 10^1) + (8 \times 10^0)] + [(2 \times 10^1) + (7 \times 10^0)],$ Expanded notation

$\quad = (1 \times 10^1) + \{(8 \times 10^0) + [(2 \times 10^1) + (7 \times 10^0)]\},$ Associative property of addition

$\quad = (1 \times 10^1) + \{[(2 \times 10^1) + (7 \times 10^0)] + (8 \times 10^0)\},$ Commutative property of addition

$\quad = (1 \times 10^1) + \{(2 \times 10^1) + [(7 \times 10^0) + (8 \times 10^0)]\},$ Associative property of addition

$$= [(1 \times 10^1) + (2 \times 10^1)] + [(7 \times 10^0) + (8 \times 10^0)], \qquad \text{Associative property of addition}$$

$$= [(1 + 2) \times 10^1] + [(7 + 8) \times 10^0], \qquad \text{Distributive property}$$

$$= (3 \times 10^1) + (15 \times 10^0), \qquad \text{Basic sums}$$

$$= (3 \times 10^1) + \{[(1 \times 10^1) + (5 \times 10^0)] \times 10^0\}, \qquad \text{Expanded notation}$$

$$= (3 \times 10^1) + \{[(1 \times 10^1) + (5 \times 10^0)] \times 1\}, \qquad 10^0 = 1$$

$$= (3 \times 10^1) + [(1 \times 10^1) + (5 \times 10^0)], \qquad \text{Multiplicative identity}$$

$$= [(3 \times 10^1) + (1 \times 10^1)] + (5 \times 10^0), \qquad \text{Associative property of addition}$$

$$= [(3 + 1) \times 10^1] + (5 \times 10^0), \qquad \text{Distributive property}$$

$$= (4 \times 10^1) + (5 \times 10^0), \qquad \text{Basic sums}$$

$$= 45. \qquad \text{Place value notation}$$

Notice in this long explanation that the Distributive Property justifies the addition of tens and tens, and ones and ones. The Associative and Commutative Properties are used over and over to group and order the terms so that the Distributive Property may be used. When we use column addition, that is when we use the familiar addition algorithm, the adding of the digits in the various columns is justified by the reasons stated in the long form above. The illustrated example shows the "carrying" of one ten. The same method is used to "carry" hundreds, thousands, and so forth.

The explanation above used numerals in the familiar decimal system. The same algorithm may be used with numerals written in any place value system regardless of the base.

The place values for the octal system are given in Table 5.1. The Basic Sums for the octal system are given in Table 5.2.

Table 5.1

Place Value in Octal System			
eight^3	eight^2	eight^1	eight^0
or	or	or	or
five hundred twelve	sixty-four	eight	one

Table 5.2

+	0	1	2	3	4	5	6	7
0	0	1	2	3	4	5	6	7
1	1	2	3	4	5	6	7	10
2	2	3	4	5	6	7	10	11
3	3	4	5	6	7	10	11	12
4	4	5	6	7	10	11	12	13
5	5	6	7	10	11	12	13	14
6	6	7	10	11	12	13	14	15
7	7	10	11	12	13	14	15	16

Consider the sum $34_{(eight)} + 42_{(eight)}$.

$$34_{(eight)} + 42_{(eight)} = [(3 \times eight^1) + (4 \times eight^0)]$$
$$+ [(4 \times eight^1) + (2 \times eight^0)].\text{—Expanded notation.}$$

If the commutative and associative properties are applied in a similar manner to their use in addition in the decimal system, we have

$$[(3 \times eight^1) + (4 \times eight^1)] + [(4 \times eight^0) + (2 \times eight^0)].$$

Using the distributive property we obtain

$$[(3 + 4) \times eight^1] + [(4 + 2) \times eight^0]$$
$$= (7 \times eight^1) + (6 \times eight^0).\text{—Basic Sums.}$$
$$= 76_{(eight)}.\text{—Place value notation.}$$

Since in the octal system the number eight is written $10_{(eight)}$, we could have substituted the numeral $10_{(eight)}$ for the word "eight" in the above explanation.

In the familiar addition algorithm we would have

$$34_{(eight)}$$
$$+42_{(eight)}$$
$$\overline{76_{(eight)}}$$

Study the addition in the octal system below. The explanation is written at the right.

$$23_{(eight)} \qquad 3 + 6 = 11_{(eight)} \qquad 11 + 2 = 13_{(eight)}$$

$$46_{(eight)}$$
$$+72_{(eight)}$$
$$163_{(eight)}$$

Write the 3 in the one's column and carry 1 eight.

$$1 + 2 = 3_{(eight)} \qquad 3 + 4 = 7_{(eight)} \qquad 7 + 7 = 16_{(eight)}$$

5.3. THE SUBTRACTION ALGORITHM

The operation of subtraction is the inverse operation of addition. That is, if a and b are whole numbers and $a \geq b$, then $a - b = c$ means $b + c = a$.

There is an important property of subtraction which is illustrated in the statements below.

$$(9 + 8) - (4 + 3) = (9 - 4) + (8 - 3),$$
$$17 - 7 = 5 + 5,$$
$$10 = 10,$$
$$(7 + 3) - (5 + 1) = (7 - 5) + (3 - 1),$$
$$10 - 6 = 2 + 2,$$
$$4 = 4.$$

In general, it is true that if a, b, c, and d are whole numbers with $a \geq c$ and $b \geq d$, then $(a + b) - (c + d) = (a - c) + (b - d)$.

We shall accept this property, which we shall call the *subtraction property*, without proof. It is vital in the explanation of the subtraction algorithm.

Let us now subtract $83 - 47$, justifying each step. We know that $83 - 47 = n$ means that $47 + n = 83$. Remembering that when we subtract 47 from 83 we must *rename* 83 so that it is possible to subtract ones from ones and tens from tens, let us first justify this renaming or *regrouping* as it is commonly called.

$83 = (8 \times 10^1) + (3 \times 10^0),$	Expanded notation
$= (8 \times 10^1) + (3 \times 1),$	$10^0 = 1$
$= [(7 + 1) \times 10^1] + (3 \times 1),$	Basic sums
$= [(7 \times 10^1) + (1 \times 10^1)] + (3 \times 1),$	Distributive property
$= (7 \times 10^1) + [(1 \times 10^1) + (3 \times 1)],$	Associative property of addition

$$= (7 \times 10^1) + [(10 \times 1) + (3 \times 1)],$$

Commutative property of multiplication and $10^1 = 10$

$$= (7 \times 10^1) + [(10 + 3) \times 1],$$

Distributive property

$$= (7 \times 10^1) + (13 \times 1),$$

Place value notation

$$= 70 + 13.$$

Place value notation and multiplicative identity

We have now renamed 83 as $70 + 13$. Then,

$$83 - 47 = (70 + 13) - [(4 \times 10^1) + (7 \times 10^0)],$$

Expanded notation

$$= (70 + 13) - (40 + 7),$$

Place value notation

$$= (70 - 40) + (13 - 7),$$

Subtraction property

$$= [(7 \times 10) - (4 \times 10)] + [13 - 7],$$

Place value notation

$$= [(7 - 4) \times 10] + 6,$$

Distributive property of multiplication over subtraction and basic sum

$$= (3 \times 10) + (6 \times 1),$$

Basic sums and multiplicative identity.

$$= 36.$$

Place value notation

In the familiar subtraction algorithm this is generally written

$$
\begin{array}{rcccl}
83 &=& 80 + 3 &=& 70 + 13 \\
-47 &=& 40 + 7 &=& 40 + 7 \\
\hline
& & & & 30 + 6 = 36.
\end{array}
$$

We use the same algorithm to subtract numbers in any place value system of numeration.

Observe the octal system subtraction examples below:

$$
\begin{array}{r}
476_{(eight)} \\
-232_{(eight)} \\
\hline
244_{(eight)}
\end{array}
\qquad
\begin{array}{r}
275_{(eight)} \\
-104_{(eight)} \\
\hline
171_{(eight)}
\end{array}
$$

$$
\begin{array}{rcl}
42_{(eight)} &=& 30_{(eight)} + 12_{(eight)} \\
-26_{(eight)} &=& 20_{(eight)} + 6_{(eight)} \\
\hline
& & 10_{(eight)} + 4_{(eight)} = 14_{(eight)}
\end{array}
$$

EXERCISE 5.1

1. Below is a proof that $6 + 8 + 9 = 9 + 8 + 6$. Give a reason for each step in the proof.

    a. $(6 + 8) + 9 = 6 + (8 + 9)$
    b. $ = (8 + 9) + 6$
    c. $ = (9 + 8) + 6$

Find the following sums in the bases indicated.

2. $46_{\text{(eight)}}$
   $72_{\text{(eight)}}$

3. $73_{\text{(eight)}}$
   $67_{\text{(eight)}}$

4. $104_{\text{(five)}}$
   $232_{\text{(five)}}$
   $113_{\text{(five)}}$

5. $1011_{\text{(two)}}$
   $101_{\text{(two)}}$
   $1111_{\text{(two)}}$

6. $49\chi_{\text{(twelve)}}$
   $7\varepsilon4_{\text{(twelve)}}$

7. $423_{\text{(six)}}$
   $454_{\text{(six)}}$

Subtract the following in the bases indicated.

8. $234_{\text{(eight)}}$
   $104_{\text{(eight)}}$

9. $721_{\text{(eight)}}$
   $437_{\text{(eight)}}$

10. $924_{\text{(twelve)}}$
    $3\chi\varepsilon_{\text{(twelve)}}$

11. $1010_{\text{(two)}}$
    $111_{\text{(two)}}$

5.4. THE MULTIPLICATION ALGORITHM

The explanation of the multiplication algorithm is greatly simplified if we use the familiar rule of annexing a "0" to a numeral for the product of the number and ten; by annexing two zeros to the numeral to multiply the number by 100; and so on. Everyone is familiar with this rule of multiplying a number by a power of 10.

Let us discover why this rule works. The rule states that to multiply 10×58 we annex a zero to the numeral 58 and the product is 580. Here is the justification.

$10 \times 58 = 58 \times 10$ Commutative property of multiplication

$ = [(5 \times 10^1) + (8 \times 10^0)] \times 10^1$ Expanded notation and $10^1 = 10$.

$ = [(5 \times 10^1) \times 10^1] + [(8 \times 10^0) \times 10^1]$ Distributive property

$ = [5 \times (10^1 \times 10^1)] + [8 \times 10^1]$ Associative property of multiplication, $10^0 = 1$, and multiplication identity

$$= (5 \times 10^2) + (8 \times 10^1) \qquad\qquad 10^1 \times 10^1 = 10 \times 10 = 10^2$$

$$= (5 \times 10^2) + (8 \times 10^1) + (0 \times 10^0) \qquad\qquad n \times 0 = 0$$

$$= 580 \qquad\qquad\qquad \text{Place value notation}$$

The same technique is used to prove the rule for multiplication by 100, 1000, and so forth.

Just as the addition algorithm depends primarily upon the commutative and associative properties of addition and the distributive property, the multiplication algorithm depends on the commutative and associative properties of multiplication and the distributive property. For example, we multiply 63×34.

$$63 \times 34 = 63 \times [(3 \times 10^1) + (4 \times 10^0)] \qquad\qquad \text{Expanded notation}$$
$$= [63 \times (3 \times 10^1)] + [63 \times (4 \times 10^0)] \qquad\qquad \text{Distributive property}$$
$$= [(63 \times 3) \times 10^1] + [(63 \times 4) \times 10^0] \qquad\qquad \text{Associative property of multiplication}$$
$$= [(3 \times 63) \times 10^1] + [(4 \times 63) \times 10^0] \qquad\qquad \text{Commutative property of multiplication}$$

$$= (\{3 \times [(6 \times 10^1) + (3 \times 10^0)]\} \times 10^1) +$$
$$(\{4 \times [(6 \times 10^1) + (3 \times 10^0)]\} \times 10^0) \qquad\qquad \text{Expanded notation}$$
$$= (\{[3 \times (6 \times 10^1)] + [3 \times (3 \times 10^0)]\} \times 10^1) +$$
$$(\{[4 \times (6 \times 10^1)] + [4 \times (3 \times 10^0)]\} \times 10^0) \qquad\qquad \text{Distributive property}$$
$$= (\{[(3 \times 6) \times 10^1] + [(3 \times 3) \times 10^0]\} \times 10^1) +$$
$$(\{[(4 \times 6) \times 10^1] + [(4 \times 3) \times 10^0]\} \times 10^0) \qquad\qquad \text{Associative property of multiplication}$$
$$= \{[(18 \times 10^1) + (9 \times 10^0)] \times 10^1\} +$$
$$\{[(24 \times 10^1) + (12 \times 10^0)] \times 10^0\} \qquad\qquad \text{Basic products}$$
$$= ([(18 \times 10^1) \times 10^1] + [(9 \times 10^1)]) +$$
$$[(24 \times 10^1) + (12 \times 10^0)] \qquad\qquad \text{Distributive property, } 10^0 = 1 \text{ Multiplicative identity}$$

$$= \{[18 \times (10^1 \times 10^1)] + (9 \times 10^1)\}$$
$$+ \{(24 \times 10^1) + (12 \times 10^0)\} \qquad\qquad \text{Associative property of multiplication}$$
$$= [18 \times (10^1 \times 10^1)] + [(9 \times 10^1) +$$
$$(24 \times 10^1)] + (12 \times 10^0) \qquad\qquad \text{Associative property of multiplication}$$
$$= (18 \times 100) + [(9 + 24) \times 10^1] + (12 \times 10^0) \qquad\qquad \text{Distributive property, } 10^1 \times 10^1 = 100$$

$$= 1800 + (33 \times 10^1) + (12 \times 10^0) \qquad\qquad \text{Multiplication by 100, addition algorithm}$$

$$= 1800 + 330 + 12 \qquad\qquad \text{Multiplication by 10, } 100 = 1,\ 12 \times 1 = 12$$

$$= 2142. \qquad\qquad \text{Addition algorithm.}$$

Now let us look at the multiplication algorithm in its familiar vertical form.

$$
\begin{array}{r}
34 \\
63 \\
\hline
102 = 3 \times 34 \\
2040 = 60 \times 34 \\
\hline
2142
\end{array}
$$

There are really four products involved, as shown in the slightly longer form below.

$$
\begin{array}{r}
34 \\
63 \\
\hline
12 = \ 3 \times 4 \\
90 = \ 3 \times 30 \\
240 = 60 \times 4 \\
1800 = 60 \times 30 \\
\hline
2142
\end{array}
$$

Notice that

$$
\begin{aligned}
12 &= 12 \times 10^0, \\
90 &= 9 \times 10^1, \\
240 &= 24 \times 10^1, \\
1800 &= 18 \times 10^2 = 18 \times 10^1 \times 10^1.
\end{aligned}
$$

These products are easily found in the lengthy explanation already given.

Just as the addition and subtraction algorithms may be used in any place value system of numeration, so may the multiplication algorithm.

The Basic Products of the octal system are given in Table 5.3.

Using these with the pattern of the multiplication algorithm we can now do multiplication examples in the octal system. Study the examples below.

$$
\begin{array}{r}
32_{\text{(eight)}} \\
5_{\text{(eight)}} \\
\hline
202_{\text{(eight)}}
\end{array}
\qquad\qquad
\begin{array}{r}
47_{\text{(eight)}} \\
6_{\text{(eight)}} \\
\hline
352_{\text{(eight)}}
\end{array}
$$

Table 5.3

×	0	1	2	3	4	5	6	7
0	0	0	0	0	0	0	0	0
1	0	1	2	3	4	5	6	7
2	0	2	4	6	10	12	14	16
3	0	3	6	11	14	17	22	25
4	0	4	10	14	20	24	30	34
5	0	5	12	17	24	31	36	43
6	0	6	14	22	30	36	43	52
7	0	7	16	25	34	43	52	61

$$432_{(eight)}$$
$$\underline{25_{(eight)}}$$
$$2602$$
$$\underline{1064}$$
$$13442_{(eight)}$$

$$572_{(eight)}$$
$$\underline{47_{(eight)}}$$
$$5126$$
$$\underline{2750}$$
$$34626_{(eight)}$$

5.5. THE DIVISION ALGORITHM

Division is related to both the operation of subtraction and the operation of multiplication. Since division is the inverse of multiplication,

$$12 \div 6 = 2 \longrightarrow 6 \times 2 = 12.$$

Division may also be interpreted as repeated subtraction. If we subtract 6 from 12 it takes two successive subtractions of 6 to obtain a remainder of 0.

$$
\begin{array}{r}
12 \\
-\ 6 \quad -1 \\
\hline
6 \\
-\ 6 \quad -1 \\
\hline
0
\end{array}
\Big\} 2
\qquad
\begin{aligned}
& 12 = (1 \times 6) + 6, \\
& 12 = (1 \times 6) + (1 \times 6).
\end{aligned}
$$

Although division of one whole number by another is not always possible, there is a division property for any ordered pair of whole numbers. For example, although $6 \div 4$ is not a whole number, we do know that we can subtract 4 from 6 once, with a remainder of 2, that is, $6 = (4 \times 1) + 2$.

Observe the following ordered pairs of whole numbers and the statement to the right of each ordered pair.

$(9, 6)$ $9 = (6 \times 1) + 3,$
$(18, 4)$ $18 = (4 \times 4) + 2,$
$(26, 12)$ $26 = (12 \times 2) + 2,$
$(39, 17)$ $39 = (17 \times 2) + 5.$

In general, if a and b are whole numbers, there is a unique pair of whole numbers q and r, such that

$$a = bq + r$$

and $r \geq 0$ and $r < b$. We usually write this $0 \leq r < b$ and read it "r greater than or equal to zero and r less that b." The whole numbers a and b are called the *dividend* and the *divisor*, respectively. The whole number q is called the *quotient*. The whole number r is called the *remainder*. This property is called the *division algorithm*. We shall accept the division algorithm without proof.

If $r = 0$, we say that a is *divisible* by b or a is a *multiple* of b. We also say that b is a *factor* or a *divisor* of a.

If a and b are small numbers, it is easy to find q and r. If a and b are large, we use the familiar pattern shown below for $a = 4826$ and $b = 36$.

$$
\begin{array}{r}
134 \\
36\overline{)4826} \\
36 \\
\hline
122 \\
108 \\
\hline
146 \\
144 \\
\hline
2
\end{array}
\qquad 4826 = (36 \times 134) + 2
$$

Now let us analyze this familiar pattern. We are looking for the largest multiple of 36 which we can subtract from 4826. The simplest way to find this multiple of 36 is to consider first the products that have 1, 10, 100, or 1000 (that is, powers of 10) as factors, because it is very easy to multiply by powers of ten.

Let us write the familiar pattern in this way.

$$
\begin{array}{r}
134 \\
36\overline{)4826} \\
3600 \quad = 36 \times 100 \\
\overline{1226} \\
1080 \quad = (36 \times 3) \times 10 \\
\overline{146} \\
144 \quad = 36 \times 4 \\
\overline{2}
\end{array}
$$

We know that $36 \times 1000 = 36{,}000$ and $36 \times 100 = 3600$. Since $36{,}000 > 4826$, the best basic multiple is 36×100. Now

$$36 \times 100 = 3600,$$

and

$$2 \times (36 \times 100) = 7200 > 4826.$$

We subtract 3600 from 4826 and there is a remainder of 1226. Now we inspect multiples of 10×36:

$$
\begin{aligned}
(36 \times 10) \times 1 &= 36 \times 10 = 360, \\
(36 \times 10) \times 2 &= 36 \times 20 = 720, \\
(36 \times 10) \times 3 &= 36 \times 30 = 1080, \\
(36 \times 10) \times 4 &= 36 \times 40 = 1440 > 1226.
\end{aligned}
$$

We subtract 1080 from 1226, and there is a remainder of 146. We now inspect multiples of 1×36:

$$
\begin{aligned}
(36 \times 1) \times 1 &= 36 \times 1 = 36, \\
(36 \times 1) \times 2 &= 36 \times 2 = 72, \\
(36 \times 1) \times 3 &= 36 \times 3 = 108, \\
(36 \times 1) \times 4 &= 36 \times 4 = 144, \\
(36 \times 1) \times 5 &= 36 \times 5 = 180 > 146.
\end{aligned}
$$

We subtract 144 from 146 and there is a remainder of 2. Since $2 < 36$ we have completed the division process.

This process may be written in horizontal form.

$$4826 = (36 \times 100) + 1226,$$
$$= (36 \times 100) + [(36 \times 30) + 146],$$
$$= [(36 \times 100) + (36 \times 30)] + 146,$$
$$= [36 \times (100 + 30)] + 146,$$
$$= (36 \times 130) + 146,$$
$$= (36 \times 130) + [(36 \times 4) + 2],$$
$$= [(36 \times 130) + (36 \times 4)] + 2,$$
$$= [36 \times (130 + 4)] + 2,$$
$$= (36 \times 134) + 2.$$

Examination of the preceding shows that the division algorithm depends on (1) the associative property of addition and (2) the distributive property. The only other requirements are the renaming of numbers, and the fact that the subtractions are possible.

Now let us use this same process to do the division example $467_{(eight)} \div 36_{(eight)}$. Written in the familiar form this is

$$36_{(eight)}\overline{)467_{(eight)}}.$$

Now let us find the largest multiple of $36_{(eight)}$ which can be subtracted from $467_{(eight)}$.

$$36_{(eight)} \times 100_{(eight)} = 3600_{(eight)} > 467_{(eight)},$$
$$36_{(eight)} \times 10_{(eight)} = 360_{(eight)},$$
$$(36_{(eight)} \times 10_{(eight)}) \times 2_{(eight)} = 740_{(eight)} > 467_{(eight)}.$$

Then

$$
\begin{array}{r}
1 \\
36_{(eight)}\overline{)467_{(eight)}} \\
360_{(eight)} = 36_{(eight)} \times 10_{(eight)} \\
\overline{107_{(eight)}}
\end{array}
$$

Now let us try multiples of $36_{(eight)} \times 1_{(eight)}$.

$$36_{(eight)} \times 1_{(eight)} = 36_{(eight)},$$
$$36_{(eight)} \times 2_{(eight)} = 74_{(eight)},$$
$$36_{(eight)} \times 3_{(eight)} = 132_{(eight)} > 107_{(eight)}.$$

We now subtract $74_{(eight)}$ from $107_{(eight)}$.

$$12_{(eight)}$$
$$36_{(eight)} \overline{)467_{(eight)}}$$
$$360_{(eight)} = 36_{(eight)} \times 10_{(eight)},$$
$$107_{(eight)}$$
$$74_{(eight)} = 36_{(eight)} \times 2_{(eight)}.$$
$$13_{(eight)}.$$

We see that $13_{(eight)} < 36_{(eight)}$ and so the division process is completed and

$$467_{(eight)} = [36_{(eight)} \times 12_{(eight)}] + 13_{(eight)}.$$

Study the division examples in the octal system which are shown below. Since all the numerals below are written in the octal system the subscripts have been omitted.

$$52$$
$$5\overline{)326}$$
$$310 = 5 \times 50$$
$$16$$
$$12 = 5 \times 2$$
$$4$$

$$51$$
$$7\overline{)437}$$
$$430 = 7 \times 50$$
$$7$$
$$7 = 7 \times 1$$
$$0$$

$$112$$
$$37\overline{)4366}$$
$$3700 = 37 \times 100$$
$$466$$
$$370 = 37 \times 10$$
$$76$$
$$76 = 37 \times 2$$
$$0$$

EXERCISE 5.2

1. Do the following multiplications in the bases indicated.

$$234_{(eight)} \qquad 436_{(twelve)}$$
$$\underline{7_{(eight)}} \qquad \underline{9_{(twelve)}}$$

$$346_{(eight)} \qquad 3\chi5_{(twelve)}$$
$$\underline{25_{(eight)}} \qquad \underline{\chi\varepsilon_{(twelve)}}$$

2. Below is a proof that $6 + 6 = 2 \times 6$. Give a reason for each step in the proof.

a. $6 + 6 = (6 \times 1) + (6 \times 1),$
b. $\qquad = 6 \times (1 + 1),$

    c. $= 6 \times 2,$
    d. $= 2 \times 6.$

3. Below is a proof that $5 + 5 + 5 = 3 \times 5$. Give a reason for each step in the proof.

    a. $(5 + 5) + 5 = [(5 \times 1) + (5 \times 1)] + 5,$
    b. $= [5 \times (1 + 1)] + 5,$
    c. $= (5 \times 2) + 5,$
    d. $= (5 \times 2) + (5 \times 1),$
    e. $= 5 \times (2 + 1),$
    f. $= 5 \times 3,$
    g. $= 3 \times 5.$

4. Below is a proof that $(2 \times 9) \times 5 = 9 \times (5 \times 2)$. Give a reason for each step in the proof.

    a. $(2 \times 9) \times 5 = 5 \times (2 \times 9),$
    b. $= (5 \times 2) \times 9,$
    c. $= 9 \times (5 \times 2).$

5. What is the largest multiple of 64 that can be subtracted from 3864?

6. What is the largest multiple of 94 that can be subtracted from 10,766?

7. Find q and r of the division algorithm given the ordered pair (a, b) below. That is, find q and r in the statement $a = (b \times q) + r$.

    a. $(26,5)$.   b. $(138,7)$.   c. $(266,19)$.
    d. $(844,28)$.   e. $(366,37)$.

Do the following divisions in the bases indicated.

    8. $463_{(eight)} \div 6_{(eight)}$.
    9. $964_{(twelve)} \div 9_{(twelve)}$.
   10. $1342_{(five)} \div 24_{(five)}$.
   11. $1011_{(two)} \div 101_{(two)}$.

CHAPTER 6

Informal Geometry

6.1. INFORMAL AND FORMAL GEOMETRY

Before we begin our discussion of this unit, we must be sure that we understand the difference between formal and informal geometry. Formal geometry is developed as a deductive system. That is, certain terms are taken as undefined; certain statements, called *axioms* or *postulates,* about these undefined terms, are accepted as true without proof; other words are defined in terms of the undefined terms, and statements, called *theorems,* are proved by a process of logical deduction. The objects studied in formal geometry are abstract and have no existence in the world of real things.

Informal geometry calls attention to what may be thought of as geometric properties of familiar objects. For example, we develop mathematical ideas of points, lines, planes, curves, angles, and space by studying some of the models of these ideas in the physical world around us. Informal geometry is studied through observation, intuition, experimentation, and reasoning by induction. Informal geometry is sometimes called *intuitive geometry.*

6.2. UNDEFINED TERMS*

Every definition must eventually depend upon ideas and words which have not been defined. It is impossible to define every term. If we attempt to define every term we become involved in what is known as *circular*

---

*This topic was discussed in Chapter 2, but because of its importance it will be reviewed here.

reasoning. For example, if you look up the meaning of a word in the dictionary, you will find this word defined in terms of other words. If you continue looking up the words used in the definition, you soon may find that you are going around in a circle. That is, one of the words which you are looking up is defined in terms of the original word whose meaning you are seeking.

For example, suppose you use the dictionary to find the meaning of "to investigate". You may find the following:

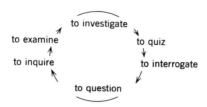

To avoid circular reasoning there are some words which we shall not attempt to define. We shall accept them as undefined. In geometry, two of these terms are *point* and *line.*

6.3. POINTS

A *point* may be thought of as a precise location. It cannot be seen or felt; it has no size. Points are represented by dots on a paper or as the end of a sharply pointed pencil. These representations are merely attempts to symbolize the idealized geometric entity we call a point. The point which we represent by a dot, no matter how small the dot, covers many locations.

A point is a fixed location. If we mark a dot to fix a particular location and then erase the dot, the location still remains. The point has not disappeared, only the representation of it has been erased. Just as the symbol "4" is not the number four, this dot, ·, is not a point but merely a pictorial representation of a point.

6.4. SPACE

Now that we understand the concept of a point, we may define *geometric space* or *space.* Space is the set of all points. That is, space consists of all locations in the universe.

6.5. LINES

Suppose we represent two points in space by the two dots in Figure

6.1. We label these dots with the letters A and B, and call the points point A and point B.

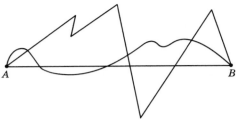

Figure 6.1

We now trace a path from A to B. We may trace infinitely many such paths. Several are drawn in Figure 6.1. All such paths are called *curves*. One of the paths from A to B is a "straight line". If we use our fingers to hold a piece of string, the various positions of the string represent paths between the two points represented by our fingers. The special path that is represented by the string pulled taut is called a *line segment*. Figure 6.2 shows a representation of a line segment between the two points represented by M and N.

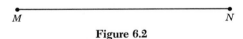

Figure 6.2

The symbol used for this line segment is $\overline{MN}$ or $\overline{NM}$. M and N represent the two *endpoints*. A line segment is a set of points which includes the endpoints. A line segment exists independent of its representation; if the printed path in Figure 6.2 were removed, the line segment would remain, since it is a set of locations.

A line may be thought of as an extension in both directions of a line segment. It is represented by the symbol $\overleftrightarrow{AB}$, where A and B are any two points on the line. We represent a line as shown in Figure 6.3. The arrows on the ends are to suggest that a line extends indefinitely in both directions.

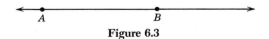

Figure 6.3

6.6. PLANES

Let us now consider a subset of the set of points of space called a *plane*. Again we do not define a plane, but we describe its relationship to lines and points, and thus get a good idea of what is meant by a plane.

Any flat surface such as the top of a table, the floor, a sheet of paper, or a wall suggests the idea of a mathematical plane. Like the line, a plane is unlimited in extent. That is, any flat surface used to represent a plane is only a representation of a part of the plane. The drawings in Figure 6.4 are representations of parts of planes.

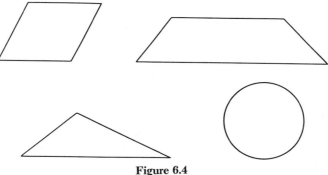

Figure 6.4

6.7. PROPERTIES OF LINES AND PLANES

From the representation of a line segment, it is easy to discover intuitively the following property of a line.

Property 1 *Through any two points in space there is exactly one line, or simply, two points in space determine one line.*

Suppose we think of two points on a plane as represented in Figure 6.5. We can draw exactly one line through these two points, because two points determine one line. This line will always lie in the plane.

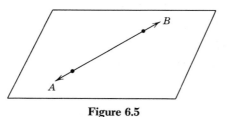

Figure 6.5

Property 2   *If a line contains two different points of a plane, it lies in the plane.*

Consider a line through two points. How many planes contain this line? Think of two points on the spine of a book; each page of the book is a different plane passing through these two points. Or, we may think of the hinges of a door as the two points. Since the door, which represents a part of a plane, can swing freely, it is easy to see that many planes contain the two points, and consequently the line determined by the two points. We may generalize:

Property 3   *A line lies on infinitely many planes, or infinitely many planes contain a line.*

Three points may all lie on one line or they may determine three lines. The points *A*, *B*, and *C* in Figure 6.6a all lie on the same line. Such points are called *collinear points*. The points *R*, *S*, and *T* are not on a line, but determine three lines as shown in Figure 6.6b. Such points are called *noncollinear*.

We know that a three-legged stool always sits firmly on the floor, whereas a four-legged table may wobble. Because of this, photographers use a tripod to support their cameras. This example suggests:

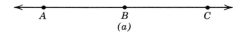

(a)

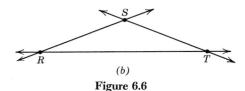

(b)

Figure 6.6

Property 4   *Through three noncollinear points there is exactly one plane.*

Now let us consider two lines in space. If the two lines lie in a plane they either intersect as shown in Figure 6.7a or have no points in common as shown in Figure 6.7b. Two lines in a plane are called *parallel lines* if they have no points in common. Two different lines in a plane are called *intersecting lines* if they have any points in common. If two different lines in a plane intersect, they intersect in a single point.

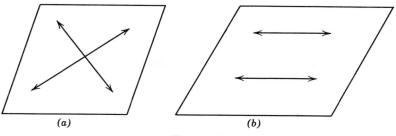

Figure 6.7

Property 5 *If two different lines intersect, they intersect in a single point.*

If two lines intersect they must lie in the same plane. If two lines are parallel they must lie on the same plane.

Property 6 *If two different lines intersect, exactly one plane contains both of them.*

Property 7 *If two different lines are parallel, they lie on the same plane.*

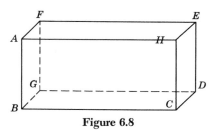

Figure 6.8

Consider the drawing in Figure 6.8 of what is called a rectangular parallelopiped. The line determined by A and H and the line determined by B and C are parallel. We write $\overleftrightarrow{AH} \parallel \overleftrightarrow{BC}$ and read this "$\overleftrightarrow{AH}$ is parallel to $\overleftrightarrow{BC}$." The following pairs of lines are parallel:

$$\overleftrightarrow{AH} \parallel \overleftrightarrow{BC}$$
$$\overleftrightarrow{AB} \parallel \overleftrightarrow{HC}$$
$$\overleftrightarrow{HC} \parallel \overleftrightarrow{ED}$$
$$\overleftrightarrow{AH} \parallel \overleftrightarrow{EF}$$
$$\overleftrightarrow{FG} \parallel \overleftrightarrow{HC}.$$

Are there other pairs of lines in Figure 6.8 that are parallel?
The following pairs of lines are intersecting:

$$\overleftrightarrow{AB} \text{ and } \overleftrightarrow{BC}$$
$$\overleftrightarrow{AH} \text{ and } \overleftrightarrow{HC}$$
$$\overleftrightarrow{DE} \text{ and } \overleftrightarrow{CD}, \text{ and so forth.}$$

Line $\overleftrightarrow{BC}$ and line $\overleftrightarrow{ED}$ are neither parallel nor intersecting. They are called *skew lines*. Skew lines are two lines in space that are neither parallel nor intersecting. Could two lines that lie in a plane be skew?

If a line and a plane intersect, their intersection is either a point or the entire line. A pencil may represent a portion of a line. A sheet of paper represents a portion of a plane. When you write on the paper with the pencil, the pencil (line) intersects the paper (plane) in only one point, the point where the pencil lead touches the paper. If you lay the pencil down on the paper the line represented by the pencil is in the plane represented by the paper.

Property 8   *If a line and a plane intersect their intersection is either one point or the entire line.*

Of course, a line and a plane may not intersect. In this case we say the line and the plane are parallel.

Figure 6.9 shows the relationship between a line and a plane. Figure 6.9*a* shows a line intersecting a plane in one point, Figure 6.9*b* shows a line lying in a plane, and Figure 6.9*c* shows a line parallel to a plane.

Figure 6.10 shows the relationship between two planes. In Figure 6.10*a* the two planes have no points in common and are called *parallel*. The intersection of these two sets of points is the empty set. Figure 6.10*b* shows the intersection of the two planes.

Property 9   *If two planes intersect, their intersection is a line.*

6.8.   SEPARATION OF SPACE

Think of a plane, represented by a wall. The wall separates space into three disjoint sets of points: those in front of the wall, those in the wall, and those behind the wall. We say that a plane separates space into two *half-spaces*. The term "half-space" may be misleading. It is a geometric idea, not a quantity. The separating plane does not lie in either half-space; it is called the *boundary* of each half-space.

In Figure 6.11, since the line segment joining A and B does not intersect the plane, points A and B are said to be in the same half-space. Points B and C are said to be in different half-spaces since the line seg-

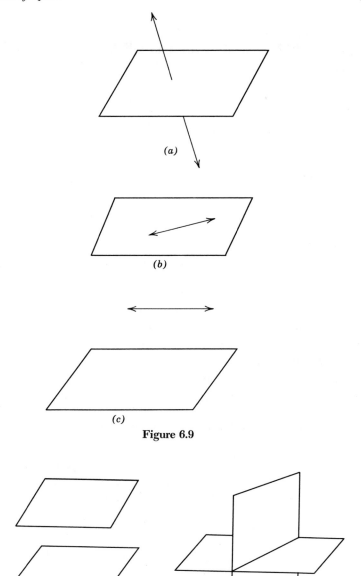

(a)

(b)

(c)

Figure 6.9

(a)

(b)

Figure 6.10

ment joining them intersects the plane. Point *D* is in the plane and hence is in neither half-space.

Just as a plane separates space into two half-spaces, a line separates the plane into two *half-planes*. (See Figure 6.12)

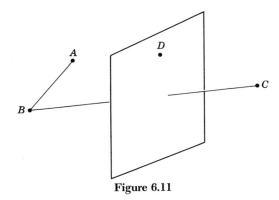

Figure 6.11

If we consider this sheet of paper as a representation of a plane we see that the line in Figure 6.12 separates the points of the plane into three disjoint sets: two *half-planes* and the line called the *boundary*. Points *A* and *C* lie in the same half-plane because a line segment joining them does not intersect the line. Points *A* and *B* lie in different half-planes because a line segment joining them intersects the line. Point *D* lies in neither half-plane, it lies on the boundary.

A point separates a line into three disjoint sets of points: the set consisting of the point itself, and two sets of points called *half-lines*.

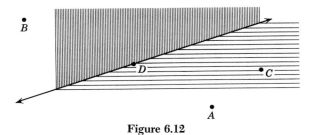

Figure 6.12

In Figure 6.13 the point *P* separates the line into the set of points to the left of *P* and the set of points to the right of *P* and the set consisting of *P*. We use the symbol $\overrightarrow{PC}$ to denote the half-line to the right of *P* which includes point *C*. The open dot signifies that *P* is not included.

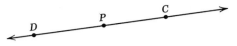

Figure 6.13

EXERCISE 6.1

1. On the map, name the point which represents the street intersection of:

a. Kingshighway & Walsh
b. Hampton & Itaska
c. Gravois & Kingshighway
d. Goethe & Murdock
e. Watson & Delor
f. Jamieson & Walsh
g. Watson & Goethe

A	B	C	D	E	Watson
F	G	H	I	J	Jamieson
K	L	M	N	O	Hampton
P	Q	R	S	T	Murdock
U	V	W	X	Y	Kingshighway

Gravois   Itaska   Goethe   Delor   Walsh

2. The diagram at right represents a seating chart. State the initial of the students who sit on the seats described:

a. Third row from the front, second seat from the left.
b. Front row, center seat.
c. Back row, third seat from the right.
d. Second row from the back, second seat from the left.

P	Q	R	S	T
K	L	M	N	O
F	G	H	I	J
A	B	C	D	E

Front

3. In the figure name

a. three planes.
b. two skew lines.
c. two parallel lines.
d. two intersecting lines.
e. a pair of parallel planes.
f. three planes that intersect in a point.
g. two planes that intersect in a line.
h. three lines that intersect in a point.

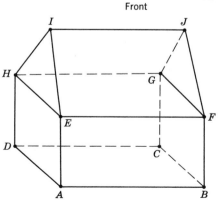

4. Are the following statements true or false? Give reasons for your answer.
   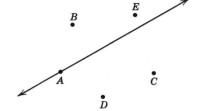
   a. Points *B* and *E* are in the same half-plane.
   b. Points *B* and *D* are in the same half-plane.
   c. Points *D* and *C* are in different half-planes.
   d. Point *A* is in the same half-plane as Point *C*.

5. Two points in space are contained in the following:
   a. Only one plane.
   b. Many planes, but we could count them.
   c. More planes than can be counted.

6. Complete this sentence: Two intersecting planes in space intersect in a

——— .

7. How many lines can be drawn through four points, a pair of them at a time, if the points be in the same plane, but no three in the same line?

8. Given two points *A* and *B* as shown below.

   ·*A*

          ·*B*

   a. How many line segments can you draw with endpoints *A* and *B*?
   b. How many lines are there that contain both *A* and *B*?

9. How many different lines may contain the following?
   a. One certain point.
   b. A certain pair of points.

10. Draw figures to show that the intersection set of two given line segments may be the following:
   a. The empty set.
   b. A point.
   c. A line segment.

11. A line has
   a. one end point,
   b. two end points,
   c. no end points.

12. A line segment has
   a. one end point,
   b. two end points,
   c. no end points.

13. Describe the set which is the intersection of two planes.
14. Describe the set which is the intersection of a line and a plane.

15. Describe the two possible sets which are the intersection of three planes.
16. How many lines are determined by two points?
17. How many lines are determined by three non-collinear points?
18. Define a curve.
19. Which of the following are representations of a part of a plane?
    a. a ball. b. table top. c. chalkboard.
    d. apple. e. pencil. f. wall.

20. List ten physical representations of

    a. a line segment,
    b. a plane.

21. If possible, make sketches in which the intersection of a line and a plane is

    a. the empty set,
    b. a line.

22. Name a one-to-one correspondence between the points in line *k* and the points on line *j*.

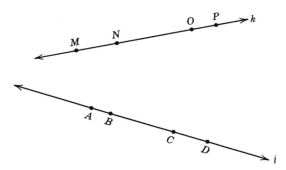

23. Describe the intersection of the following curves.

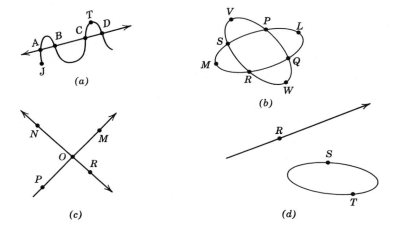

24. How many points are there on a line; on a plane; in space?

6.9. RAYS

There is another set of points which is important. That is the set of points in a half-line and its boundary. This set of points is called a *ray*. Thus, in Figure 6.13, a ray may consist of all the points to the right of P, including the point P. We use the symbol $\overrightarrow{PC}$ to signify this ray. A ray has only one endpoint. Thus $\overrightarrow{PC}$ is different from $\overrightarrow{CP}$. $\overrightarrow{PC}$ is the set of points on the line $\overleftrightarrow{PC}$ to the right of point P, including point P; $\overrightarrow{CP}$ is the set of points on the line $\overleftrightarrow{PC}$ to the left of C, including point C.

From our knowledge of a line, we can assert that a line contains infinitely many rays since any point on the line may serve as the endpoint of a ray. Since there are only two directions in a line from a fixed point, there are only two distinct rays on a line with the fixed point as the common endpoint.

In a plane there are an unlimited number of rays with a common endpoint, as shown in Figure 6.14.

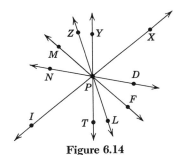

Figure 6.14

6.10 ANGLES

An *angle* is the union of two rays which have a common endpoint, but which are not parts of the same line. The common endpoint of the two rays is called the *vertex* of the angle. Angles are named by three points of the angle including the endpoint and a point on each ray. The symbol for angle is $\angle$. The angles in Figure 6.15 are: (a) $\angle ABC$ or $\angle CBA$; (b) $\angle RST$ or $\angle TSR$; (c) $\angle PQR$ or $\angle RQP$; (d) $\angle XYZ$ or $\angle ZYX$. Angles may have many names if each represents the same set of points. For example, in Figure 6.15,

a. $\angle ABC = \angle CBA = \angle DBE = \angle EBD$,

b. $\angle RST = \angle TSR = \angle USV = \angle VSU$,
c. $\angle PQR = \angle RQP = \angle WQL = \angle LQW$,
d. $\angle XYZ = \angle ZYX = \angle OYK = \angle KYO$.

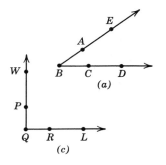 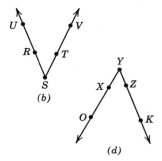

Figure 6.15

An angle separates a plane into three disjoint sets of points: the set of points of the angle itself, and the two sets of points called the *interior* and the *exterior* of the angle. In Figure 6.16, the set of points represented by the vertical shading is called the interior of the angle, and the set of points represented by the horizontal shading is called the exterior of the angle.

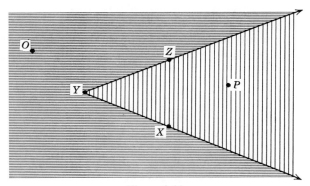

Figure 6.16

Point O lies outside the angle, and point P lies inside the angle. Point Z is on the angle. The way to determine the interior of an angle is to use the separation property of a line in a plane. In Figure 6.17 $\angle XYZ$ is determined by the rays $\overrightarrow{YX}$ and $\overrightarrow{YZ}$. These rays determine the lines $\overleftrightarrow{YX}$ and $\overleftrightarrow{YZ}$.

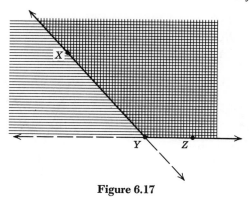

Figure 6.17

Line $\overleftrightarrow{YX}$ separates the plane into two half-planes, and Z lies in one of these. This half-plane is marked by vertical shading. Line $\overleftrightarrow{YZ}$ separates the plane into two half-planes, and X lies in one of them. This half-plane is marked by horizontal shading. That portion of the plane which is cross hatched is the interior of $\angle XYZ$.

6.11   TRIANGLES

A *triangle* is a set of three noncollinear points and the points of the three line segments joining them. A triangle may also be defined as the union of three line segments. Each of the three points, which are the end-points of the line segments, is called a *vertex* of the triangle. We name the triangle by the points which are its vertices. The symbol for the triangle is $\triangle$. Figure 6.18 shows $\triangle ABC$ which may also be called $\triangle BAC$ or $\triangle CBA$.

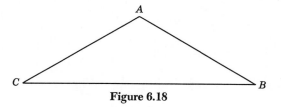

Figure 6.18

A triangle determines three angles called the *angles of the triangle.* Although $\angle ACB$ is an angle of $\triangle ABC$, not all of the points of $\angle ACB$ are points of the triangle. This is shown in Figure 6.19. Notice that Q is a point of $\angle ACB$ but not a point of $\triangle ABC$. The same is true of $\angle CBA$ and $\angle BAC$.

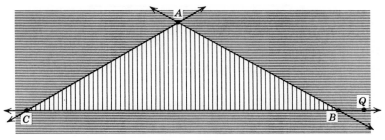

Figure 6.19

The triangle separates the plane into three disjoint sets of points: the set of points of the triangle, the set of points in the interior of the triangle and the set of points in the exterior of the triangle. The set of points in the interior of the triangle is shown in Figure 6.19 by vertical line segments; the set of points in the exterior is shown by horizontal line segments.

EXERCISE 6.2

1. Draw points A and B.
   a. Draw a ray with end point A.
   b. Draw a ray with end point B.
   c. Draw $\overline{AB}$
   d. Draw $\overrightarrow{AB}$.

2. Which of the following are true statements? A ray has
   a. one end point,
   b. two end points,
   c. no end points.

3. Consider the figure at the right.
   a. What is the vertex of $\angle BAC$?
   b. Is point C in the interior or exterior of $\angle BAD$?
   c. Is $\overline{AC}$ in the interior or exterior of $\angle BAD$?

4. Consider the line below.

   a. What is the union of $\overline{PQ}$ and $\overrightarrow{QS}$?
   b. What is the union of $\overline{PR}$ and $\overrightarrow{QS}$?
   c. What is the union of $\overrightarrow{PS}$ and $\overrightarrow{RS}$?

5. Which of the following statements are true?

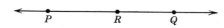

a. A line $\overleftrightarrow{PQ}$ is a set of points.

b. Point R separates the line $\overleftrightarrow{PQ}$ into two rays.

c. Point P lies on $\overrightarrow{RQ}$.

d. Line segments $\overline{PQ}$, $\overline{QR}$, and $\overline{PR}$ are sets of points.

e. Point P is an endpoint of $\overline{PR}$.

6. Which of the points in the figure at the right are:

    a. on the triangle?

    b. in the interior region?

    c. in the exterior region?

7. Define an angle.

8. Define a triangle.

9. Given the angles below.

    a. Name each angle.

    b. Name the vertex of each angle.

    c. Name the points in the interior of each angle.

    d. Name the points in the exterior of each angle.

    e. Name the points on each angle.

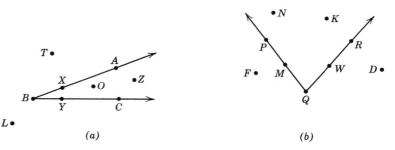

(a)   (b)

10. Which of the following statements are true?

    a. If a point is on a side of an angle, then it is not in the interior of the angle.

    b. If a line contains the vertex of an angle and a point of the exterior, then it contains no other point of the angle.

    c. A ray from the vertex of an angle is in the interior of the angle.

    d. If two rays have a common end point then they lie on the same line.

11. Name all the angles shown in the figure below.

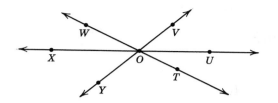

12. In △ ABC at the right, name the

   a. vertices,
   b. sides,
   c. angles.

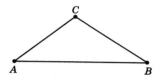

13. Use the figure below to answer the following:

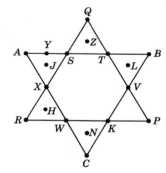

   a. Which points are in the interior of △ ABC?
   b. Which points are in the interior of △ QPR?
   c. Which points are in the exterior of △ ABC?
   d. Which points are in the exterior of △ PQR?
   e. What is the intersection set of △ ABC and △ PQR?

14. Name all of the triangles in the figure below.

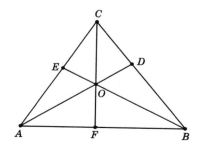

15. Draw a picture of two triangles whose intersection consists of

    a. one point,   b. two points,   c. three points,
    d. four points,   e. five points,   f. six points.

16. Draw a picture of a triangle and a line whose intersection is

    a. the empty set,
    b. one point,
    c. two points.

17. Draw a picture of a triangle and an angle whose intersection is

    a. the empty set,
    b. two points,
    c. four points.

6.12. SIMPLE CLOSED CURVES

A *curve* is merely a set of points which can be traced without lifting a pencil from the paper. The drawings in Figure 6.20 are pictures of curves.

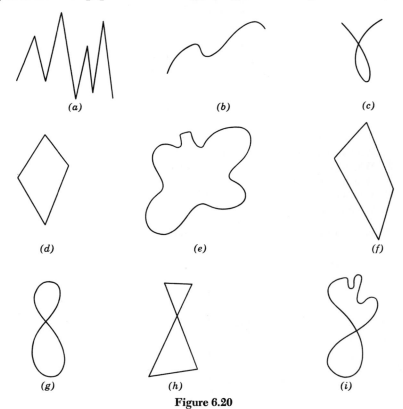

Figure 6.20

Figures 6.20a, 6.20b, and 6.20c are called *open curves;* the others are *closed curves.* In tracing a picture of a closed curve it is possible to begin tracing at any point and return to the starting point without lifting the pencil. Figures 6.20d, 6.20e, and 6.20f are *simple closed curves.* By simple closed curve we mean a set of points in a plane represented by a drawn path that begins and ends at the same point and does not intersect itself. The triangle is an example of a simple closed curve.

A closed curve separates the plane into three sets of points: the interior, the exterior and the curve itself. The interior of any simple closed curve is called a *region.* The curve is called the *boundary* of the region. The region together with the boundary is called a *closed region.*

6.13. POLYGONS

A simple closed curve which is the union of several line segments is called a *polygon.* If it is the union of three line segments, it is a *triangle;* of four line segments, a *quadrilateral;* of five lines segments a *pentagon;* of six line segments, a *hexagon;* of seven line segments, a *heptagon;* of eight line segments, an *octagon.*

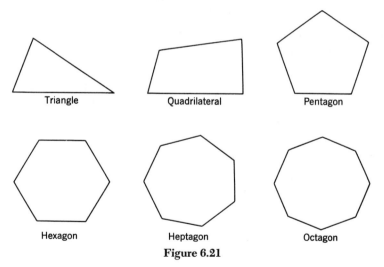

Triangle   Quadrilateral   Pentagon

Hexagon   Heptagon   Octagon

Figure 6.21

EXERCISE 6.3

1. Which of the following are simple closed curves?

 a. triangle   b. line segment
 c. ray   d. angle
 e. line   f. square
 g. hexagon   h. rectangle

2. Look at a map of the United States. Which of the boundaries of the states below are simple closed curves?

    a. Utah
    b. Missouri
    c. Hawaii

3. Draw a simple closed curve which is

    a. the union of four line segments,
    b. the union of six line segments,
    c. the union of eight line segments.

4. Consider the capital letters as ordinarily printed. Which of them are closed curves? Which of them are simple closed curves?

5. Consider the digits 0, 1, 2, 3, 4, 5, 6, 7, 8, 9. Which are simple closed curves?

6. Draw a picture of a closed curve that is not simple.

7. Draw a simple closed curve. Name the three sets of points into which the curve separates the plane.

8. Draw a picture if possible, of

    a. a triangle that is not a simple closed curve,
    b. a pentagon that is not a simple closed curve,
    c. a hexagon that is not a simple closed curve.

9. Define a polygon.

10. Which of the curves below are not simple closed curves?

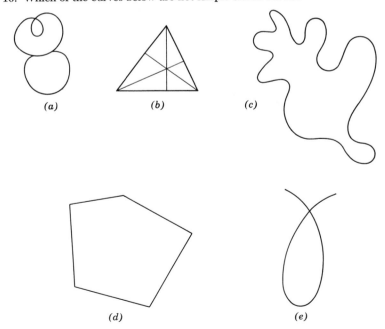

    (a)   *(b)*   *(c)*

    (d)   *(e)*

11. Which of these simple closed curves are pictures of polygons?

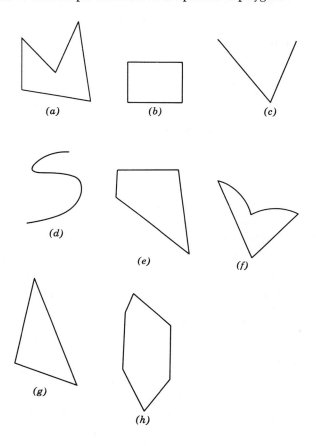

12. Which of the pictures in Problem 11 are quadrilaterals?
13. Which of the curves below are simple closed curves?

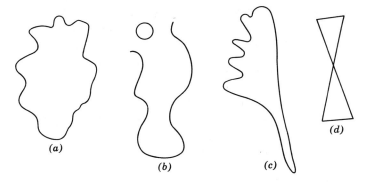

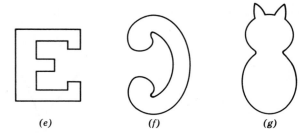

(e)   (f)   (g)

14. The curve below does not intersect itself. Why is it not a simple closed curve?

Use the picture at the right to answer the following.

15. What is the intersection of closed curve *ABH* and closed curve *CDEGH?*

16. What points are in the interior of closed curve *ABH?*

17. What points are in the exterior of closed curve *ABH?*

18. Name a closed curve containing points *G, H,* and *D.*

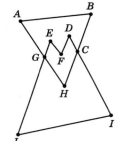

6.14. CONGRUENCE

Congruence is a complex idea with many consequences in geometry. It applies to geometric figures of all kinds. We shall confine ourselves to an intuitive idea of congruence, that is, if one geometric figure is an exact replica of another, we shall say that the two figures are congruent.

The best way to determine whether or not two line segments are congruent is to use a compass. If the points of a compass are separated and made to cover the end points of the first segment and then, on being transferred to the second segment, cover the endpoints of the second segment, the two segments are said to be congruent. The line segments in Figure 6.22 are congruent.

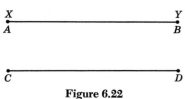

Figure 6.22

We use the symbol $\cong$ for congruent and write $\overline{AB} \cong \overline{CD}$. We do not say $\overline{AB} = \overline{CD}$ because equality means "the same as," and $\overline{AB}$ is not the same line segment as $\overline{CD}$. Although $\overline{CD}$ fits and matches $\overline{AB}$, it is evident that C and A do not name the same points, nor do B and D. It is true, of course, if segments are equal, they are also congruent. Hence,

$$\overline{AB} = \overline{XY} \qquad \text{and} \qquad \overline{AB} \cong \overline{XY}.$$

6.15. CONGRUENT ANGLES

If two angles, $\angle\,ABC$ and $\angle\,DEF$, are given, we can take as a representation of $\angle\,ABC$ a tracing, say $\angle\,A'B'C'$, and make the ray $\overrightarrow{B'C'}$ fall on $\overrightarrow{EF}$, with $\overrightarrow{B'A'}$ falling in the same half-plane as $\overrightarrow{ED}$ and with B' falling on E as shown in Figure 6.23. Now if $\overrightarrow{B'A'}$ falls on $\overrightarrow{ED}$ we say that

$$\angle\,ABC \cong \angle\,DEF.$$

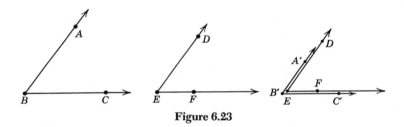

Figure 6.23

It is important to remember that angles may be congruent although the parts of the rays represented in the drawing may not be congruent. For example,

$$\angle\,PQR \cong \angle\,XYZ \text{ in Figure 6.24.}$$

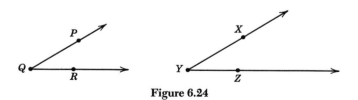

Figure 6.24

There is a special angle of importance called a *right angle*, which may be illustrated thus. Take any point Q not on $\overleftrightarrow{AB}$. Draw $\overrightarrow{PQ}$. We now have two angles, $\angle APQ$ and $\angle BPQ$. If $\angle APQ \cong \angle BPQ$, we say that $\angle APQ$ and $\angle BPQ$ are both right angles. Thus in Figure 6.25b, $\angle APQ$ and $\angle BPQ$ are right angles; in Figure 6.25a they are not.

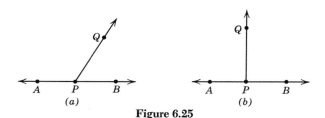

Figure 6.25

6.16.   CIRCLES

The *circle* is a simple closed curve having a point, O, in its interior, such that if P and Q are any two points on the circle, then $\overline{OP} \cong \overline{OQ}$. The point, O, is called the *center* of the circle. The center is not a point of the circle. A line segment with one endpoint at the center and the other endpoint on the circle is called a *radius*. In Figure 6.26, $\overline{OP}$, $\overline{OQ}$, $\overline{OT}$, and $\overline{OS}$ are all radii of the circle. All radii of a given circle are congruent.

The *diameter* of a circle is a line segment whose endpoints lie on the circle and which contains the center of the circle. In Figure 6.26, $\overline{QR}$ is a diameter of the circle.

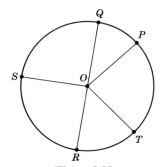

Figure 6.26

A portion of the circle is called an *arc*. Any two points on a circle separates the circle into two arcs. For example, points Q and T in Figure 6.26 separate the circle into the arc containing point P and the arc containing point S. These arcs are written

$$\overset{\frown}{QPT} \text{ and } \overset{\frown}{QST}.$$

EXERCISE 6.4

1. Which of the following line segments are congruent?

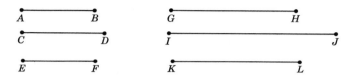

2. Which of the following angles are right angles?

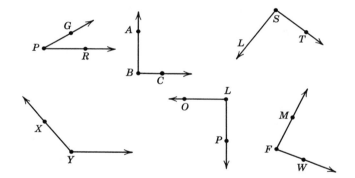

3. In the circle at the right name:

   a. a radius,
   b. a diameter,
   c. a point on the circle,
   d. a point on the interior,
   e. a point on the exterior,
   f. an arc,
   g. the center.

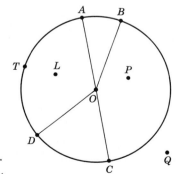

4. Complete the following statements:

   a. If $\overline{AB} \cong \overline{CD}$ and $\overline{AB} \cong \overline{PQ}$, then _____ .
   b. If $\overline{AB} \cong \overline{CD}$ and $\overline{DC} \cong \overline{EF}$, then _____ .

5. Given a line segment $\overline{PQ}$ and a point R on a line k, how many points T are on k such that $\overline{PQ} \cong \overline{RT}$?

6. For any circle what is the intersection of all its diameters?

7. Draw two circles in such a way that their intersection is

    a. the empty set,
    b. a single point.

8. What is the intersection set of the circle and the curve shown below?

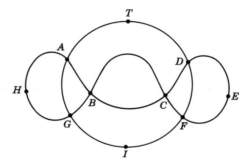

6.17.   CONGRUENT TRIANGLES

In Figure 6.27, the three triangles represented are congruent. If $\triangle DEF$

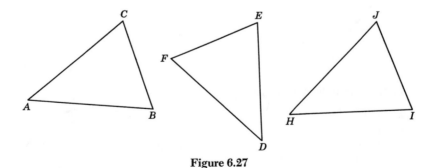

Figure 6.27

were traced on paper and the paper cut along the sides of the triangle, the paper pattern would represent the triangle and its interior region. The paper pattern of $\triangle DEF$ could be placed on $\triangle ABC$ and would fit exactly. If the vertex D were placed on vertex A of $\triangle ABC$ with $\overline{DF}$ along $\overline{AC}$, vertex F would fall on vertex C and vertex E would fall on vertex B. In these two triangles there would be six pairs of congruent line segments and angles:

$$\overline{AB} \cong \overline{DE} \qquad \angle\, CAB \cong \angle\, FDE$$
$$\overline{BC} \cong \overline{EF} \qquad \angle\, ABC \cong \angle\, DEF$$
$$\overline{AC} \cong \overline{DF} \qquad \angle\, BCA \cong \angle\, EFD$$

We say that $\triangle ABC \cong \triangle DEF$. Care must be taken in writing this statement, for we must be sure that corresponding letters are names for matching parts. In this instance, it would be incorrect to say $\triangle ABC \cong \triangle FED$ since $\angle\, CAB \cong \angle\, FDE$ and not to $\angle\, DFE$. We then say side $\overline{AB}$ of $\triangle ABC$ corresponds to side $\overline{DE}$ of $\triangle DEF$, and we call $\overline{AB}$ and $\overline{DE}$ *corresponding sides*. Further, we say that $\angle\, CAB$ of $\triangle ABC$ corresponds to $\angle\, FDE$ of $\triangle DEF$ and call $\angle\, CAB$ and $\angle\, FDE$ *corresponding angles*. In other words, pairs of congruent sides or angles are called corresponding sides or angles of the two triangles. In Figure 6.27, $\triangle DEF \cong \triangle HIJ$. Then $\angle\, FDE$ and $\angle\, JHI$ are corresponding angles, and $\overline{DE}$ and $\overline{HI}$ are corresponding sides. Name other pairs of corresponding sides and angles.

We conclude from the above that two triangles are congruent if their corresponding angles and their corresponding sides are congruent. We ask ourselves how many corresponding parts of a triangle must be congruent before we can conclude that the triangles are congruent.

In formal geometry the following theorems are proved. We will accept them without proof.

Two triangles are congruent if THE FOLLOWING APPLIES:

THEOREM 1.   Three sides of one triangle are congruent respectively to three sides of the other triangle.

THEOREM 2.   Two sides and the included angle of one triangle are congruent respectively to two sides and the included angle of the other triangle.

THEOREM 3.   Two angles and the side which lies between them are congruent respectively to the two angles and the side which lies between them of the other triangle.

6.18.   CONSTRUCTING CONGRUENT ANGLES

Suppose we wish to draw an angle congruent to $\angle\, ABC$. This can be done as illustrated below.

ANGLE TO BE COPIED	NEW ANGLE	DIRECTIONS
		1. Draw a ray $\overrightarrow{DE}$
		2. Place the point of the compass on B. Draw an arc that meets the sides of $\angle ABC$ at P and Q. Without changing the compass setting, put the point of the compass on D and draw a similar arc which cuts $\overrightarrow{DE}$ at R.
		3. Place the compass point on P and the compass pencil point on Q to get the distance. Do not change the compass setting. Place the compass point on R and make a mark S as shown.
		4. Draw $\overrightarrow{DS}$. $\angle FDE \cong \angle ABC$

6.19. CONSTRUCTING CONGRUENT TRIANGLES

Suppose we wish to draw a triangle congruent to $\triangle ABC$ in Figure 6.28.

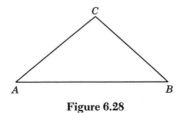

Figure 6.28

We start by laying off a segment $\overline{A'B'}$ congruent to $\overline{AB}$.

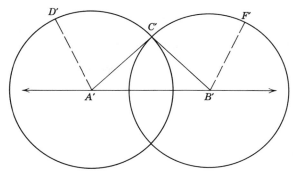

Figure 6.29

Then we take a line segment $\overline{A'D'}$ congruent to $\overline{AC}$, and using it as a radius, we draw a circle with center at A'. Now we take a segment $\overline{B'F'}$ congruent to $\overline{BC}$; using it as a radius, we draw a circle with center at B'. These two circles, in Figure 6.29, will intersect in two points. Label one of them C' and draw $\overline{A'C'}$ and $\overline{B'C'}$. Now $\triangle ABC$ and $\triangle A'B'C'$ are congruent because the three sides of $\triangle ABC$ are respectively congruent to the three sides of $\triangle A'B'C'$. Why?

A second method of drawing a triangle congruent to $\triangle ABC$ in Figure 6.28 is given below. Lay off $\overline{A'B'} \cong \overline{AB}$. We must now construct an angle with vertex at A' and one side $\overline{A'B'}$ congruent to $\angle CAB$. Figure 6.30 shows $\overrightarrow{A'K}$ drawn so that $\angle KA'B' \cong \angle CAB$.

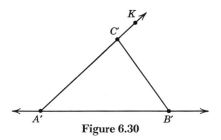

Figure 6.30

We may now follow two different methods which are given below.

Method 1. Make $\overline{A'C'} \cong \overline{AC}$ on ray $\overrightarrow{A'K}$. Draw $\overline{B'C'}$ thus getting $\triangle A'B'C'$; $\triangle A'B'C'$ has two sides and an included angle congruent respectively to two sides and an included angle of $\triangle ABC$, and hence $\triangle ABC \cong \triangle A'B'C'$. This method is shown in Figure 6.30.

Method 2. Draw $\overrightarrow{B'L}$ so that $\angle LB'A' \cong \angle CBA$. The rays $\overrightarrow{A'K}$ and $\overrightarrow{B'L}$ will intersect in a point labeled C'. We now have $\triangle A'B'C'$ which is congruent to $\triangle ABC$ because two angles and the side which lies between them are congruent respectively to the corresponding angles and the side that lies between them of $\triangle ABC$. This method is shown in Figure 6.31.

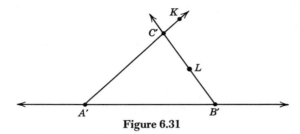

Figure 6.31

6.20.   CLASSIFICATION OF TRIANGLES

Triangles can be classified by comparing their sides or their angles.

1. If three sides of a triangle are congruent, the triangle is equilateral.
2. If two sides of a triangle are congruent, the triangle is isosceles.
3. If three angles of a triangle are congruent, the triangle is equiangular.
4. If no two sides of a triangle are congruent, the triangle is scalene.
5. If two angles of a triangle are congruent, the triangle is isosceles.
6. If one angle of a triangle is a right angle, the triangle is a right triangle.

In Figure 6.32, $\triangle ABC$ is equilateral as well as equiangular; $\triangle DEF$ is isosceles; $\triangle PQR$ is scalene; and $\triangle HIJ$ is a right triangle.

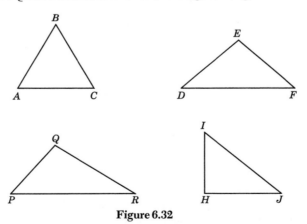

Figure 6.32

6.21.   CLASSIFICATION OF QUADRILATERALS

Quadrilaterals may be classified in the same way as triangles, that is, by listing special properties of their sides or angles. For example;

1. *Scalene Quadrilateral:* None of its sides congruent.

2. *Trapezoid:* One pair of its nonintersecting sides are parallel line segments.

3. *Parallelogram:* Both pairs of its non-intersecting sides are parallel line segments; these sides are congruent.

4. *Rectangle:* A parallelogram whose angles are congruent; these angles are right angles.

5. *Square:* A rectangle with four congruent sides.

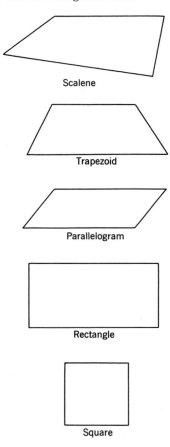

Scalene

Trapezoid

Parallelogram

Rectangle

Square

EXERCISE 6.5

1. Which of the following are true statements?

   a. All squares are rectangles.
   b. All right triangles are isosceles.
   c. All parallelograms are rectangles.
   d. All rectangles are squares.
   e. All right triangles are scalene triangles.

2. Which of the following pairs of triangles are always congruent?

    a. Two equilateral triangles,
    b. Two right triangles,
    c. Two isosceles triangles,
    d. Two scalene triangles,
    e. Two equiangular triangles.

3. Name the corresponding parts of the triangles below.

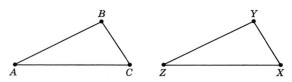

4. Construct a triangle with sides congruent to these line segments.

    _____   _____   _____

5. Sketch congruent pairs of

    a. triangles
    b. rectangles
    c. squares
    d. hexagons.

6. Define a square.
7. Define a rectangle.
8. Define a quadrilateral.

CHAPTER 7

Number Sentences

7.1. MATHEMATICAL SENTENCES

Mathematical sentences may be statements. For example, the following mathematical sentences are statements because they can be labeled *True* or *False*.

$$6 + 3 = 9 \qquad \text{True}$$
$$6 + 9 < 4 \qquad \text{False}$$
$$(7 \cdot 3) + 5 > 2 \qquad \text{True}$$
$$18 \div 6 = 15 + 3 \qquad \text{False}$$

Other mathematical sentences may have statement form but are not statements because, as stated, they may not be given a truth value. The mathematical sentences

$$n + 6 = 9,$$
$$5n > 4,$$
$$7 \div 6 > n + 2$$

have statement form but may not be given a truth value as they stand. Such sentences are called *open sentences* or simply, *sentences*.

Mathematical sentences have verbs which express a relationship between numbers. We use symbols to represent these verbs or verb phrases.

The symbols we will use most often in mathematical sentences are the following:

Symbol	Verb or verb phrase
$=$	equals or is equal to
$<$	is less than
$>$	is greater than
$\neq$	is not equal to
$\not<$	is not less than
$\not>$	is not greater than.

A mathematical sentence which contains the verb "equals" is called an *equality* or an *equation*. A mathematical sentence which contains the verb phrase "is greater than" or "is less than" is called an *inequality*.

7.2. OPEN SENTENCES

An example of an open sentence is $n + 9 = 14$. The letter, n, in this case, is a symbol that stands for an unspecified number. We call such a symbol a *variable*. This open sentence is true if we replace the symbol, n, by 5. It is false for all other replacements. A mathematical sentence may contain one or more variables. The symbol that is used for the variable in a sentence is immaterial. For example, instead of n in the open sentence $n + 9 = 14$, we might have used $\square$, x, y, $\triangle$, ?, or $\diamondsuit$ for the variable, n. Thus

$$\square + 9 = 14,$$
$$x + 9 = 14,$$
$$y + 9 = 14,$$
$$\triangle + 9 = 14,$$
$$? + 9 = 14,$$
$$\diamondsuit + 9 = 14,$$

are all forms of the same open sentences; only the symbol for the variable is different. The symbols $\square$, $\triangle$, and $\diamondsuit$ are called *frames*. They are usually used as symbols for variables in the primary grades.

7.3. SOLUTION SETS

A set of numbers either implied or explicitly stated as permissible replacements of the variable in an open sentence, is called the *replacement set*, the *domain of the variable*, or, simply, the *domain*. The subset from the replacement set whose elements make the open sentence a true statement, is called the *solution set,* or *truth set,* of the open sentence. Every element in the solution set is called a *solution.*

Let us consider the open sentence $5n + 2 = 17$. Let the domain of the variable be

$$D = \{1, 2, 3, 4, 5\}.$$

We now wish to find the solution set for the sentence $5n + 2 = 17$ by trying each replacement.

Replace n by 1:
$$(5 \times 1) + 2 = 17$$
$$5 + 2 = 17$$
$$7 = 17. \qquad \text{False}$$

Replace n by 2:
$$(5 \times 2) + 2 = 17$$
$$10 + 2 = 17$$
$$12 = 17. \qquad \text{False}$$

Replace n by 3:
$$(5 \times 3) + 2 = 17$$
$$15 + 2 = 17$$
$$17 = 17. \qquad \text{True}$$

Replace n by 4:
$$(5 \times 4) + 2 = 17$$
$$20 + 2 = 17$$
$$22 = 17. \qquad \text{False}$$

Replace n by 5:
$$(5 \times 5) + 2 = 17$$
$$25 + 2 = 17$$
$$27 = 17. \qquad \text{False}$$

We see that 3 is the only member of the domain for which the sentence $5n + 2 = 17$ is true. Hence, the solution set is $\{3\}$, and 3 is the solution for the sentence $5n + 2 = 17$.

Now let us find the solution set for the inequality $5n - 6 > 20$.

Let the domain be

$$D = \{4, 5, 6, 7\}.$$

Replace n by 4:
$$(5 \times 4) - 6 > 20$$
$$20 - 6 > 20$$
$$14 > 20. \qquad \text{False}$$

Replace n by 5:
$$(5 \times 5) - 6 > 20$$

$$25 - 6 > 20$$
$$19 > 20. \quad \text{False}$$

Replace n by 6: $\quad (5 \times 6) - 6 > 20$
$$30 - 6 > 20$$
$$24 > 20. \quad \text{True}$$

Replace n by 7: $\quad (5 \times 7) - 6 > 20$
$$35 - 6 > 20$$
$$29 > 20. \quad \text{True}$$

Hence, the solution set is $\{6, 7\}$, and the solutions of $5n - 6 > 20$ are 6 and 7.

In both examples above the domain was a finite set. Now let us consider an example in which the domain is an infinite set. Consider the sentence $x - 7 > 5$ in which the domain is the set of whole numbers $D = \{0, 1, 2, 3, \ldots\}$.

Since D is an infinite set, it is impossible to attempt to replace x by every element in D as we did in the examples above. We know that $12 - 7 = 5$, hence if x is replaced by 12 or any number less than 12, the sentence $x - 7 > 5$ will be false.

If we replace x by 13, we see

$$13 - 5 > 7$$
$$8 > 7$$

which is true. Hence, 13 is a member of the solution set. But any number greater than 13 will also make the sentence true. Therefore, the solution set is $\{13, 14, 15, \ldots\}$.

Now let us find the solution set of the inequality $x + 2 < 2$.

Let the domain be the set of whole numbers $D = \{0, 1, 2, \ldots\}$.

Since 0 is the least whole number and $0 + 2 = 2$, we see that there is no whole number that satisfies the sentence $x + 2 < 2$. Hence, the solution set is the empty set.

7.4. EQUIVALENT OPEN SENTENCES

Sometimes several sentences have the same solution set. Such sentences are called *equivalent sentences*. For example,

$$y + 7 = 9,$$
$$9 = y + 7,$$
$$9 - y = 7,$$

$$9 - 7 = y,$$
$$7 = 9 - y,$$
$$y = 9 - 7,$$

are equivalent sentences because the solution set for each sentence is $\{2\}$. Equivalent sentences are important in solving verbal problems. For example, consider the problem: Nancy has \$7. She wishes to buy a skirt that costs \$12. How much money must she save before she can buy the skirt?

Each of the following sentences is a mathematical translation of the conditions given in the problem.

$$
\begin{array}{ll}
7 + n = 12, & 12 = 7 + n, \\
12 - 7 = n, & n = 12 - 7, \\
12 - n = 7, & 7 = 12 - n, \\
n + 7 = 12, & 12 = n + 7.
\end{array}
$$

EXERCISE 7.1

1. Which of the following statements are true?

   a. $4 + 7 > 9$,
   b. $3 + 6 = 9 - 7$,
   c. $(26 \times 18) = 42 > 72$,
   d. $97 + 83 = 77 + 43$.

2. Write the following as open mathematical sentences. Use the letter n for the variable.

   a. Seven plus a number is equal to sixteen.
   b. The sum of nine and this number is equal to fourteen.
   c. Twenty less than this number is sixty.
   d. This number plus twelve is greater than forty-six.
   e. Five times this number added to seven is less than sixty-nine.

3. Find the solution set for the sentences below. The domain is the set of whole numbers, $\{0, 1, 2, 3, 4, \ldots\}$.

   a. $n - 14 = 77$,
   b. $n + 6 > 9$,
   c. $19 < n - 4$,
   d. $4t = 16$,
   e. $k - 4 < 15$,
   f. $2p + 5 < 40$,
   g. $m - 7 < 11$,
   h. $4 + k > 16$.

4. Which of the following mathematical sentences have the same solution set?

   a. $7n + 6 > 39$,
   b. $2n - 3 < 7$,
   c. $5x - 4 > 21$,
   d. $y < 5$,
   e. $4k + 1 > 6$.

5. What is the distinction between a solution and a solution set?
6. Name the variables in each of the following mathematical sentences.

   a. $7x + 9 > 15$,
   b. $2 + \square = 27$,
   c. $3n + 9 > 5n - 2$,
   d. $7 + \triangle < 92$.

7. Which of the following have the null set as the solution set? The domain is the set of whole numbers.

   a. $x^2 + 1 = 0$,
   b. $2x + 1 > 3$,
   c. $5x - 7 < 5$,
   d. $2 > x$,
   e. $5x + 3 > 15$.

8. How many elements are in the solution set of $x = 2$?
9. Which of the sentences in Problem 3 are equations? Which are inequalities?
10. What is another name for domain?
11. What is a frame?
12. Translate the following number sentences into word sentences.

   a. $12 + 6 = 18$.   b. $3 \times 10 = 30$.
   c. $17 < 5 \times 25$.   d. $4 + 6 \neq 27 - 7$.

13. Which of the following statements are true?

   a. The symbol ">" is read "is less than."
   b. The symbol "$\neq$" is read "is not equal to."
   c. The symbol "$=$" denotes "is the same as."
   d. A statement may be both true and false at the same time.
   e. $n + 6 = 15$ is an open sentence.
   f. $n + 7 = 9$ and $9 - 7 = n$ are equivalent sentences.
   g. $7 + 6 < 15$ is an equality.
   h. $6 + 40 > 4$ is an inequality.

14. What is another name for solution set?

7.5. COMPOUND OPEN SENTENCES

Sometimes we are asked to solve compound open sentences. For example, we may be asked to solve the conjunction

$$n > 2 \text{ and } n < 9.$$

We know that a conjunction is true, if, and only if, both of its components are true. Hence, the sentence $n > 2$ and $n < 9$ is true only when $n > 2$ is true and $n < 9$ is true. If the domain is the set of whole numbers, the solution set of $n > 2$ is $\{3, 4, 5, \ldots\}$, and the solution set of $n < 9$ is $\{0, 1, 2, 3, 4, 5, 6, 7, 8\}$. Notice that the solution set of $n > 2$ is an infinite set; the solution set of $n < 9$ is a finite set.

Since the compound sentence $n > 2$ and $n < 9$ is true if and only if $n > 2$ is true and $n < 9$ is true, the solution set of the compound sentence is the intersection set of the two solution sets. That is, the solution set is

$$\{3, 4, 5, \ldots\} \cap \{0, 2, 3, 4, 5, 6, 7, 8\}.$$

Hence, the solution set is the set of elements common to these two sets, that is, $\{3, 4, 5, 6, 7, 8\}$.

The conjunction $n > 2$ and $n < 9$ is generally written in the shortened form $2 < n < 9$, and is read "2 is less than n, and n is less than 9" or "n is greater than 2 and less than 9."

Now let us solve the disjunction $x > 7$ or $x = 7$ where the domain is the set of whole numbers. The solution set of $x > 7$ is $\{8, 9, 10, \ldots\}$, and the solution set of $x = 7$ is $\{7\}$.

Recalling that a disjunction is true if one or the other or both of its components are true, we find that the solution set of $x > 7$ or $x = 7$ is the union of the solution set of $x > 7$ and the solution set of $x = 7$. That is, the solution set is

$$\{8, 9, 10, \ldots\} \cup \{7\} = \{7, 8, 9, \ldots\}.$$

The sentence $x > 7$ or $x = 7$ is generally written in the shorthand form $x \geq 7$ which is read "x is greater than 7 or x is equal to 7" or, "x is greater than or equal to 7." The symbol $\geq$ is a combination of the symbols $>$ and $=$.

Often we encounter situations involving even more complex sentences. For example, consider the sentence, "Candidates for the Civic Mathematics Fellowship must be between the ages of 20 and 35 inclusive." Suppose x represents the age of the eligible candidate. He must be at least 20 years old; that is, $20 \leq x$. But he must not be older than 35 years old; that is, $35 \geq x$. These conditions are described in the conjunction

$$20 \leq x \text{ and } x \leq 35$$

or,

$$20 \leq x \leq 35.$$

This shortened form of the sentence is read, "20 is less than or equal to x, and x is less than or equal to 35" or, "x is greater than or equal to 20 and less than or equal to 35." The conjunction $20 \leq x \leq 35$ is made up of two other compound sentences which are disjunctions. Consider the disjunction $20 \leq x$. This says

$$20 < x \text{ or } 20 = x.$$

The solution set of $20 < x$ is $\{21, 22, \ldots\}$. The solution set of $x = 20$ is $\{20\}$. Since $20 \leq x$ is a disjunction, the solution set is the union of $\{21, 22, \ldots\}$ and $\{20,\}$, that is, $\{20, 21, 22, \ldots\}$.

Consider the disjunction $x \leq 35$. This says

$$x < 35 \text{ or } x = 35.$$

The solution set of $x < 35$ is $\{1, 2, \ldots, 34\}$.
The solution set of $x = 35$ is $\{35\}$.
The solution set of $x \leq 35$ is the union of $\{1, 2, \ldots, 34\}$ and $\{35,\}$, that is, the set $\{1, 2, 3, \ldots, 35\}$.
The solution set of the conjunction $20 \leq x \leq 35$ is the intersection of the solution sets of $20 \leq x$ and $x \leq 35$; that is, $\{20, 21, \ldots\} \cap \{1, 2, 3, \ldots, 35\}$ $= \{20, 21, \ldots, 35\}$.

7.6. GRAPHING SOLUTION SETS

On the number line we can picture the solution set of a number sentence with one variable. This picture is called the *graph* of the solution set. The graph of a set of points is the collection of points on the number line which represent the set.

Let us consider the sentence $x \leq 6$ where the domain is the set of whole numbers.
The solution set of $x \leq 6$ is

$$\{0, 1, 2, 3, 4, 5, 6\}.$$

The graph of this solution set is shown below.

Now let us graph the solution set of $2 < x < 9$ where the domain is the set of whole numbers.

The solution set of $2 < x < 9$ is $\{3, 4, 5, 6, 7, 8\}$. The graph of this solution set is shown below

Now let us graph the solution set of $x > 10$. Again let the domain be the set of whole numbers.

The solution set is $\{11, 12, 13, \ldots\}$.

The graph of this solution set is shown below.

We draw an arrow on the right above the number line to indicate that all the points to the right are members of the solution set.

EXERCISE 7.2

Solve the following compound sentences. The domain is the set of whole numbers.

1. $x \geq 5$.
2. $2 < x < 9$.
3. $x + 9 \leq 15$.
4. $y + 11 \geq 27$.
5. $x > 9$ and $x < 27$.
6. $x \geq 20$ and $x \leq 35$.
7. $x \geq 19$ and $x \leq 47$.
8. $x \geq 15$ or $x \leq 10$.
9. $x \geq 26$ or $x \leq 97$.
10. Graph the solution set of Problem 1.
11. Graph the solution set of Problem 2.
12. Graph the solution set of Problem 3.
13. Graph the solution set of Problem 4.
14. Graph the solution set of Problem 5.
15. Graph the solution set of Problem 6.
16. Graph the solution set of Problem 7.
17. Graph the solution set of Problem 8.
18. Graph the solution set of Problem 9.
19. How do you read $2 < x < 9$?
20. How do you read $3 \leq n \leq 15$?
21. How do you read $p \geq 25$?
22. How do you read $r \leq 17$?
23. A man weighs 40 pounds more than his twelve-year old son. Their combined weight is less than 280 pounds. How much does the boy weigh?

24. Mr. Wright and Mr. Carlson agree to furnish at least $10,000 capital to start a new business. If Mr. Carlson furnishes $500 more than Mr. Wright, what is the least that Mr. Wright can contribute?

7.7. SENTENCES WITH TWO VARIABLES

Even at the primary level one encounters problems which are solved by sentences involving more than one variable. Suppose a child is told that he may have five cookies from a plate containing round chocolate cookies and square gingerbread cookies. Since there are two kinds of cookies, the number sentence to solve this problem contains two variables. If ◯ represents the number of chocolate cookies and ☐ represents the number of gingerbread cookies, the number sentence representing this problem is

$$\bigcirc + \square = 5.$$

Since the sentence involves two variables, each solution in the solution set will be an ordered pair of numbers. Since the child is only permitted to have five cookies, the domain for each variable is $\{0, 1, 2, 3, 4, 5\}$. If the first choice is one chocolate cookie and four gingerbread cookies, we have the ordered pair $(1, 4)$ which is a solution of the sentence. The possible solutions are listed in Table 7.1.

Table 7.1

◯	☐
0	5
1	4
2	3
3	2
4	1
5	0

The solution set is a set of ordered pairs $\{(0, 5), (1, 4), (2, 3), (3, 2), (4, 1), (5, 0)\}$. We see that the ordered pair $(3, 3)$ is not a solution since $3 + 3 \neq 5$.

Now let us solve the sentence $x + y = 9$ where the domain for each variable is the set of whole numbers. The largest value x can have is 9 since any larger whole number cannot be added to another whole number and have a sum of 9.

The solution set for this sentence is $\{(9,0)\ (8,1),\ (7,2),\ (6,3),\ (5,4),\ (4,5),\ (3,6),\ (2,7),\ (1,8),\ (0,9)\}$. Because the solutions are ordered pairs the solution $(4,5)$ is not the same as the solution $(5,4)$.

Let us find the solution set of $x + y < 8$ in which the domain of each variable is the set of whole numbers. We see that x can never be larger than 7. Hence, the possible values for x are $0, 1, 2, 3, 4, 5, 6, 7$. If $x = 0$, y can be any whole number less than 8. This gives the ordered pairs

$$(0,7),\ (0,6),\ (0,5),\ (0,4),\ (0,3),\ (0,2),\ (0,1),\ (0,0)$$

If $x = 1$, y can be any whole number less than 7. This gives the ordered pairs

$$(1,6),\ (1,5),\ (1,4),\ (1,3),\ (1,2),\ (1,1),\ (1,0).$$

If $x = 2$, y can be any whole number less than 6. This gives the ordered pairs

$$(2,5),\ (2,4),\ (2,3),\ (2,4),\ (2,1),\ (2,0).$$

If $x = 3$, y can be any whole number less than 5. This gives the ordered pairs

$$(3,4),\ (3,3),\ (3,2),\ (3,1),\ (3,0).$$

Continuing in this fashion, we find that the solution set is

$$\left\{ \begin{array}{l} (0,7),\ (0,6),\ (0,5),\ (0,4),\ (0,3),\ (0,2),\ (0,1),\ (0,0), \\ (1,6),\ (1,5),\ (1,4),\ (1,3),\ (1,2),\ (1,1),\ (1,0), \\ (2,5),\ (2,4),\ (2,3),\ (2,2),\ (2,1),\ (2,0), \\ (3,4),\ (3,3),\ (3,2),\ (3,1),\ (3,0), \\ (4,3),\ (4,2),\ (4,1),\ (4,0), \\ (5,2),\ (5,1),\ (5,0), \\ (6,1),\ (6,0), \\ (7,0). \end{array} \right\}$$

7.8. GRAPHING ORDERED PAIRS

In graphing ordered pairs of numbers we need two number rays, called *axes*. We arrange them so that one is horizontal and one is vertical, as shown in Figure 7.1.

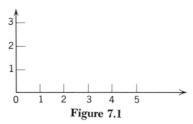

Figure 7.1

We will call the horizontal axis the *first axis* and the vertical axis the *second axis*. (In the more common terminology, these are the *x*-axis and *y*-axis respectively.) Now we draw lines to form a lattice as shown in Figure 7.2.

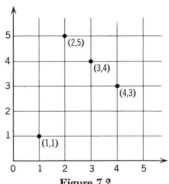

Figure 7.2

The intersections of these lines are called *lattice points*. Each lattice point represents an ordered pair of whole numbers. Some of the ordered pairs represented on the lattice in Figure 7.2 are labeled. Using a lattice which is called a *lattice plane* we can graph the solution set of a sentence containing two variables.

The solution set of $x + y = 5$ is $\{(5,0), (4,1), (3,2), (2,3), (1,4), (0,5)\}$. The graph of this solution set is shown in Figure 7.3.

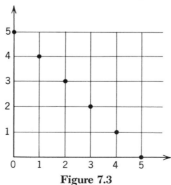

Figure 7.3

Let us solve the sentence $x = y$, in which the domain is the set of whole numbers, and graph the solution set. Since $x = y$, the ordered pairs which are solutions must have the first member equal to the second member. Hence, some solutions are $(2, 2)$, $(3, 3)$, $(4, 4)$.

The solution set will be every ordered pair of the form (a, a) in which a is a whole number. The solution set of this sentence will be an infinite set. Now let us graph the solution set. The graphs of the solution are all the lattice points on the line drawn in the lattice in Figure 7.4.

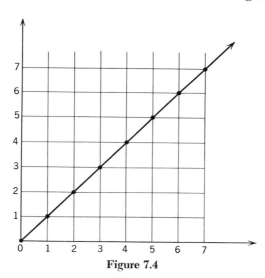

Figure 7.4

EXERCISE 7.3

   1. Graph the following ordered pairs.

      a. $(7, 3)$ b. $(2, 1)$ c. $(2, 7)$
      d. $(1, 1)$ e. $(3, 1)$ f. $(5, 9)$

Solve the following sentences. Let the domain of the variables be $\{1, 2, 3, 4, 5\}$.

   2. $x + y = 9$.
   3. $x - y = 3$.
   4. $x + y > 5$.
   5. $x + y < 14$.
   6. $2x < y$.
   7. Graph the solution set of Problem 2.
   8. Graph the solution set of Problem 3.
   9. Graph the solution set of Problem 4.
  10. Graph the solution set of Problem 5.
  11. Graph the solution set of Problem 6.

In Problems 12–15 solve the following sentences. Let the domain of the variables be the set of whole numbers.

12. $x + y = 9$.
13. $2x + y < 12$.
14. $x - y < 16$.
15. $3x + y < 24$.
16. Draw the graph of the solution set of Problem 9.
17. Draw the graph of the solution set of Problem 15.

CHAPTER **8**

Topics in Number Theory

8.1. FIGURATE NUMBERS

Most people are intrigued by unusual numbers. Even though they may not attach to them any special significance, it does amuse most people to see a car with the license number ABC–123, a telephone number like 234–5678, or a dollar bill with the serial number G56565656W. The ancient Greeks were similarly fascinated by special numbers. Since they were particularly interested in the subject of geometry, they singled out numbers with which they were able to associate various geometrical figures; such numbers were called *figurate numbers*. They studied the numbers $1, 3, 6, 10, \ldots$, for example, and called them *triangular numbers*. The choice of this name is easy to understand if we look at Figure 8.1.

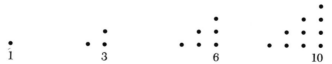

Figure 8.1 Triangular numbers.

The Greeks were also interested in the *square numbers* (Figure 8.2*a*) $1, 4, 9, 16, \ldots$, the *pentagonal numbers* (Figure 8.2*b*) $1, 5, 12, 22, \ldots$,

155

hexagonal numbers and others referring to more complicated geometrical figures.

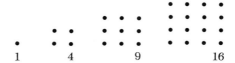

Figure 8.2a   Square numbers.

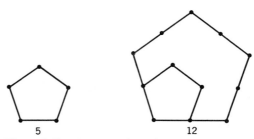

Figure 8.2b   Pentagonal numbers.

In each case only a few of these special numbers are shown in Figures 8.1 and 8.2. If necessary, we could find the eighteenth or the twentieth triangular number by drawing the corresponding geometrical figure and counting the dots. This, of course, would be a very tedious job. Let us see if there is not a simpler method by which these numbers can be computed.

Let us first consider the square numbers. It is easy to see that they follow a definite arithmetical pattern. The first one is 1, or 1×1; the second is 4, or $2 \times 2 = 2^2$; the third is 9, or $3 \times 3 = 3^2$; and so on. This leads us to the generalization that the sixth square number is $6 \times 6 = 6^2 = 36$; the tenth square number is $10 \times 10 = 10^2 = 100$; and in general the nth square number is $n \times n = n^2$. This explains why we read 3^2 as "three squared."

Let us see whether or not we can find a similar formula for finding the nth triangular number. We have

$$
\begin{array}{ll}
\text{1st} & 1 \\
\text{2nd} & 1 + 2 = 3, \\
\text{3rd} & 1 + 2 + 3 = 6, \\
\text{4th} & 1 + 2 + 3 + 4 = 10.
\end{array}
$$

Each successive triangular number is thus obtained by adding another row of dots containing one more dot than the previous bottom row. Thus,

5th $1 + 2 + 3 + 4 + 5 = 15,$
6th $1 + 2 + 3 + 4 + 5 + 6 = 21,$

.

.

.

kth $1 + 2 + 3 + \ldots + k,$

where k is any counting number.

This method of finding any desired triangular number entails a good deal of work if k is large. To simplify this task we shall develop a formula for finding the kth triangular number without actually having to add all the counting numbers from 1 to k.

It is a well-known fact that the area of a rectangular region is given by the product of its length and width. Look at Figure 8.3.

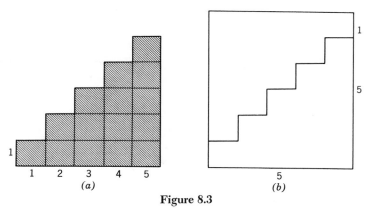

Figure 8.3

If we consider the total shaded figure formed by squares we find that its area is equal to 15 square units; that is,

$$1 + 2 + 3 + 4 + 5 = 15.$$

If we take *two* such figures and fit them together as in Figure 8.3b, we get a rectangular region whose width is 5, and whose length is $5 + 1 = 6$, and whose area is $5 \times (5 + 1) = 30$. In other words, twice the sum of $1 + 2 + 3 + 4 + 5$ is equal to $5 \times (5 + 1)$.

We can use this argument to find a formula for the kth triangular number, which we have shown is given by the sum of $1 + 2 + 3 + \ldots + k$. If we draw a figure like the shaded part in Figure 8.3*a* in which there are k square units in the bottom row its total area will be equal to $1 + 2 + 3 + \ldots + k$. Combining two such figures in the same way as before, we will obtain a rectangular region whose length is $k + 1$ and whose width is k. The total area of this rectangular region is $k \times (k + 1)$, and this represents twice the sum of the counting numbers from 1 to k. Thus,

$$2 \times (1 + 2 + \ldots + k) = k(k + 1)$$

or the sum of the first k natural numbers is $\dfrac{k(k + 1)}{2}$.

8.2. SUBSETS OF THE WHOLE NUMBERS

If we have a set we can separate it into subsets in many ways. For example, if we consider the set of persons in a class, we may separate them into two subsets, the set of men and the set of women, or we may separate them into the subset of persons over 21 years of age and the subset of persons 21 years of age or younger.

Similarly we may separate the set of whole numbers into subsets in various ways. We may separate them into the subset of even numbers and the subset of odd numbers. We are going to study some of these special subsets of whole numbers.

All whole numbers are either *even* or *odd*. Even numbers are those which are divisible by two without a remainder. Even numbers are, therefore, multiples of two. It is easy to see that $0, 2, 4, 6, 8$, and 10 are divisible by two and hence are even numbers. Every even number may be represented by $2n$ where n must be a whole number. For example, $58 = 2 \times n$ where $n = 29$ because $2 \times 29 = 58$.

When any whole number is divided by two, the remainder is either zero or one. Since even numbers are divisible by two, the remainder when an even number is divided by two is zero. Hence, all odd numbers have a remainder of one when divided by two. Therefore all odd numbers may be represented by $2n + 1$ where n must be a whole number. It is easy to see that $1, 3, 5, 7$, and 9 are odd numbers.

$$
\begin{aligned}
1 &= (2 \times 0) + 1, \\
3 &= (2 \times 1) + 1, \\
5 &= (2 \times 2) + 1, \\
7 &= (2 \times 3) + 1, \\
9 &= (2 \times 4) + 1.
\end{aligned}
$$

8.3. PROPERTIES OF EVEN AND ODD NUMBERS

We can convince ourselves in observing examples such as

$$2 + 2 = 4,$$
$$4 + 6 = 10,$$
$$8 + 16 = 24,$$
$$26 + 34 = 60,$$

that the sum of two even numbers is always an even number. Similarly we see that the product of two even numbers is an even number. Observe that

$$12 \times 6 = 72 \ = 2 \times 36,$$
$$8 \times 4 = 32 \ = 2 \times 16,$$
$$42 \times 6 = 252 = 2 \times 126.$$

In fact, it is quite easy to prove that the sum of any two even numbers is an even number. Let the two even numbers be $2p$ and $2s$, where p and s are whole numbers. We wish to show that $2p + 2s$ is an even number. We use the Distributive Property to make $2p + 2s = 2(p + s)$. Since p and s are whole numbers, $p + s$ is a whole number. Hence, $2(p + s)$ is a whole number of the form $2n$.

Since the sum of any two even numbers is again an even number, we say that the set of even numbers is closed under addition.

We will now show that the product of two even numbers is an even number. Let the two even numbers again be represented by $2p$ and $2s$, where s and p are whole numbers. Then $2p \times 2s = 2 \times (p \times 2 \times s) = 2(2ps)$. But since p, s, and 2 are whole numbers, their product is a whole number, and hence, $2 \times (2ps)$ is two times a whole number and is an even number. The set of even numbers is therefore closed under multiplication.

That the set of odd numbers is not closed under addition is shown by the sums $3 + 5 = 8$ and $9 + 7 = 16$. In fact, the sum of any two odd numbers is an even number.

The set of odd numbers is closed under multiplication. That is, the product of two odd numbers is always an odd number. A few examples illustrate that the product of two odd numbers is an odd number:

$$3 \times 9 = 27,$$
$$5 \times 7 = 35,$$
$$9 \times 9 = 81.$$

It can also be shown that the sum of an even number and an odd number is an odd number and that the product of an odd number and an even number is an even number. Table 8.1 summarizes these results. In the table E represents an even number and O represents an odd number.

Table 8.1

+	E	O
E	E	O
O	O	E

×	E	O
E	E	E
O	E	O

EXERCISE 8.1

1. Draw figures, using dots, of the first ten triangular numbers.
2. Draw figures, using dots, of the first five pentagonal numbers.
3. What is the

    a. 4th square number?
    b. 7th square number?
    c. 12th square number?
    d. 39th square number?

4. Use the formula to find the following triangular numbers.

    a. 15th   b. 36th   c. 100th
    d. 27th   e. 54th   f. 200th

5. Every even number may be represented by $2n$, where n is a whole number. Every odd number may be represented by $2n + 1$, where n is a whole number. Write each of the following as $2n$ or $2n + 1$.

    a. 9   b. 18   c. 32   d. 37
    e. 137   f. 152   g. 263   h. 2384
    i. 5381   j. 6472   k. 13,841   l. 42,427

6. Write the set of those even numbers greater than 12 but less than 50.
7. Write the set of odd numbers that are greater than 83 but less than 99.
8. Using Table 8.1, tell whether the following name odd or even numbers.

    a. $E \times (O + O)$ b. $(E \times O) + (O \times O)$
    c. $(E + O) \times (E + E)$ d. $O \times (E + E) \times (O + E)$

9. Prove that the product of two odd numbers is an odd number.
10. Prove that the sum of two odd numbers is an even number.
11. Define an even number.
12. Which of the following represent an even number? Which an odd number? (The symbol "n" stands for any counting number.)

a. n b. $2n$ c. $2n + 1$
d. $2n - 1$ e. $2n + 2$ f. $n + 1$

13. How can we tell from looking at the factors that the product $11 \times 4 \times 5$ is an even number?

14. Is $1001_{(two)}$ even or odd?

15. Is $12_{(three)}$ even or odd?

16. Which of the following are true statements?

     a. Adding 1 to any odd number gives an even number.
     b. Adding 1 to an even number gives an even number.
     c. The product of four even numbers is an even number.
     d. The product of two even numbers and two odd numbers is an odd number.
     e. Subtracting 1 from an odd number gives an even number.
     f. An even number is always divisible by 2.
     g. The quotient of an odd number divided by 1 is odd.

17. What number is a factor of every counting number?

18. What number is a divisor of every counting number?

19. Which of the following sets are closed under the operation of multiplication? of addition?

     a. even numbers   b. odd numbers

8.4. PRIME NUMBERS AND COMPOSITE NUMBERS

We have just shown that the set of whole numbers may be separated into two disjoint sets, the set of even numbers and the set of odd numbers.

Let us now omit zero from the set of whole numbers and consider only the set of counting numbers, $\{1, 2, 3, \ldots\}$. We separate the set of counting numbers into three disjoint sets. Let set A contain those counting numbers that have only one divisor; let set P contain those counting numbers that have only two divisors, and let set C contain those counting numbers that have more than two divisors.

The set A will contain only one element, the number 1.

The set P will contain only those numbers other than 1 that are divisible by 1 and themselves. Such numbers are called *prime numbers* or simply *primes*.

$$P = \{2, 3, 5, 7, 11, 13, 17, 19, 23, \ldots\}.$$

All the other counting numbers will belong to set C.

$$C = \{4, 6, 8, 9, 10, 12, 14, 15, 16, 18, \ldots\}.$$

The numbers in set C are called *composite numbers* or simply *composites*.

Notice that the number 2 belongs to P because the only divisors of 2 are 1 and 2. The number 4 belongs to C because it has divisors $1, 2,$ and 4.

Observe that there are infinitely many primes and infinitely many composites. The only even prime is 2. Why?

8.5. THE SIEVE OF ERATOSTHENES

About 2200 years ago a Greek mathematician and scientist devised a scheme, called the *Sieve of Eratosthenes,* for finding all the prime numbers among the counting numbers less than some particular counting number. His method sieved out all the numbers that are not primes and left only the primes. Let us use his method to find all the primes less than 50. We will write in a table all the numbers greater than 1 but less than 50.

$$
\begin{array}{cccccccccc}
 & 2 & 3 & \not{4} & 5 & \not{6} & 7 & \not{8} & \not{9} & \not{10} \\
11 & \not{12} & 13 & \not{14} & \not{15} & \not{16} & 17 & \not{18} & 19 & \not{20} \\
\not{21} & \not{22} & 23 & \not{24} & \not{25} & \not{26} & \not{27} & \not{28} & 29 & \not{30} \\
31 & \not{32} & \not{33} & \not{34} & \not{35} & \not{36} & 37 & \not{38} & \not{39} & \not{40} \\
41 & \not{42} & 43 & \not{44} & \not{45} & \not{46} & 47 & \not{48} & \not{49}
\end{array}
$$

Let us leave the prime number 2, and scratch out every second number after 2. All the numbers which we have scratched out are divisible by 2 and hence are not primes. The next number is 3 which is a prime. Now let us scratch out every third number after 3. All the numbers which we have scratched out are divisible by three and hence are not prime numbers. The next number not scratched out is 5 which is a prime. Now let us scratch out every fifth number which is a multiple of 5 and hence, not a prime. The next number not scratched out is 7, a prime. Scratch out every seventh number. Continuing in this manner we can find all the prime numbers less than 50. They are the following:

$$2, 3, 5, 7, 11, 13, 17, 19, 23, 29, 31, 37, 41, 43, 47.$$

Notice that in the sieve some numbers, such as 24, are scratched out more than once. This happens because 24 is divisible by more than one prime number. In fact, it is divisible by both 2 and 3.

In performing the procedure of finding all of the primes less than 50, you may have observed that it was not necessary to strike out multiples of 11 because they were already stricken out in previous steps. This was also true of multiples of 13, 17, 19, and all primes less than 50. In searching for the primes less than 50, the largest prime necessary to use in the sieve method was 7. We ask ourselves if this was a coincidence, or is there some general property which can be used.

We are always sure to reach the end of the sieve process when we have crossed out the proper multiples of the prime p, where p is the largest prime such than $p^2 < n$. This follows because, if $n = ab$ is a composite, at least one of the factors a and b must be such that $a^2 \leq n$ and $b^2 \leq n$; that is, $a \leq \sqrt{n}$ ($\sqrt{n}$ is read "the square root of n." If $\sqrt{n} = a$, then $a^2 = n$. Thus, $\sqrt{25} = 5$ because $5^2 = 25$) and $b \leq \sqrt{n}$. Otherwise, if $a > \sqrt{n}$ and $b > \sqrt{n}$, we would have $n = ab > \sqrt{n} \cdot \sqrt{n} = n$, an obvious contradiction. Hence, if n is not crossed out when the proper multiples of p (and of all the smaller primes) have been eliminated, then n must be a prime.

This, of course, gives us a way of determining whether or not a given number is prime. For example, let us test whether or not 101 is a prime. Since $10 \times 10 = 100$ and $11 \times 11 = 121$, we need only test those primes less than 10, that is, $2, 3, 5,$ and 7, as possible factors of 101. Since none of these, $2, 3, 5,$ or 7, are factors of 101, we conclude that 101 is a prime.

8.6. FACTORS

In $3 \times 5 = 15$, 3 and 5 are called *factors*, and 15 is called the *product*. If we write 3×5 as another name for 15, we call this expression a *factor expression*. In general, if $n = a \times b$, a and b are called factors of n.

Various factor expressions of 24 are

$$1 \times 24,$$
$$2 \times 12,$$
$$3 \times 8,$$
$$4 \times 6,$$
$$2 \times 2 \times 2 \times 3.$$

It is observed that 1 and the number itself are always factors of a given number. For any given number, all possible factors (which are also divisors) should be given. For example, the factors of 24 are $1, 2, 3, 4, 6, 8, 12,$ and 24.

When we look for the factors of a small number, knowledge of the multiplication facts enables us to find every product expression with two factors. For large numbers, the method of division is usually more satisfactory. For example, is 3 a factor of 143?

$$
\begin{array}{r}
47 \\
3\overline{)143} \\
12 \\
\hline
23 \\
21 \\
\hline
2
\end{array}
$$

Since 143 ÷ 3 gives a remainder 2, we conclude that 3 is not a factor of 143. Is 3 a factor of 345?

$$
\begin{array}{r}
115 \\
3\overline{)345} \\
3 \\
\hline
4 \\
3 \\
\hline
15 \\
15 \\
\hline
0
\end{array}
$$

Since 345 ÷ 3 = 115, we conclude that 3 is a factor of 345.

Another method of factoring a counting number is a *factor tree*. A factor tree is a means of showing how a counting number is built from small factors. A factor tree for 48 is shown below:

$$
\begin{array}{c}
48 \\
\diagup \diagdown \\
6 \times 8
\end{array}
$$

By extending the drawing, 48 is pictured as $2 \times 3 \times 8$.

$$
\begin{array}{c}
48 \\
\diagup \diagdown \\
6 \times 8 \\
\diagup \diagdown \\
2 \times 3
\end{array}
$$

In a further extension of this the drawing, 48 is pictured as $2 \times 3 \times 2 \times 4$.

Another extension shows the *complete factorization* of 48; that is, it shows the product expression of 48, all of whose factors are primes.

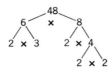

EXERCISE 8.2

1. Define a prime number.
2. List the even prime numbers.
3. What is the union of the set of prime numbers and the set of composite numbers?
4. What is the intersection of the set of prime numbers and the set of composite numbers?
5. Use the Sieve of Eratosthenes to find all the prime numbers less than 200.
6. Which of the following are primes?

    a. 127   b. 319   c. 313
    d. 649   e. 1321   f. 403

7. Make a factor tree factoring each of the following into prime factors.

    a. 72   b. 68   c. 188   d. 436

8. In 1742 a mathematician named Goldbach conjectured that every even number greater than 4 is the sum of two odd primes. To this day nobody has proved Goldbach's Conjecture either true or false.
Write the following even numbers as the sum of two odd primes.

    a. 14   b. 18   c. 28
    d. 68   e. 144   f. 268

9. When a whole number is divided by 3, the remainder is 0, 1, or 2. Let A, B, and C be the set of whole numbers for which the remainders are 0, 1, and 2, respectively. The first four members of A are 0, 3, 6, and 9.

    a. What are the first four members of C?
    b. What are the first five members of B?
    c. Are A, B, and C disjoint sets or overlapping sets?
    d. What is $A \cup B \cup C$?

Verify, using numerical examples, that

    e. The sum of a member of B and a member of C is a member of A.
    f. The sum of a member of A and a member of B is a member of B.
    g. The product of any two members of A is a member of A.
    h. The product of a member of B and a member of C is a member of C.

10. Which of the following have 3 as a factor?

   a. 374   b. 627   c. 861
   d. 8043   e. 7061   f. 87765

11. List all the factors of

   a. 12   b. 17   c. 45
   d. 36   e. 29   f. 18

12. Two odd primes whose difference is 2 are called *twin primes*. For example, 3 and 5 are *twin primes*. Give five examples of twin primes.

13. Every prime of the form $4n + 1$, where n is a counting number, may be represented as the sum of two squares. For example,

$$5 = 2^2 + 1^2 \qquad 13 = 3^2 + 2^2$$
$$17 = 4^2 + 1^2 \qquad 41 = 5^2 + 4^2$$

Write the following primes as the sum of two squares.

   a. 73   b. 89
   c. 97   d. 61

8.7. THE FUNDAMENTAL THEOREM OF ARITHMETIC

A prime number can be expressed as a product of counting numbers in only one way, namely the product of itself and 1. Thus,

$$7 = 7 \times 1,$$
$$11 = 11 \times 1,$$
$$23 = 23 \times 1,$$
and $$101 = 101 \times 1.$$

A composite number has more than one factor expression. For example, some factor expressions for 48 are

$$48 = 1 \times 48$$
$$= 2 \times 24$$
$$= 3 \times 16$$
$$= 4 \times 12$$
$$= 6 \times 8$$
$$= 2 \times 3 \times 8$$
$$= 2 \times 3 \times 4 \times 2$$
$$= 2 \times 2 \times 2 \times 2 \times 3.$$

The factor expression $2 \times 2 \times 2 \times 2 \times 3 = 2^4 \times 3$ is called the *com-*

plete factorization or *prime factorization* of 48. It expresses 48 as a product of primes.

Every composite number can be factored; that is, it can be written as the product of at least two factors, each of which is smaller than the original number. If one or more of these factors is composite, it can be written as the product of still smaller factors. This process cannot go on indefinitely since the factors are getting smaller. Eventually we must come to a factor expression each of whose factors is a prime. For example,

$$
\begin{aligned}
144 &= 6 \times 24 \\
&= 2 \times 3 \times 24 \\
&= 2 \times 3 \times 3 \times 8 \\
&= 2 \times 3 \times 3 \times 4 \times 2 \\
&= 2 \times 3 \times 3 \times 2 \times 2 \times 2,
\end{aligned}
$$

or

$$
\begin{aligned}
144 &= 12 \times 12 \\
&= 3 \times 4 \times 12 \\
&= 3 \times 4 \times 2 \times 6 \\
&= 3 \times 2 \times 2 \times 2 \times 6 \\
&= 3 \times 2 \times 2 \times 2 \times 2 \times 3,
\end{aligned}
$$

or

$$
\begin{aligned}
144 &= 8 \times 18 \\
&= 2 \times 4 \times 18 \\
&= 2 \times 2 \times 2 \times 18 \\
&= 2 \times 2 \times 2 \times 2 \times 9 \\
&= 2 \times 2 \times 2 \times 2 \times 3 \times 3.
\end{aligned}
$$

Notice that although in each case above we started with a different factor expression, the complete factorization was the same except for the order in which the prime factors were written.

This example leads to the statement of the *Fundamental Theorem of Arithmetic:*

> Every composite number can be written as a product of primes in one, and only one, way except for the order in which the prime factors are written.

We do not present the proof of this theorem, but it can be found in any Theory of Numbers text.

8.8. DIVISIBILITY TESTS

Before we discuss methods for factoring composite numbers completely, we shall discuss tests for divisibility by certain counting numbers. The justification of the tests that follow depends upon a basic fact concerning the divisibility of the sum of two numbers by a given number.

Suppose we ask: "Is $30 + 24$ divisible by 6?" The answer is "yes," and the reason for the answer is as follows:

$$30 + 24 = (6 \times 5) + (6 \times 4)$$
$$= 6 \times (5 + 4). \qquad \text{(Distributive property)}$$

Hence, $30 + 24$ is divisible by 6, because both the addends, 30 and 24, are divisible by 6.

Similarly, $35 + 45$ is divisible by 5, because both 35 and 45 are divisible by 5.

$$35 + 45 = (5 \times 7) + (5 \times 9)$$
$$= 5 \times (7 + 9)$$

In general, $a + b$ is divisible by c if both a and b are divisible by c. We shall call this property the *divisibility property of a sum*.

Let us now discover a rule for testing when a number is divisible by 2. A number is divisible by 2 if and only if the units digit of its numeral is $0, 2, 4, 6,$ or 8. The reason for this is that every power of ten except $10^0 = 1$ is divisible by 2. Hence, the number is divisible by 2 if and only if the units digit of its decimal numeral is divisible by 2, that is, $0, 2, 4, 6,$ or 8.

For example, let us consider the number 6784, which may be written in expanded form as

$$(6 \times 10^3 + 7 \times 10^2 + 8 \times 10^1) + 4,$$

that is, the sum of two addends. Since every power of ten is divisible by 2, the first addend

$$(6 \times 10^3 + 7 \times 10^2 + 8 \times 10^1)$$

is divisible by 2. It follows from the Divisibility Property of a Sum that the number

$$(6 \times 10^3 + 7 \times 10^2 + 8 \times 10^1) + 4$$

is divisible by 2 if 4 is divisible by 2, that is, if the units digit of the numeral is divisible by 2. Since 2 divides 4, 6784 is divisible by 2.

We see that we only need look at the units digit of its decimal numeral to tell whether or not a number is divisible by 2. A similar test may be used to tell whether a number is divisible by 5 and 10. A number is divisible by 5 if, and only if, the last digit in its decimal numeral is 0 or 5. A number is divisible by 10 if, and only if, the last digit in its decimal numeral is 0.

The tests for divisibility by 5 and 10 are justified in a similar way as the test for divisibility by 2.

In the case of divisibility by 3 or 9, the problem is not so simple as for divisibility by 2, 5, or 10. Study the two columns of numerals below.

A	B
30	10
21	11
12	22
63	13
24	14
15	25
36	16
27	17
18	28
39	29

None of the numbers represented by the numerals in column *B* are divisible by 3 in spite of the fact that every possible digit appears in the units place. In column *A* every number represented by the numerals is divisible by 3, and again every possible digit appears in the units place. The units digit of a numeral, therefore, tells us nothing about divisibility by 3.

The same numerals are repeated in Table 8.2, and for each numeral the sum of its digits is shown. Notice that all of the numerals in the first column of Table 8.2 (that is, all of the numerals which represent numbers divisible by 3) have something in common; the sum of the digits of these numerals is divisible by 3. In the numerals which represent numbers not divisible by 3, this is not so; the sum of the digits of the numerals is not divisible by 3. This is true for all numbers. A number is divisible by 3 if the sum of the digits in its decimal numeral is divisible by 3; otherwise the number is not divisible by 3.

Table 8.2

Numeral	Sum of Digits	Numeral	Sum of Digits
30	$3 + 0 = 3$	10	$1 + 0 = 1$
21	$2 + 1 = 3$	11	$1 + 1 = 2$
12	$1 + 2 = 3$	22	$2 + 2 = 4$
63	$6 + 3 = 9$	13	$1 + 3 = 4$
24	$2 + 4 = 6$	14	$1 + 4 = 5$
15	$1 + 5 = 6$	25	$2 + 5 = 7$
36	$3 + 6 = 9$	16	$1 + 6 = 7$
27	$2 + 7 = 9$	17	$1 + 7 = 8$
18	$1 + 8 = 9$	28	$2 + 8 = 10$
39	$3 + 9 = 12$	29	$2 + 9 = 11$

We illustrate this with an example.

$$
\begin{aligned}
642 &= (6 \times 10^2) + (4 \times 10^1) + (2 \times 10^0) \\
&= (6 \times 100) + (4 \times 10) + 2 \\
&= 6(99 + 1) + 4(9 + 1) + 2 \\
&= (6 \times 99) + (6 \times 1) + (4 \times 9) + (4 \times 1) + 2 \\
&= [(6 \times 99) + (4 \times 9)] + (6 + 4 + 2)
\end{aligned}
$$

We see that the first addend, $[(6 \times 99) + (4 \times 9)]$, is divisible by 3. If the sum, 642, is divisible by 3, the second addend, $(6 + 4 + 2)$, must be divisible by 3, and this addend is the sum of the digits in 642.

The test for divisibility by 9 is similar to the test for divisibility by 3.

In the example above, the addend $[(6 \times 99) + (4 \times 9)]$ is divisible by 9; hence, the number 642 is divisible by 9 if the second addend, $(6 + 4 + 2)$, is divisible by 9, using the Divisibility Property of a Sum. This addend is the sum of the digits of 642.

Therefore, we state that if a number is divisible by 3, the sum of the digits of its decimal numeral must be divisible by 3, and that a number is divisible by 9 if the sum of the digits of its decimal numeral is divisible by 9.

If a counting number n is divisible by another counting number, m, then it is divisible by any factor of m. For example, if n is divisible by 6, then it must be divisible by 2 and 3 since $2 \times 3 = 6$.

8.9. COMPLETE FACTORIZATION

A composite number may be factored into its prime factors; that is, it may be factored completely by drawing a factor tree. This method is fine for small numbers, but it is a rather long, tedious process for large numbers.

There is a more systematic way of factoring a composite number completely. This is a method of successive divisions and is called the *consecutive primes method*. We shall illustrate this method by an example. Let us factor 144 completely; that is, let us find the prime factorization of 144. We begin with the smallest prime, 2, and see whether or not it is a factor of 144. We see by inspection that 144 is divisible by 2.

$$144 = 2 \times 72$$

Since 2 is a factor of 72, and $72 = 2 \times 36$, therefore

$$144 = 2 \times 2 \times 36.$$

We see that 2 is also a factor of 36, $36 = 2 \times 18$, therefore

$$144 = 2 \times 2 \times 2 \times 18.$$

Again, 2 is a factor of 18 and we have

$$144 = 2 \times 2 \times 2 \times 2 \times 9.$$

Since 2 is not a factor of 9, we try the next prime, 3. We see that

$$144 = 2 \times 2 \times 2 \times 2 \times 3 \times 3 = 2^4 \times 3^2.$$

Since all of the factors in this expression are primes, we have factored 144 completely. The essential results of this method may be written in this shortened form:

$$
\begin{array}{r}
2\overline{)144} \\
2\overline{)72} \\
2\overline{)36} \\
2\overline{)18} \\
3\overline{)9} \\
3
\end{array}
$$
$\qquad 144 = 2 \times 2 \times 2 \times 2 \times 3 \times 3 = 2^4 \times 3^2.$

Study the following examples which show the complete factorization
of 1500, 405, and 198.

$$2\underline{)1500} \qquad\qquad 3\underline{)405} \qquad\qquad\qquad\qquad$$
$$2\underline{)750} \qquad\qquad 3\underline{)135} \qquad\qquad 2\underline{)198}$$
$$3\underline{)375} \qquad\qquad 3\underline{)45} \qquad\qquad 3\underline{)99}$$
$$5\underline{)125} \qquad\qquad 3\underline{)15} \qquad\qquad 3\underline{)33}$$
$$5\underline{)25} \qquad\qquad\quad 5 \qquad\qquad\qquad 11$$
$$\quad 5$$

$$1500 = 2^2 \times 3 \times 5^3 \qquad 405 = 3^4 \times 5 \qquad 198 = 2 \times 3^2 \times 11$$

EXERCISE 8.3

1. Find the prime factors of
    a. 288   b. 365   c. 216   d. 404

2. Factor completely the following:
    a. 4   b. 484   c. 245
    d. 3333   e. 1001   f. 21700

3. Write four factor expressions for
    a. 36   b. 56   c. 84
    d. 125   e. 832   f. 700

4. State the Fundamental Theorem of Arithmetic.
5. Which of the following are divisible by 2?

    a. 1076   b. 2076   c. 58731
    d. 27399   e. 80275   f. 83211
    g. 909191   h. 20931   i. 72642

6. Which of the numbers in Exercise 5 are divisible by 3?
7. Which of the numbers in Exercise 5 are divisible by 9?
8. Which of the numbers in Exercise 5 are divisible by 6?
9. What is a quick way to test for the divisibility by 45?
10. Find a rule for divisibility by 15.
11. Find all the divisors of 1350.
12. Given $346xy$, where x and y are one of the digits $0, 1, 2, 3, \ldots, 9$. Find all
possible values of x and y such that $346xy$ is divisible by

    a. 3   b. 6   c. 9

13. Determine in several different ways the prime factorization of each of the
following numbers. In each case verify the Fundamental Theorem of Arithmetic.

    a. 72   b. 60   c. 56   d. 96

14. Find all the pairs of factors for each of the following.

    a. 36   b. 16   c. 48
    d. 64   e. 206   f. 148

15. What is the largest prime that divides each of the following?

    a. 421   b. 299   c. 176
    d. 4235   e. 5246   f. 8088

16. Which of the following statements are true?

    a. If a number is divisible by 4, it is divisible by 2.
    b. If a number is not divisible by 3, then it is not divisible by 9.
    c. If a number has a units digit 6, it is divisible by 6.
    d. If a number is divisible by 3 and by 4, then it is divisible by 7.

17. Let $N = (2 \cdot 3 \cdot 5 \cdot 7, \ldots, 101) + 1$, where the number in parentheses is the product of all primes up to and including 101.

    a. What is the remainder when you divide N by 2?
    b. What is the remainder when you divide N by 3?
    c. What is the remainder when you divide N by 101?
    d. If N is a prime, is it a prime greater than or less than 101?
    e. If N is not a prime and has a prime factor M, is M greater than or less than 101? Why?
18. Name two values of s for which 7^3 will divide $7^2 \cdot s$.
19. What is the least value of s for which 7^4 will divide $7^2 \cdot s$?
20. What is the remainder when you divide the following by 9?

    a. 10   b. 10^2 c. 10^3
    d. 10^4 e. 10^{50} f. 10^n

21. When is a number divisible by 7 in the octal system?
22. Is it true that if a numeral of a number in the base three system ends in 2 that the number is even? Give a numerical example to substantiate your answer.

8.10. GREATEST COMMON FACTOR

Consider the numbers 10 and 12. We see that both 10 and 12 are even numbers, hence they are both divisible by 2. In other words, we can say that 2 is a factor of both 10 and 12. Because 2 is a factor of both of these numbers, we say it is a *common factor* of the numbers.

All whole numbers are multiples of 1, and thus, 1 is a common factor of all whole numbers. Therefore when we look for common factors of several numbers, we only need look for numbers other than 1. What factors other than 1 are common factors of 12 and 30?

$$12 = 1 \times 12 = 2 \times 6 = 3 \times 4 = 2 \times 2 \times 3$$
$$30 = 1 \times 30 = 2 \times 15 = 3 \times 10 = 5 \times 6 = 2 \times 3 \times 5$$

The set of factors of 12 is $\{1, 2, 3, 4, 6, 12\}$. The set of factors of 30 is $\{1, 2, 3, 5, 6, 10, 15, 30\}$. Hence, the common factors of 12 and 30 are the elements of the intersection of these two sets. The common factors of 12 and 30 are 1, 2, 3, and 6.

Do the numbers 10 and 21 have any common factor?

$$10 = 2 \times 5 = 1 \times 10$$
$$21 = 3 \times 7 = 1 \times 21$$

The set of factors of 10 is $\{1, 2, 5, 10\}$
The set of factors of 21 is $\{1, 3, 7, 21\}$

Hence, 10 and 21 have only one common factor, 1.

Some sets of numbers have many common factors and some sets have only 1 as a common factor.

We found that 12 and 30 had common factors 1, 2, 3, and 6. The largest common factor of 12 and 30 is 6. Generally, this greatest common factor is more useful in mathematics than other common factors.

Writing the set of all factors of a number is sometimes troublesome, particularly if the number has many factors. An easier way to find the greatest common factor of several numbers is the use of their prime factors. Suppose we want to find the greatest common factor of 72 and 90.

$$72 = 2^3 \times 3^2 = (2 \times 3 \times 3) \times 2 \times 2$$
$$90 = 2 \times 3^2 \times 5 = (2 \times 3 \times 3) \times 5$$

Notice that each number has 2 as a common factor, and 3^2 as a common factor. Hence, the greatest common factor of 72 and 90 is $2 \times 3^2 = 18$.

The *greatest common factor* is also called the *greatest common divisor* (GCD). Symbolically we write

$$(8, 12) = 4,$$

and read this symbol "the greatest common divisor of 8 and 12 is 4." If the GCD of two numbers is 1 we say the two numbers are *relatively prime*.

8.11. EUCLID'S ALGORITHM

A method of finding the GCD of two numbers was developed by Euclid and is called *Euclid's algorithm*. Euclid's algorithm is based on the division algorithm for whole numbers. This relation may be stated in the following form: If a and b are any whole numbers, unique whole numbers, q and r, may be found such that $a = (b \times q) + r$, where $0 \leqslant r < b$.

Euclid's algorithm is applied as follows:

We wish to find the GCD of 391 and 544. Divide the larger, 544, by the smaller, 391.

$$
\begin{array}{r}
1 \\
391\overline{)544} \\
391 \\
\hline
153
\end{array}
$$

The remainder is 153. As we will see later, the GCD of 391 and 544 is equal to the GCD of this remainder, 153, and the given number, 391. Symbolically, we write this $(544, 391) = (391, 153)$.

This procedure is repeated. Since each remainder is less than the one before, a zero remainder must eventually be obtained.

$$
\begin{array}{r}
2 \\
153\overline{)391} \\
306 \\
\hline
85
\end{array}
\qquad
\begin{array}{r}
1 \\
85\overline{)153} \\
85 \\
\hline
68
\end{array}
\qquad
\begin{array}{r}
1 \\
68\overline{)85} \\
68 \\
\hline
17
\end{array}
\qquad
\begin{array}{r}
4 \\
17\overline{)68} \\
68 \\
\hline
0
\end{array}
$$

$(544, 391) = (391, 153) = (153, 85) = (85, 68) = (68, 17) = 17.$

When the division comes out even, as with 17 and 68, then the smaller number (17) is obviously a divisor of both itself and of the larger number (68) and so must be the GCD.

To see the "why" of the process, consider the division algorithm resulting from the division of 544 by 391.

$$544 = (391 \times 1) + 153.$$

Any divisor of both 544 and 391 must also divide 153. (Divisibility Property of a Sum). Therefore, the GCD of 391 and 544 is also a divisor of the remainder, 153, and 391. If it is not the greatest such divisor, then we would have

$$(391, 544) < (153, 391).$$

This is impossible, for it may be seen from the same division relationship that $(153, 391)$, being a divisor of 153 and 391, is also a divisor of 544, so that $(153, 391)$ is a divisor of 391 and 544 and hence cannot exceed $(391, 544)$.

To understand this explanation more easily, let us examine the division algorithm written as shown below.

1. $544 = (391 \times 1) + 153$
2. $391 = (153 \times 2) + 85$
3. $153 = (85 \times 1) + 68$
4. $85 = (68 \times 1) + 17$
5. $68 = (17 \times 4) + 0$

From step 5 we see that 17 divides 68. Since 17 divides 68 and itself, from step 4 we see that it must divide 85. Since 17 divides 68 and 85, we see (3) that it must divide 153. In this same manner we see that 17 must divide both 391 and 544 and hence is a common divisor of 544 and 391.

Now we must show that 17 is the *greatest common divisor* of 544 and 391. Suppose there is a common divisor of 544 and 391 that is greater than 17. Let us call the divisor N. Step 1 shows that since N divides 544 and 391 it must divide 153. From 2 we see that N must divide 85. Continuing in this fashion, we see that N must divide 17, but $N > 17$; hence it is impossible for it to divide 17, and therefore 17 is the GCD of 544 and 391.

8.12. LEAST COMMON MULTIPLE

You already know a great deal about multiples of numbers, for example,

1. All whole numbers are multiples of 1.
2. The even numbers, $0, 2, 4, \ldots$, are multiples of 2.
3. The members of $\{0, 3, 6, 9, \ldots\}$ are multiples of 3.

In fact, we can list a set of multiples of any counting number.

The number 2 is an even number and the number 3 is an odd number. At first sight, these two numbers do not seem to have much in common. Yet, when we look at the set of multiples of 2;

$$\{0, 2, 4, 6, 8, 10, 12, \ldots\},$$

and the set of multiples of 3:

$$\{0, 3, 6, 9, 12, 15, \ldots\},$$

we see that they do have something in common. Some of the multiples of 2 are also multiples of 3. For example, 6 is a multiple of both 2 and 3. There are many such numbers divisible by both 2 and 3. In fact, the set of multiples of 6 are all multiples of 2 and 3. Numbers which are multiples of more than one number are called *common multiples* of those numbers.

Let us look at the set of multiples of 3:

$$\{0, 3, 6, 9, 12, \ldots\},$$

and the set of multiples of 4:

$$\{0, 4, 8, 12, 16, 20, 24, \ldots\}.$$

The numbers that these two sets have in common are the common multiples of 3 and 4. They are $\{0, 12, 24, 36, \ldots\}$.

Common multiples are very useful in arithmetic. For example, when we add by the usual method $\frac{1}{2} + \frac{1}{3}$ we must get a common denominator which is a common multiple of the two denominators.

A pair of counting numbers have many common multiples. The smallest of these common multiples is called the *Least Common Multiple* (LCM) of the pair. The least common multiple of a pair of counting numbers is defined as the smallest counting number that is a multiple of each member of the pair of the given numbers.

Notice that 0 is a common multiple of any set of whole numbers. We are interested only in the common multiples other than 0.

Suppose we wanted to find the least common multiple greater than 0, of 12 and 20. First we list the sets of multiples of each of the two numbers.

Set of multiples of 12: $\{12, 24, 36, 48, 60, 72, 84, \ldots\}$
Set of multiples of 20: $\{20, 40, 60, 80, 100, \ldots\}$

The set of common multiples of 12 and 20 is $\{60, 120, 180, \ldots\}$. The least number in this set is 60. Therefore, 60 is the least common multiple of 12 and 20.

Another way to find the least common multiple of two numbers is to use their prime factorization. Suppose we want to find the least common multiple of 144 and 64. We factor the two numbers completely.

$$144 = 2^4 \times 3^2,$$
$$64 = 2^6.$$

In order to be divisible by 64, the LCM must have 2^6 as a factor. To be divisible by 144 it must also have factors 3^2 and 2^4. Since 2^4 is a factor of 2^6, the LCM of 144 and 64 is $2^6 \times 3^2 = 396$.

This same method may be used to find the LCM of more than two numbers. Suppose we wish to find the LCM of 24, 15, and 20.

$$24 = 2^3 \times 3,$$
$$15 = 5 \times 3,$$
$$20 = 5 \times 2^2.$$

In order to be divisible by 24, the LCM must have 2^3 and 3 as factors; to be divisible by 15, it must also have the factor 5. Since these three factors include the factors of 20, the LCM is $2^3 \times 3 \times 5 = 120$.

EXERCISE 8.4

1. Use sets of divisors to find the GCD of the following.

   a. 16 and 56   b. 65 and 135   c. 66 and 99

2. List all the common divisors of 84 and 196.
3. List all the common divisors of 144 and 84.
4. Find the GCD of the following pairs of numbers.

   a. $45, 75$ b. $21, 77$ c. $84, 198$
   d. $72, 175$ e. $36, 108$ f. $144, 196$

5. Use Euclid's algorithm to find the GCD of the following pairs of numbers.

   a. $(7232, 1806)$ b. $(504, 142)$
   c. $(97, 21)$ d. $(80301, 972)$

6. Find the GCD of the following sets of numbers by the prime factorization method.

   a. $84, 198$ b. $72, 175$
   c. $144, 196$ d. $36, 108$
   e. $36, 148, 356$ f. $723, 72, 81$

7. Find the GCD of

   a. $(0, 6)$ b. $(0, 9)$ c. $(0, 18)$
   d. What can you say about the GCD of $(0, n)$ where n is any counting number?

8. Which of the following pairs of numbers are relatively prime?

a. $(16, 9)$ b. $(17, 87)$ c. $(64, 137)$
d. $(2187, 36)$ e. $(70, 105)$ f. $(846, 937)$

9. What is the GCD of q and p if they are both prime numbers?
10. What is the GCD of two relatively prime numbers?
11. Find the LCM of the following pairs of numbers.

a. $4, 18$ b. $6, 26$
c. $36, 42$ d. $36, 54$
e. $303, 33$ f. $125, 75$

12. What is the LCM of two relatively prime numbers?
13. Find the LCM of the following sets of numbers, using the prime factorization method.

a. $16, 36$ b. $36, 27$ c. $96, 84$
d. $4, 18, 36$ e. $36, 56, 72$ f. $42, 90, 135$

14. Write 0 as a multiple of

a. 5 b. 7 c. 8 d. n

CHAPTER 9

Fractions

9.1. THE WORD "FRACTION"

The term "fraction" as commonly used has two meanings. Sometimes it means "fractional symbol," that is, a symbol for a number, and sometimes it means "fractional number." In common usage the word "fraction" means both number and numeral. For example, in the statement, "the fraction $\frac{3}{4}$ is greater than zero," the word "fraction" means "fractional number." In the statement, "1 is the numerator of the fraction $\frac{1}{2}$," the word "fraction" means "fractional symbol."

In this text we shall use "fraction" as it is commonly used if the meaning is clear. If there is a necessity to emphasize the distinction between the number and its symbol we shall use "fractional number" and "fractional symbol," respectively.

9.2. DEFINITION OF FRACTIONS

The concept of a fractional number arises in counting situations when a unit region or a unit length is divided into a number of congruent subregions or sublengths. Just as we have numbers to count the objects in a set, we also have numbers to indicate the subunits of a unit region or a unit length.

Any region may be considered as a unit region, and any length may be considered as a unit length. For example, each region in Figure 9.1 is a unit region divided into a number of congruent subregions by dotted line segments. Table 9.1, part A, indicates the number of congruent subregions in each unit region of Figure 9.1. In Figure 9.2 we have shaded certain of the congruent subregions. In Table 9.1, part B, the number of congruent regions which have been shaded in each unit region is indicated.

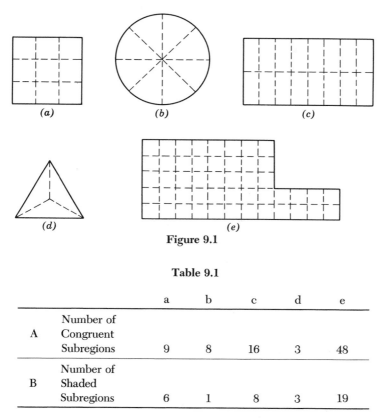

(a)   *(b)*   *(c)*

(d)   *(e)*

Figure 9.1

Table 9.1

		a	b	c	d	e
A	Number of Congruent Subregions	9	8	16	3	48
B	Number of Shaded Subregions	6	1	8	3	19

For each unit region we now have a pair of numbers corresponding to the number of shaded congruent subregions in the unit regions and the total number of congruent regions in the unit regions. Thus the pairs of numbers corresponding to the unit regions in Figure 9.2 are

     a. $(6, 9)$,
     b. $(1, 8)$,
     c. $(8, 16)$,
     d. $(3, 3)$,
     e. $(19, 48)$.

In the symbol $(6, 9)$, the 6 means that 6 subregions have been shaded and the 9 means that the unit region is divided into 9 congruent subregions. Thus, we associate with each unit region in Figure 9.2 an *ordered*

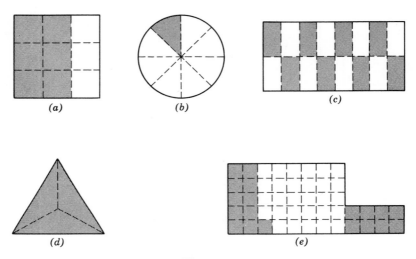

Figure 9.2

pair of numbers. The first number in the ordered pair indicates the number of congruent subregions chosen (shaded, in this case), and the second number in the ordered pair indicates the total number of congruent regions in the unit region. (Note that $(0, 5)$ may name a fractional number. It means that none of five congruent subregions of a unit region has been chosen. Physically, this situation is meaningful. On the other hand, 0 never appears as the second member of an ordered pair which is the symbol for a fractional number. We never consider the given set of congruent regions to consist of *no* unit region.)

We see that we may name a fractional number by an ordered pair. Another way of naming a fractional number is by using the familiar fraction symbol. Thus, the symbol $\frac{6}{9}$ names the same fractional number as the symbol $(6, 9)$. This fraction symbol, $\frac{6}{9}$, is read "six over nine" or "six-ninths." Then

$$\tfrac{1}{8} = (1, 8),$$
$$\tfrac{8}{16} = (8, 16),$$
$$\tfrac{3}{3} = (3, 3),$$
$$\tfrac{19}{48} = (19, 48).$$

The symbol $\tfrac{1}{8}$ has three parts: the 1, the 8, and the horizontal bar separating them. This symbol is called a *common fraction*. The whole number represented by the numeral above the bar is called the *numerator*. The whole number represented by the numeral below the bar is called the *denominator*. Notice that in Figure 9.3a the unit region is divided into two congruent subregions, and one is shaded; this is recorded as $\tfrac{1}{2}$. In Figure 9.3b the unit region is divided into four congruent subregions and two are shaded; this is recorded as $\tfrac{2}{4}$. In both cases the same area of the region has been shaded. Hence $\tfrac{1}{2}$ and $\tfrac{2}{4}$ name the same fractional number, and we write

$$\tfrac{1}{2} = \tfrac{2}{4}.$$

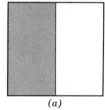 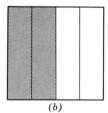

(a)   (b)

Figure 9.3

Every fraction in set F below names the same fractional number:

$$F = \{\tfrac{1}{2}, \tfrac{2}{4}, \tfrac{3}{6}, \tfrac{4}{8}, \tfrac{5}{10}, \ldots\}.$$

Notice that

$$\frac{1}{2} = \frac{1 \cdot 2}{2 \cdot 2} = \frac{2}{4},$$

$$\frac{2}{4} = \frac{2 \cdot 2}{4 \cdot 2} = \frac{4}{8},$$

$$\frac{1}{2} = \frac{1 \cdot 5}{2 \cdot 5} = \frac{5}{10} \text{ and so forth.}$$

This leads to the discovery of an important property of fractions: If $\frac{a}{b}$ is a fraction (b, of course, cannot be zero), then

$$\frac{a}{b} = \frac{a \cdot c}{b \cdot c}, \; c \neq 0.$$

Property 1 *Any fraction may be renamed by multiplying its numerator and denominator by the same counting number.*

For example:

$$1. \; \frac{5}{8} = \frac{5 \cdot 3}{8 \cdot 3} = \frac{15}{24},$$

$$2. \; \frac{3}{7} = \frac{3 \cdot 5}{7 \cdot 5} = \frac{15}{35}.$$

This property may be thought of in a different way. Notice that

$$\frac{15}{35} = \frac{3}{7}$$

and

$$\frac{15 \div 5}{35 \div 5} = \frac{3}{7}.$$

Here we see that a fraction may be renamed by dividing its numerator and denominator by the same counting number.

Property 2 *Any fraction may be renamed by dividing its numerator and denominator by one of their common factors.*

For example:

$$\frac{50}{170} = \frac{50 \div 10}{170 \div 10} = \frac{5}{17},$$

$$\frac{6}{18} = \frac{6 \div 6}{18 \div 6} = \frac{1}{3},$$

$$\frac{24}{64} = \frac{24 \div 8}{64 \div 8} = \frac{3}{8}.$$

A fractional number has many names. For example, all the fractions in set A are names for the same fractional number; the *simplest name* for that number is $\frac{2}{3}$.

$$A = \{\tfrac{2}{3}, \tfrac{4}{6}, \tfrac{6}{9}, \tfrac{8}{12}, \tfrac{10}{15}, \ldots\}.$$

We see that the simplest name for a fractional number is the fraction in the set with the least numerator and denominator. The numerator and denominator of this fraction are relatively prime. The numerator and denominator of each of the other fractions in the set have a common factor. Consequently, we may state

Property 3   *The simplest name of a fractional number is that fraction whose numerator and denominator are relatively prime.*

To decide whether or not a given fraction is the simplest name of a fractional number, we must look for common factors of the numerator and denominator. The simplest way to do this is to factor both numerator and denominator into their prime factors. For example, suppose we wish to rename $\tfrac{216}{576}$ by its simplest name.
Factoring the numerator and denominator into their prime factors we have

$$216 = 2 \cdot 2 \cdot 2 \cdot 3 \cdot 3 \cdot 3,$$
$$576 = 2 \cdot 2 \cdot 2 \cdot 2 \cdot 2 \cdot 2 \cdot 3 \cdot 3.$$

The highest common factor of these two numbers is

$$2 \cdot 2 \cdot 2 \cdot 3 \cdot 3 = 72.$$

Using Property 2, we have

$$\frac{216}{576} = \frac{216 \div 72}{576 \div 72} = \frac{3}{8}.$$

Notice that 3 and 8 are relatively prime. We can always rename a fraction to simplest form by dividing numerator and denominator by the highest common factor of the two numbers. For example,

a. $\dfrac{8}{12} = \dfrac{(2 \cdot 2 \cdot 2) \div (2 \cdot 2)}{(2 \cdot 2 \cdot 3) \div (2 \cdot 2)} = \dfrac{2}{3},$

b. $\dfrac{15}{24} = \dfrac{(3 \cdot 5) \div 3}{(2 \cdot 2 \cdot 2 \cdot 3) \div 3} = \dfrac{5}{8},$

$$\text{c. } \frac{15}{100} = \frac{(3\cdot 5) \div 5}{(2\cdot 2\cdot 5\cdot 5) \div 5} = \frac{3}{20}.$$

We now ask ourselves, when are two fractions equal? If two fractions have the same denominators, it is obvious that they are equal if and only if they have the same numerators. Thus

$$\frac{1}{2} = \frac{1}{2},$$

$$\frac{2}{3} = \frac{2}{3},$$

$$\frac{a}{b} = \frac{a}{b}.$$

If two fractions have different denominators, it is always possible to rename them so that they have the same denominator. For example,

$$\frac{2}{3} = \frac{4}{6}$$

because

$$\frac{2}{3} = \frac{2\cdot 2}{3\cdot 2} = \frac{4}{6} \quad \text{and} \quad \frac{6}{9} = \frac{18}{27}$$

because

$$\frac{6\cdot 3}{9\cdot 3} = \frac{18}{27}.$$

Notice the following fractions:

a. $\frac{2}{3} = \frac{4}{6}$ b. $\frac{5}{9} = \frac{15}{27}$ c. $\frac{8}{15} = \frac{24}{45}$ d. $\frac{5}{7} = \frac{10}{14}$

In the equalities above we observe that

a. $2\cdot 6 = 3\cdot 4,$ b. $5\cdot 27 = 9\cdot 15,$
c. $8\cdot 45 = 15\cdot 24,$ d. $5\cdot 14 = 10\cdot 7.$

We may conclude from this observation that if we have two fractions, $\frac{a}{b}$ and $\frac{c}{d}$, they are equal if and only if $ad = bc$.

Property 4   *Two fractions with the same denominators are equal if their numerators are equal.*

Property 5 *Two fractions, $\frac{a}{b}$ and $\frac{c}{b}$, with different denominators are equal if and only if $ad = bc$.*

EXERCISE 9.1

1. Give the ordered pairs associated with the shaded subregions in each unit region in the illustration.

 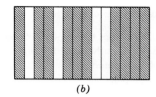 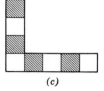

<table>
<tr><td>(a)</td><td>(b)</td><td>(c)</td></tr>
</table>

2. Give the ordered pairs associated with the unshaded subregions in each unit region in the illustration.

3. Write fractions that name the shaded area in the unit regions in the illustration.

4. Write fractions that name the unshaded area in the unit regions in the illustration.

5. Write fractions that name the same fractional numbers as these ordered pairs:

    a. $(7, 18)$.   b. $(0, 3)$.   c. $(5, 4)$.
    d. $(2, 4)$.   e. $(1, 5)$.   f. $(9, 12)$.
    g. $(4, 16)$.   h. $(7, 8)$.   i. $(12, 34)$.

6. List five fractions that name the fractional number three-fourths.

7. List the ordered pairs associated with the fractions you listed in Problem 6.

8. Illustrate each of the following fractions by using it as the measure of a region of a unit square.

    a. $\frac{3}{4}$.   b. $\frac{5}{8}$.   c. $\frac{2}{3}$.   d. $\frac{5}{16}$.

9. Name the numerator and the denominator of each fraction.

    a. $\frac{9}{16}$.   b. $\frac{3}{8}$.   c. $\frac{17}{85}$.   d. $\frac{35}{100}$.

10. Represent the following sets of fractional numbers by fractions having the same denominator.

    a. $\frac{3}{4}, \frac{2}{3}, \frac{5}{6}$.   b. $\frac{5}{2}, \frac{7}{8}, \frac{3}{5}$.
    c. $\frac{5}{17}, \frac{7}{51}, \frac{9}{34}$.   d. $\frac{9}{8}, \frac{3}{7}, \frac{2}{3}$.
    e. $\frac{9}{7}, \frac{13}{21}, \frac{11}{42}$.   f. $\frac{3}{5}, \frac{2}{3}, \frac{7}{8}$.

11. Find the simplest name for the fractional numbers named by the following fractions.

    a. $\frac{8}{12}$.   b. $\frac{9}{27}$.   c. $\frac{15}{65}$.
    d. $\frac{36}{148}$.   e. $\frac{216}{576}$.   f. $\frac{169}{130}$.

12. Which of these pairs of fractions name the same fractional number?

    a. $\frac{72}{192}, \frac{9}{72}$.   b. $\frac{84}{168}, \frac{75}{150}$.

    c. $\frac{9}{16}, \frac{3}{4}$.   d. $\frac{24}{100}, \frac{54}{225}$.

    e. $\frac{16}{136}, \frac{68}{578}$.   f. $\frac{14}{5}, \frac{28}{14}$.

13. How can you decide whether or not two fractions name the same fractional number?

14. Which of the following statements are true?

    a. The fraction symbol $\frac{5}{13}$ names the same fractional number as $(10, 26)$.

    b. The fractions $\frac{3}{4}$ and $\frac{9}{16}$ name the same fractional number.

    c. The first member of an ordered pair is the numerator of the fraction associated with the ordered pair.

15. Find n to make the following statements true.

    a. $\dfrac{3}{5} = \dfrac{n}{125}$ b. $\dfrac{7}{8} = \dfrac{105}{n}$

    c. $\dfrac{5}{12} = \dfrac{480}{n}$ d. $\dfrac{2}{3} = \dfrac{n}{24}$

    e. $\dfrac{9}{16} = \dfrac{108}{n}$ f. $\dfrac{13}{15} = \dfrac{65}{n}$

9.3. FRACTIONS AND THE NUMBER LINE

Although we may use any region in defining fractions, let us now, for uniformity, use only congruent squares as unit regions, and let us subdivide them into congruent subregions only by means of vertical line segments. Thus in Figure 9.3a the successive unit regions have been divided into two, three, four, and eight congruent subregions by one, two, three, and seven vertical lines.

Figure 9.3a

Let us now put a succession of these unit regions side by side on a line as shown in Figure 9.4. Then let us divide each of the unit regions into four congruent subregions as shown. Let us agree to indicate the choice of subregions by taking successive ones starting at the extreme left and to record our choice, in fraction form, beside the lower right hand corner of the last chosen subregion. The fractions below the line in Figure 9.4

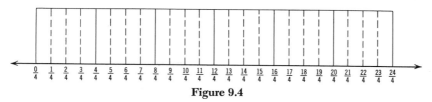

Figure 9.4

illustrate our choices of subregions. Thus, $\frac{0}{4}$ means that we have chosen none of the subregions; $\frac{3}{4}$ means that we have chosen three of the subregions; $\frac{10}{4}$, that we have chosen ten of the subregions; and so on. Although $\frac{0}{4}$ may look peculiar, physically this situation is quite meaningful and useful. It is quite apparent that $\frac{0}{4}$ means that you have chosen none of the subregions of the unit region. In other words, you have probably guessed that $\frac{0}{4}$ is another name for zero (this will be discussed later). The fraction $\frac{10}{4}$ means that we have divided several congruent unit regions into four congruent subregions each, and chosen ten of these subregions. For example, if you cut three pies into four pieces each (each piece is a congruent subregion, and the pie is the unit region), then $\frac{10}{4}$ can be interpreted as serving ten of these pieces.

Now let us consider our unit regions as though placed on a line, with each region divided into a different number of congruent subregions. To illustrate, Figure 9.5 shows a unit region divided into two congruent subregions by dotted line segments and into three congruent subregions by dashed line segments.

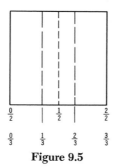

Figure 9.5

We see from Figure 9.6 that fractional numbers can be represented as points on a number line. On the number line we can locate the point representing any fractional number. For example, suppose we wished to locate the point representing $\frac{5}{16}$. We divide the part of the number line

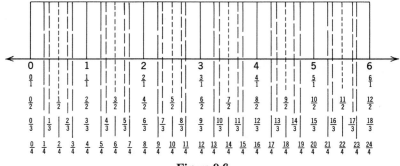

Figure 9.6

between 0 and 1 into sixteen congruent sublengths. The point at the right hand end of the fifth part represents $\frac{5}{16}$, as is shown in Figure 9.7.

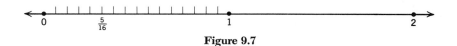

Figure 9.7

Figure 9.8 shows the number line with the points between 0 and 3 representing the fractional numbers named by fractions with denominators 1, 2, 4, and 8.

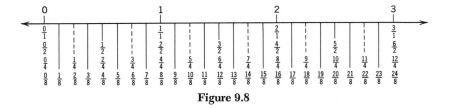

Figure 9.8

9.4. ORDERING FRACTIONS

Fractions with the same denominator present themselves in a very definite order. For example,

$$\tfrac{0}{8}, \tfrac{1}{8}, \tfrac{2}{8}, \tfrac{3}{8}, \tfrac{4}{8}, \tfrac{5}{8}, \ldots \quad .$$

Thus fractions with the same denominator are ordered by their numerators. We see that each succeeding fractional number represented by the fractions in the sequence above is greater than the preceding one:

$$\tfrac{0}{8}<\tfrac{1}{8}<\tfrac{2}{8}<\tfrac{3}{8}<\tfrac{4}{8}<\tfrac{5}{8}<\ldots$$

because

$$0<1<2<3<4<5<\ldots$$

In general, the following property is true:

Property 6   *The fraction $\dfrac{a}{b}$ is greater than the fraction $\dfrac{c}{b}$ if $a>c$, and $\dfrac{a}{b}$ is less than $\dfrac{c}{b}$ if $a<c$.*

It is now possible to decide the order of any two fractional numbers. All that is necessary is to rename the fractions representing these numbers, so that they have the same denominators, and to apply Property 6. For example, let us order $\tfrac{2}{3}$ and $\tfrac{5}{8}$:

$$\tfrac{2}{3}=\tfrac{16}{24} \quad \text{and} \quad \tfrac{5}{8}=\tfrac{15}{24},$$

$$\tfrac{16}{24}>\tfrac{15}{24}$$

therefore

$$\tfrac{2}{3}>\tfrac{5}{8}.$$

Observe the following:

$$\tfrac{2}{3}>\tfrac{1}{2} \quad \text{and} \quad 2\cdot2>3\cdot1,$$
$$\tfrac{1}{3}<\tfrac{5}{8} \quad \text{and} \quad 1\cdot8<3\cdot5,$$
$$\tfrac{5}{6}=\tfrac{5}{6} \quad \text{and} \quad 5\cdot6=5\cdot6,$$
$$\tfrac{10}{3}>\tfrac{5}{2} \quad \text{and} \quad 10\cdot2>3\cdot5,$$
$$\tfrac{7}{2}>\tfrac{15}{8} \quad \text{and} \quad 7\cdot8>2\cdot15.$$

These observations lead us to the following generalization:

Property 7   *If $\dfrac{a}{b}$ and $\dfrac{c}{d}$ are any two fractions, then*

$$\frac{a}{b}<\frac{c}{d} \quad \text{if} \quad a\cdot d<b\cdot c$$

$$\frac{a}{b}=\frac{c}{d} \quad \text{if} \quad a\cdot d=b\cdot c \quad \textbf{(Property 5)}$$

$$\frac{a}{b}>\frac{c}{d} \quad \text{if} \quad a\cdot d>b\cdot c$$

Just as the order of the whole numbers shows up clearly by the position of the points on the number line corresponding to them, similarly the order of the fractional numbers is shown on the number line. The point on the number line corresponding to the whole number 8 is to the right of the point corresponding to the whole number 3, and correspondingly, $8 > 3$. Similarly, the point corresponding to the fractional number $\frac{3}{4}$ is to the right of the point corresponding to the fractional number $\frac{1}{2}$, and correspondingly, $\frac{3}{4} > \frac{1}{2}$.

EXERCISE 9.2

1. What does the symbol $\frac{9}{3}$ mean when it corresponds to a point on the number line?

2. Determine the order relation between each of the following pairs.

    a. $\frac{28}{3}, \frac{30}{4}$.   b. $\frac{17}{20}, \frac{15}{17}$.   c. $\frac{8}{11}, \frac{9}{21}$.

3. Write the following as ordered sets.

    a. $\{\frac{9}{3}, \frac{4}{3}, \frac{2}{3}, \frac{5}{3}\}$.
    b. $\{\frac{2}{3}, \frac{5}{9}, \frac{9}{9}, \frac{19}{9}, \frac{27}{9}\}$.
    c. $\{\frac{3}{4}, \frac{1}{2}, \frac{5}{8}, \frac{7}{16}, \frac{9}{4}\}$.
    d. $\{\frac{1}{3}, \frac{2}{3}, \frac{3}{8}, \frac{5}{4}\}$.

4. Order the following fractions, beginning with the least.

$$\frac{5}{4}, \frac{1}{1}, \frac{3}{2}, \frac{7}{8}, \frac{18}{6}, \frac{19}{3}, \frac{9}{9}$$

5. Use the symbols "$=$", "$<$", and "$>$" to order the following pairs of fractions:

    a. $\frac{1}{3}, \frac{9}{27}$,   b. $\frac{3}{4}, \frac{7}{8}$,   c. $\frac{3}{3}, \frac{15}{32}$,
    d. $\frac{9}{3}, \frac{5}{2}$,   e. $\frac{3}{3}, \frac{2}{2}$,   f. $\frac{68}{93}, \frac{51}{72}$.

9.5.   ADDITION OF FRACTIONAL NUMBERS

The addition of $\frac{3}{8} + \frac{2}{8}$ may be shown either on the number line or with unit regions. This is shown in Figures 9.9 and 9.10. Figures 9.10a and 9.10b show $\frac{3}{8}$ and $\frac{2}{8}$; Figure 9.10c is a model of the two regions ($\frac{3}{8}$ and $\frac{2}{8}$) on one unit region. It shows that $\frac{3}{8} + \frac{2}{8} = \frac{5}{8}$.

Figure 9.9

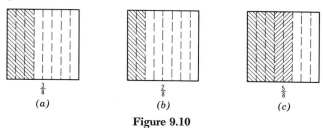

Figure 9.10

Fractions with the same denominators may also be added by adding their numerators:

$$\frac{3}{8} + \frac{2}{8} = \frac{3+2}{8} = \frac{5}{8},$$

$$\frac{7}{5} + \frac{9}{5} = \frac{7+9}{5} = \frac{16}{5},$$

$$\frac{4}{9} + \frac{7}{9} = \frac{4+7}{9} = \frac{11}{9}.$$

Thus, if $\frac{a}{b}$ and $\frac{c}{b}$ are two fractions their sum is

$$\frac{a}{b} + \frac{c}{b} = \frac{a+c}{b}.$$

If two fractional numbers named by fractions with different denominators are to be added, they are first renamed as fractions with the same denominators. They may then be added as shown. For example, to add $\frac{3}{4}$ and $\frac{2}{3}$, rename $\frac{3}{4}$ and $\frac{2}{3}$:

$$\frac{3}{4} = \frac{3 \cdot 3}{4 \cdot 3} = \frac{9}{12} \quad \text{and} \quad \frac{2}{3} = \frac{2 \cdot 4}{3 \cdot 4} = \frac{8}{12}.$$

Then

$$\frac{3}{4} + \frac{2}{3} = \frac{9}{12} + \frac{8}{12} = \frac{9+8}{12} = \frac{17}{12}.$$

The addition of any two fractions is similarly performed. First the fractions are renamed so that they have the same denominators. We do this by multiplying the numerator and the denominator of $\frac{a}{b}$ and $\frac{c}{d}$ by d and b respectively:

$$\frac{a}{b} = \frac{a \cdot d}{b \cdot d} \quad \text{and} \quad \frac{c}{d} = \frac{c \cdot b}{d \cdot b}.$$

The two fractions $\frac{ad}{bd}$ and $\frac{cd}{db}$ have the same denominators since $bd = db$. Hence

$$\frac{a}{b} + \frac{c}{d} = \frac{ad}{bd} + \frac{cb}{db} = \frac{ad + cb}{bd}.$$

9.6. SUBTRACTION OF FRACTIONAL NUMBERS

To subtract $\frac{2}{3}$ from $\frac{7}{3}$, that is to perform the subtraction $\frac{7}{3} - \frac{2}{3}$, we must find the missing addend in the number sentence $\frac{2}{3} + n = \frac{7}{3}$. Using unit regions, this operation requires that seven congruent subregions be separated into two parts, one of which measures $\frac{2}{3}$. The separation is indicated in Figure 9.11, by shading. This shows that

$$\frac{2}{3} + \frac{5}{3} = \frac{7}{3} \quad \text{or} \quad \frac{7}{3} - \frac{2}{3} = \frac{5}{3}.$$

Hence n is $\frac{5}{3}$. Figure 9.12 demonstrates the subtraction $\frac{7}{3} - \frac{2}{3}$ on the number line.

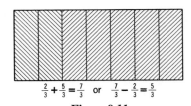

$$\frac{2}{3} + \frac{5}{3} = \frac{7}{3} \quad \text{or} \quad \frac{7}{3} - \frac{2}{3} = \frac{5}{3}$$

Figure 9.11

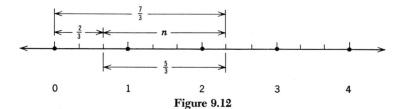

Figure 9.12

Two fractional numbers named by fractions with the same denominator may be subtracted by subtracting their numerators:

$$\frac{7}{3} - \frac{2}{3} = \frac{7-2}{3} = \frac{5}{3},$$

$$\frac{8}{12} - \frac{3}{12} = \frac{8-3}{12} = \frac{5}{12},$$

$$\frac{23}{5} - \frac{7}{5} = \frac{23-7}{5} = \frac{16}{5}.$$

If $\frac{a}{b}$ and $\frac{c}{b}$ are two fractions, then

$$\frac{a}{b} - \frac{c}{b} = \frac{a-c}{b}.$$

If two fractional numbers named by fractions with different denominators are to be subtracted, they are first renamed as fractions with the same denominator. They may be then subtracted as above. For example, to perform the subtraction $\frac{3}{4} - \frac{2}{3}$, rename $\frac{3}{4}$ and $\frac{2}{3}$:

$$\frac{3}{4} = \frac{3\cdot 3}{4\cdot 3} = \frac{9}{12} \quad \text{and} \quad \frac{2}{3} = \frac{2\cdot 4}{3\cdot 4} = \frac{8}{12}.$$

Then

$$\frac{3}{4} - \frac{2}{3} = \frac{9}{12} - \frac{8}{12} = \frac{9-8}{12} = \frac{1}{12}.$$

The subtraction of any two fractions is similarly performed. First the fractions are renamed so that the two fractions have the same denominator. This is done by multiplying the numerator and denominator of $\frac{a}{d}$ and $\frac{c}{d}$ by d and b respectively.

$$\frac{a}{b} = \frac{a\cdot d}{b\cdot d} \quad \text{and} \quad \frac{c}{d} = \frac{c\cdot b}{d\cdot b}$$

The two fractions $\frac{ad}{bd}$ and $\frac{bc}{bd}$ have the same denominator and may be subtracted, provided $ad \geq bc$. Hence,

$$\frac{a}{b} - \frac{c}{d} = \frac{ad}{bd} - \frac{bc}{bd} = \frac{ad - bc}{bd} \quad \text{if } ad \geq bc.$$

9.7. PROPERTIES OF ADDITION OF FRACTIONAL NUMBERS

Before discussing the operations of multiplication and division of fractional numbers, we shall discuss the properties of addition of fractional numbers. These are the same as the properties of the addition of whole numbers.

R-1. *Closure Property of Addition*
By definition of addition we know that

$$\frac{a}{b} + \frac{c}{b} = \frac{a + c}{b}.$$

Since a, b, and c are whole numbers with $b \neq 0$, the numerator of $\frac{a + c}{b}$ is a whole number, since the set of whole numbers is closed under addition. Since $a + c$ is a whole number and b is a whole number not equal to zero, $\frac{a + c}{b}$ is a fractional number.

R-2. *Commutative Property of Addition*
By definition of addition we know that

$$\frac{a}{b} + \frac{c}{b} = \frac{a + c}{b} \quad \text{and} \quad \frac{c}{b} + \frac{a}{b} = \frac{c + a}{b}.$$

But $a + c = c + a$ because of the commutative property of addition of whole numbers. Hence,

$$\frac{a}{b} + \frac{c}{b} = \frac{a + c}{b} = \frac{c + a}{b} = \frac{c}{b} + \frac{a}{b}.$$

R-3. *Associative Property of Addition*
We know that

$$\left(\frac{a}{b} + \frac{c}{b}\right) + \frac{d}{b} = \frac{a + c}{b} + \frac{d}{b} = \frac{(a + c) + d}{b}$$

and

$$\frac{a}{b}+\left(\frac{c}{b}+\frac{d}{b}\right)=\frac{a}{b}+\frac{(c+d)}{b}=\frac{a+(c+d)}{b}$$

but $(a+c)+d=a+(c+d)$ because of the associative property of addition of whole numbers. Hence the fractions

$$\frac{(a+c)+d}{b} \quad \text{and} \quad \frac{a+(c+d)}{b},$$

which have the same denominators and equal numerators, are equal.

R-4 Identity Element of Addition

We know that

$$\frac{a}{b}+\frac{0}{b}=\frac{a+0}{b}=\frac{a}{b},$$

and

$$\frac{0}{b}+\frac{a}{b}=\frac{0+a}{b}=\frac{a}{b},$$

so $\frac{0}{b}$, $b\neq 0$ is the additive identity for the fractional numbers.

The additive identity may be named by any of the fractions $\frac{0}{1}$, $\frac{0}{2}$, $\frac{0}{3}$, $\cdots$. Of course, there is only one additive identity since $\frac{0}{1}=\frac{0}{2}=\frac{0}{3}=\frac{0}{4}=\cdots$.

EXERCISE 9.3

1. Add the following. Give the answers in simplest form.

   a. $\frac{1}{3}+\frac{2}{3}$ b. $\frac{3}{4}+\frac{7}{4}$

   c. $\frac{4}{9}+\frac{7}{9}$ d. $\frac{4}{5}+\frac{3}{25}$

   e. $\left(\frac{2}{3}+\frac{1}{2}\right)+\frac{3}{4}$ f. $\left(\frac{3}{8}+\frac{1}{2}\right)+\frac{2}{3}$

   g. $\left(\frac{5}{6}+\frac{5}{8}\right)+\frac{3}{4}$ h. $\frac{5}{16}+\left(\frac{5}{6}+\frac{2}{3}\right)$

2. Subtract the following. Give the answers in simplest form.

   a. $\frac{3}{4}-\frac{1}{2}$ b. $\frac{5}{16}-\frac{1}{4}$

   c. $\frac{7}{8}-\frac{3}{12}$ d. $\frac{17}{12}-\frac{5}{8}$

   e. $\frac{1}{2}-\frac{3}{10}$ f. $\frac{15}{24}-\frac{3}{8}$

3. Use the fractional numbers $\frac{3}{8}$ and $\frac{2}{3}$ to illustrate the commutative property of addition for the set of fractional numbers.

4. Use the fractional numbers $\frac{2}{3}$, $\frac{2}{5}$, and $\frac{5}{16}$ to illustrate the associative property of addition for the set of fractional numbers.

5. Use the fractional numbers $\frac{1}{2}$ and $\frac{1}{4}$ to show that the operation of subtraction is not commutative for the set of fractional numbers.

6. Use the fractional numbers $\frac{5}{8}$ and $\frac{7}{8}$ to show that the set of fractional numbers is not closed under subtraction.

7. Use the fractional numbers $\frac{4}{8}$, $\frac{3}{8}$, and $\frac{2}{8}$ to show that the operation of subtraction is not associative for the set of fractional numbers.

8. Give ten fractions that name the additive identity for the set of fractional numbers.

9. For each number sentence, find a number, n, which makes the sentence true.

a. $\frac{2}{3} + n = \frac{7}{3}$, b. $\frac{5}{8} + n = \frac{23}{24}$,
c. $\frac{5}{8} - n = \frac{1}{2}$, d. $\frac{9}{12} - n = \frac{3}{4}$.

10. Perform the following operations.

a. $(\frac{3}{4} - \frac{2}{3}) + \frac{1}{2}$, b. $(\frac{2}{3} + \frac{5}{8}) - \frac{3}{4}$,
c. $\frac{25}{16} - (\frac{1}{2} + \frac{1}{8})$, d. $\frac{31}{6} - (\frac{2}{3} - \frac{1}{2})$.

9.8. MULTIPLICATION OF FRACTIONAL NUMBERS

We define the product of two whole numbers by an array. For example, the product of 3×4 is the number of elements in an array having three rows and four columns.

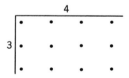

We can also illustrate the product 3×4 by means of unit regions; in Figure 9.13 there are three rows and four columns of unit regions, twelve unit regions in all.

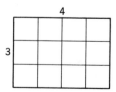

Figure 9.13

Multiplication of fractional numbers can also be shown by regions. Let us consider the product $\frac{1}{2} \times \frac{2}{3}$. First we consider a unit square, that is, a square whose side is one unit long (see Figure 9.14). Now we divide the unit square into two congruent subregions by horizontal line segments as shown in Figure 9.14a. Then we divide the unit square by vertical line segments into three congruent subregions as shown in Figure 9.14b.

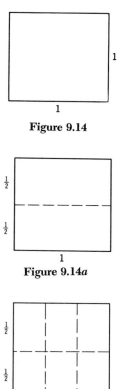

Figure 9.14

Figure 9.14a

Figure 9.14b

Observing the unit square, we see that we now have, with the horizontal and vertical line segments, divided it into six congruent subregions. To show the product $\frac{1}{2} \times \frac{2}{3}$, we shade one-half of the unit square (shading one way), and then two-thirds of the unit square (shading another way). The double shading (cross hatched) shows the set of congruent subregions which we shall define to correspond to the product $\frac{1}{2} \times \frac{2}{3}$. Of the six congruent subregions we have cross hatched two, hence

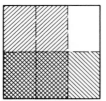

Figure 9.14c

$$\tfrac{1}{2} \times \tfrac{2}{3} = \tfrac{2}{6}.$$

Figure 9.15a illustrates $\tfrac{1}{2} \times \tfrac{3}{4}$; Figure 9.15b illustrates $\tfrac{3}{4} \times \tfrac{2}{3}$.

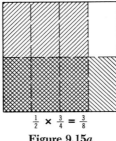

$$\tfrac{1}{2} \times \tfrac{3}{4} = \tfrac{3}{8}$$

Figure 9.15a

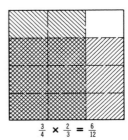

$$\tfrac{3}{4} \times \tfrac{2}{3} = \tfrac{6}{12}$$

Figure 9.15b

Figures 9.15c and 9.15d illustrate $\tfrac{1}{2} \times \tfrac{5}{3}$. Since the factors are both greater than 1 and less than 2, we construct four unit squares. We divide the four unit squares horizontally into halves and vertically into thirds by dotted line segments (Figure 9.15c).

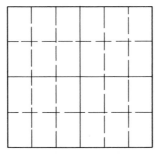

Figure 9.15c

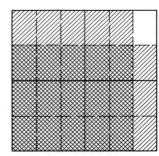

Figure 9.15d

Observe that each unit region is now divided into six congruent sub-regions. Now we shade three halves of the total region (shading one way) and five thirds of the total region (shading another way). The cross hatched portion shows the product $\tfrac{3}{2} \times \tfrac{5}{3}$. Each small subregion represents one-sixth of a unit square, and fifteen of these are cross hatched; hence $\frac{3}{2} \times \frac{5}{3} = \frac{15}{6}$.

These examples suggest that given any two fractions $\frac{a}{b}$ and $\frac{c}{d}$ their product is named by the fraction $\frac{ac}{bd}$. That is, the product of two fractional numbers $\frac{a}{b}$ and $\frac{c}{d}$ is

$$\frac{a}{b} \cdot \frac{c}{d} = \frac{ac}{bd}.$$

This definition of multiplication is illustrated by the examples below:

a. $\dfrac{3}{5} \cdot \dfrac{5}{8} = \dfrac{(3 \cdot 5)}{(5 \cdot 8)} = \dfrac{15}{40},$

b. $\dfrac{7}{3} \cdot \dfrac{2}{3} = \dfrac{(7 \cdot 2)}{(3 \cdot 3)} = \dfrac{14}{9},$

c. $\dfrac{7}{2} \cdot \dfrac{9}{16} = \dfrac{(7 \cdot 9)}{(2 \cdot 16)} = \dfrac{63}{32}.$

The definition of multiplication of two fractional numbers has two very important cases. If $c = 1$ and $d = 1$, then

$$\frac{a}{b} \cdot \frac{c}{d} = \frac{a}{b} \cdot \frac{1}{1} = \frac{a}{b}.$$

Similarly, if $a = 1$ and $b = 1$, then

$$\frac{a}{b} \cdot \frac{c}{d} = \frac{1}{1} \cdot \frac{c}{d} = \frac{c}{d}.$$

We see that the fraction $\frac{1}{1}$ is an identity element for the operation of multiplication of fractional numbers, since

$$\frac{1}{1} \cdot \frac{a}{b} = \frac{a}{b} \cdot \frac{1}{1} = \frac{a}{b}.$$

The fraction $\frac{1}{1}$ will be called an identity element. We conclude that a fraction remains unchanged when multiplied by the identity element. Notice that

$$\frac{2}{3} \cdot \frac{3}{2} = \frac{1}{1},$$

$$\frac{5}{6} \cdot \frac{6}{5} = \frac{1}{1},$$

$$\frac{a}{b} \cdot \frac{b}{a} = \frac{1}{1}.$$

We conclude that for any fraction $\frac{a}{b}$ with $a \neq 0$ (of course b is never zero!),

$$\frac{a}{b} \cdot \frac{b}{a} = \frac{1}{1}.$$

The two fractions $\frac{a}{b}$ and $\frac{b}{a}$ are called *reciprocals* of each other. The reciprocal of $\frac{3}{2}$ is $\frac{2}{3}$; the reciprocal of $\frac{a}{b}$ is $\frac{b}{a}$.

9.9. PROPERTIES OF MULTIPLICATION OF FRACTIONAL NUMBERS

The operation of multiplication of fractional numbers has all of the properties of the multiplication of whole numbers plus the reciprocal property discussed in Section 9.8.

R-5. Closure Property for Multiplication

By definition of multiplication of fractional numbers

$$\frac{a}{b} \cdot \frac{c}{d} = \frac{ac}{bd}.$$

Since a, b, c, and d are whole numbers and $b \neq 0$ and $d \neq 0$, the product ac is a whole number, and the product bd is a counting number, hence $\frac{ac}{bd}$ is a fractional number.

R-6. Commutative Property of Multiplication

By definition we know that

$$\frac{a}{b} \cdot \frac{c}{d} = \frac{ac}{bd} \quad \text{and} \quad \frac{c}{d} \cdot \frac{a}{b} = \frac{ca}{db},$$

but $ac = ca$ and $bd = db$ by the commutative property of multiplication of whole numbers. Hence,

$$\frac{a}{b} \cdot \frac{c}{d} = \frac{ac}{bd} = \frac{ca}{db} = \frac{c}{d} \cdot \frac{a}{b}.$$

R-7. Associative Property for Multiplication

$$\left(\frac{a}{b} \cdot \frac{c}{d}\right) \cdot \frac{e}{f} = \left(\frac{ac}{bd}\right) \frac{e}{f},$$ Definition of multiplication

$$= \frac{(ac)\,e}{(bd)\,f},$$ Definition of multiplication

$$= \frac{a\,(ce)}{b(df)},$$ Associative property of whole numbers

$$= \frac{a}{b} \cdot \frac{ce}{df},$$ Definition of multiplication

$$= \frac{a}{b} \cdot \left(\frac{c}{d} \cdot \frac{e}{f}\right),$$ Definition of multiplication

This proof shows that

$$\left(\frac{a}{b} \cdot \frac{c}{d}\right) \cdot \frac{e}{f} = \frac{a}{b} \cdot \left(\frac{c}{d} \cdot \frac{e}{f}\right).$$

R-8. Identity Element for Multiplication

$$\frac{a}{b} \cdot \frac{1}{1} = \frac{a \cdot 1}{b \cdot 1}$$ Definition of multiplication

$$= \frac{a}{b},$$ Identity element for multiplication of whole numbers

and

$$\frac{1}{1} \cdot \frac{a}{b} = \frac{1 \cdot a}{1 \cdot b}$$ Definition of multiplication

$$= \frac{a}{b},$$ Identity element for multiplication of whole numbers

Hence $\frac{a}{b} \cdot \frac{1}{1} = \frac{1}{1} \cdot \frac{a}{b} = \frac{a}{b}$ and $\frac{1}{1}$ is the identity element for multiplication.

The multiplicative identity may be named by any of the fractions $\frac{1}{1}$, $\frac{2}{2}$, $\frac{3}{3}$, $\frac{4}{4}$, ... Of course, there is only one multiplicative identity since

$$\tfrac{1}{1} = \tfrac{2}{2} = \tfrac{3}{3} = \tfrac{4}{4} = \ldots .$$

R-9. *Distributive Property*

$$\frac{a}{b} \cdot \left(\frac{c}{d} + \frac{e}{d}\right) = \frac{a}{b} \cdot \frac{(c + e)}{d} \qquad \text{Definition of addition}$$

$$= \frac{a(c + e)}{bd} \qquad \text{Definition of multiplication}$$

$$= \frac{(ac + ae)}{bd} \qquad \text{Distributive property of whole numbers}$$

$$= \frac{ac}{bd} + \frac{ae}{bd} \qquad \text{Definition of addition}$$

$$= \frac{a}{b} \cdot \frac{c}{d} + \frac{a}{b} \cdot \frac{e}{d}, \qquad \text{Definition of multiplication}$$

This proof shows that

$$\frac{a}{b} \cdot \left(\frac{c}{d} + \frac{e}{d}\right) = \frac{ac}{bd} + \frac{ae}{bd}.$$

R-10. *Multiplicative Inverses (Reciprocals).*

Every fractional number, $\frac{a}{b}$, with $a \neq 0$, has a multiplicative inverse $\frac{b}{a}$ such that

$$\cdot \quad \frac{a}{b} \cdot \frac{b}{a} = \frac{1}{1}.$$

9.10. DIVISION OF FRACTIONAL NUMBERS

The operation of division of fractional numbers is the inverse of the operation of multiplication of fractional numbers. Thus

$$\frac{2}{3} \div \frac{1}{4} = \frac{e}{f} \quad \text{means} \quad \frac{2}{3} = \frac{1}{4} \cdot \frac{e}{f}.$$

In general

$$\frac{a}{b} \div \frac{c}{d} = \frac{e}{f} \quad \text{means} \quad \frac{a}{b} = \frac{c}{d} \cdot \frac{e}{f}.$$

The property that every fractional number except those of the form $\frac{0}{b}$ has a multiplicative inverse is basic to the definition of division of fractional numbers.

Let us consider the division $\frac{2}{3} \div \frac{1}{4}$. Assuming that there is a fractional number $\frac{e}{f}$ such that

$$\frac{2}{3} \div \frac{1}{4} = \frac{e}{f},$$

we ask ourselves how can we determine $\frac{e}{f}$? We know that

$$\frac{2}{3} \div \frac{1}{4} = \frac{e}{f} \quad \text{means} \quad \frac{2}{3} = \frac{1}{4} \cdot \frac{e}{f}.$$

The reciprocal of $\frac{1}{4}$ is $\frac{4}{1}$ since $\frac{1}{4} \cdot \frac{4}{1} = \frac{1}{1}$.

Multiplying both $\frac{1}{4} \cdot \frac{e}{f}$ and $\frac{2}{3}$ by $\frac{4}{1}$ we get

$$\frac{4}{1} \left(\frac{1}{4} \cdot \frac{e}{f} \right) = \frac{4}{1} \cdot \frac{2}{3}.$$

Then

$$\frac{4}{1} \cdot \left(\frac{1}{4} \cdot \frac{e}{f} \right) = \left(\frac{4}{1} \cdot \frac{1}{4} \right) \cdot \frac{e}{f}, \quad \text{R-7}$$

$$= \frac{1}{1} \cdot \frac{e}{f}, \quad \text{R-10}$$

$$= \frac{e}{f}, \quad \text{R-8}$$

Hence

$$\frac{e}{f} = \frac{4 \cdot 2}{1 \cdot 3} = \frac{8}{3}, \quad \text{Definition of multiplication}$$

We have now shown that if there is a fractional number $\frac{e}{f}$ such that $\frac{2}{3} \div \frac{1}{4} = \frac{e}{f}$, then $\frac{e}{f} = \frac{8}{3}$. We will now show that $\frac{8}{3}$ is truly that number which satisfies the sentence $\frac{2}{3} \div \frac{1}{4} = \frac{e}{f}$. We know that if

$$\frac{2}{3} \div \frac{1}{4} = \frac{8}{3}$$

then

$$\frac{1}{4} \cdot \frac{8}{3} = \frac{2}{3}.$$

But

$$\frac{1}{4} \cdot \frac{8}{3} = \frac{1 \cdot 8}{4 \cdot 3} = \frac{8}{12}$$

and $\frac{8}{12}$ is another name for $\frac{2}{3}$. As we look back at the steps in the division $\frac{2}{3} \div \frac{1}{4}$, we observe that the solution $\frac{8}{3}$ was obtained by multiplying $\frac{2}{3}$ by $\frac{4}{1}$, the reciprocal of $\frac{1}{4}$, and we can write

$$\frac{2}{3} \div \frac{1}{4} = \frac{2}{3} \cdot \frac{4}{1} = \frac{8}{3}.$$

We observe that dividing by a fractional number other than 0 gives the same result as multiplying by its reciprocal.

EXERCISE 9.4

1. Perform the following multiplications. Write your answers in simplest form.

    a. $\frac{1}{2} \times \frac{2}{3}$ b. $\frac{3}{4} \times \frac{8}{15}$

    c. $\frac{9}{25} \times \frac{5}{27}$ d. $\frac{36}{17} \times \frac{51}{48}$

    e. $\left(\frac{3}{8} \times \frac{1}{2}\right) \times \frac{2}{3}$ f. $\left(\frac{7}{8} \times \frac{5}{16}\right) \times \frac{32}{25}$

2. Use the fractional numbers $\frac{3}{4}$ and $\frac{7}{8}$ to illustrate the commutative property of multiplication for the set of fractional numbers.

3. Use the fractional numbers $\frac{3}{16}$, $\frac{1}{3}$, and $\frac{3}{4}$ to illustrate the associative property of multiplication for the set of fractional numbers.

4. List ten fractions that name the multiplicative identity for the set of fractional numbers.

5. Find the multiplicative inverses of

    a. $\frac{5}{6}$ b. $\frac{3}{8}$ c. $\frac{8}{7}$ d. $\frac{1}{4}$

    e. $\frac{3}{4}$ f. $\frac{19}{27}$ g. $\frac{2}{3}$ h. $\frac{4}{7}$

6. For each division statement below write a multiplication sentence that expresses the same relationship: for example, $35 \div n = 7$, $n \times 7 = 35$.

    a. $36 \div n = 4$ b. $n \div 7 = 9$ c. $n \div \frac{3}{4} = \frac{5}{6}$

    d. $1 \div n = 5$ e. $2 \div 11 = n$ f. $7 \div \frac{3}{4} = n$

7. For each number sentence below, find a number, n, which makes the sentence true.

a. $\frac{5}{8} \times n = \frac{1}{1}$,   b. $\frac{4}{1} \times n = \frac{1}{1}$,
c. $\frac{2}{3} \times n = \frac{1}{1}$,   d. $\frac{7}{8} \times n = \frac{1}{1}$,
e. $\frac{17}{16} \times n = \frac{1}{1}$,   f. $n \times (\frac{3}{4} \times \frac{4}{3}) = \frac{1}{1}$.

8. What property of multiplication of fractional numbers do the following statements illustrate?

a. $\frac{2}{3} \times \frac{3}{2} = \frac{1}{1}$,
b. $\frac{1}{2} \times \frac{176}{15} = (\frac{1}{2} \times \frac{150}{15}) + (\frac{1}{2} \times \frac{26}{15})$,
c. $\frac{2}{3} \times (\frac{3}{4} \times \frac{1}{2}) = (\frac{2}{3} \times \frac{3}{4}) \times \frac{1}{2}$,
d. $\frac{3}{4} \times \frac{225}{8} = (\frac{3}{4} \times \frac{200}{8}) + (\frac{3}{4} \times \frac{25}{8})$.

9. Are there any fractional numbers that have no reciprocal? What are they?

Study the following examples:

a. $\dfrac{2}{5} \div \dfrac{3}{4} = \dfrac{a}{b}$ b. $\dfrac{a}{b} \times \dfrac{3}{4} = \dfrac{2}{5}$

c. $\left(\dfrac{a}{b} \times \dfrac{3}{4}\right) \times \dfrac{4}{3} = \dfrac{2}{5} \times \dfrac{4}{3}$

d. $\dfrac{a}{b} \times \left(\dfrac{3}{4} \times \dfrac{4}{3}\right) = \dfrac{2}{5} \times \dfrac{4}{3}$

e. $\dfrac{a}{b} = \dfrac{2}{5} \times \dfrac{4}{3}$

10. Why can sentence (a) be written in the form of sentence (b)?
11. Give the reason why it is possible to derive sentence (c) from sentence (b).
12. What property of multiplication of fractional numbers is used to rewrite sentence (c) as sentence (d)?
13. What property of multiplication is used to derive sentence (e) from sentence (d)?

9.11.   SUBSETS OF THE FRACTIONAL NUMBERS

Let us consider the set of all fractional numbers which may be recorded by fractions whose denominators are 1. This set is

$$F = \{\tfrac{0}{1}, \tfrac{1}{1}, \tfrac{2}{1}, \tfrac{3}{1}, \tfrac{4}{1}, \ldots\}.$$

Let W be the set of whole numbers

$$W = \{0, 1, 2, 3, 4, 5, \ldots\}.$$

We can match the elements of sets F and W and in so doing see that there is a one-to-one correspondence between the elements of F and the elements of W.

$$\begin{array}{cccc} \frac{0}{1} & \frac{1}{1} & \frac{2}{1} & \frac{3}{1}, \dots \\ \updownarrow & \updownarrow & \updownarrow & \updownarrow \\ 0 & 1 & 2 & 3, \dots \end{array}$$

This matching preserves both the order and the fundamental operations. For example,

$$6 > 2 \quad \text{and} \quad \tfrac{6}{1} > \tfrac{2}{1};\ 6 + 2 = 8 \quad \text{and} \quad \tfrac{6}{1} + \tfrac{2}{1} = \tfrac{8}{1};$$

$$6 \cdot 2 = 12 \quad \text{and} \quad \tfrac{6}{1} \cdot \tfrac{2}{1} = \tfrac{12}{1},$$

$$7 > 5 \quad \text{and} \quad \tfrac{7}{1} > \tfrac{5}{1},\ 7 + 5 = 12 \quad \text{and} \quad \tfrac{7}{1} + \tfrac{5}{1} = \tfrac{12}{1},$$

$$7 \cdot 5 = 35 \quad \text{and} \quad \tfrac{7}{1} \cdot \tfrac{5}{1} = \tfrac{35}{1}.$$

Thus we see that so far as their order and the performance of the operations are concerned, the fractions of F and the whole numbers of W behave exactly alike. Because of this similarity between the elements of F and the whole numbers, it is customary to use the symbols "0," "1," "2," ... to denote both the whole numbers and the fractional numbers with denominator 1. That is, the symbols "0," "1," "2," ..., are regarded as other names for $\tfrac{0}{1}, \tfrac{1}{1}, \tfrac{2}{1}, \dots$.

The set of whole numbers then may be replaced, as convenient, for all the purposes of arithmetic by the set $\tfrac{0}{1}, \tfrac{1}{1}, \tfrac{2}{1}, \tfrac{3}{1}, \dots$, and vice versa.

9.12. FRACTIONS AS SYMBOLS FOR DIVISION

Observe that

$$
\begin{aligned}
20 \div 3 &= \frac{20}{1} \div \frac{3}{1} \\[2mm]
&= \frac{20}{1} \cdot \frac{1}{3} \\[2mm]
&= \frac{20 \cdot 1}{1 \cdot 3} \\[2mm]
&= \frac{20}{3}.
\end{aligned}
$$

Thus $\tfrac{20}{3}$ may be viewed either as a fraction or as a quotient of whole numbers, in this case $20 \div 3$.

In general, if a is any whole number and b is any nonzero whole number, then

$$a \div b = \frac{a}{1} \div \frac{b}{1}$$

$$= \frac{a}{1} \cdot \frac{1}{b}$$

$$= \frac{a \cdot 1}{1 \cdot b}$$

$$= \frac{a}{b}.$$

Thus if a and b are whole numbers and $b \neq 0$, $a \div b$ and $\frac{a}{b}$ are names for the same fractional number.

The division $\frac{2}{3} \div \frac{5}{6}$ may be expressed as

$$\frac{\dfrac{2}{3}}{\dfrac{5}{6}}$$

Such an expression is called a *complex fraction*. It is a fraction whose numerator and/or denominator are themselves fractions. Any fraction may be thought of as a complex fraction. For example,

$$\frac{2}{3} = \frac{\dfrac{2}{1}}{\dfrac{3}{1}}.$$

Since

$$\frac{\dfrac{a}{b}}{\dfrac{c}{d}} = \frac{a}{b} \div \frac{c}{d} = \frac{a}{b} \cdot \frac{d}{c} = \frac{ad}{bc}$$

we see that any complex fraction may be renamed as a common fraction.

9.13. MIXED NUMERALS

Since the fractional numbers are ordered we may separate the set of all fractional numbers into two disjoint subsets, one containing those fractional numbers less than 1 and the other containing those fractional numbers greater than or equal to 1. We distinguish between fractions naming fractional numbers greater than or equal to 1 by observing their numerators. A fraction with a numerator less than the denominator names a fractional number less than 1. Such fractions are sometimes called *Proper Fractions*. A fraction with a numerator greater than or equal to its denominator names a fractional number greater than or equal to 1. These fractions are sometimes called *Improper Fractions*. Every fractional number that is named by a fraction whose numerator is greater than or equal to the denominator is either a whole number or a number that can be expressed as the sum of a whole number and a fractional number less than one. For example,

$$\frac{27}{6} = \frac{24}{6} + \frac{3}{6} = 4 + \frac{3}{6} = 4 + \frac{1}{2}.$$

It is customary to write this last sum as $4\frac{1}{2}$ and read it "four and one-half." The form $4\frac{1}{2}$ is called a *mixed numeral*. Consider the fraction $\frac{27}{6} = 27 \div 6$. Then

$$27 = 4 \cdot 6 + 3.$$

But

$$27 \div 6 = (4 \cdot 6 + 3) \div 6$$

$$= \frac{4 \cdot 6}{6} + \frac{3}{6}$$

$$= 4 + \frac{3}{6}$$

$$= 4\frac{3}{6}.$$

This example illustrates one method for changing a fraction naming a fractional number greater than one to a mixed numeral.

EXERCISE 9.5

1. Write ten fractions that are members of the set F described in section 9.11.
2. Why can the members of set F be used to rename the whole numbers?
3. Write the following as common fractions.

    a. $7 \div 8$ b. $3 \div 9$ c. $17 \div 24$
    d. $18 \div 3$ e. $242 \div 15$ f. $42 \div 9$

4. Write the following as quotients of two whole numbers.

    a. $\frac{5}{12}$ b. $\frac{7}{16}$ c. $\frac{9}{2}$
    d. $\frac{342}{12}$ e. $\frac{216}{512}$ f. $\frac{42}{7}$

5. Write each common fraction below as a complex fraction.

a. $\frac{5}{8}$ b. $\frac{3}{4}$ c. $\frac{27}{2}$ d. $\frac{18}{6}$

6. Write the following complex fractions as common fractions.

a. $\dfrac{\frac{2}{3}}{\frac{1}{2}}$ b. $\dfrac{\frac{5}{16}}{\frac{3}{8}}$ c. $\dfrac{\frac{7}{15}}{\frac{30}{29}}$ d. $\dfrac{\frac{9}{16}}{\frac{5}{12}}$

7. Write the following fractions as mixed numerals.

a. $\frac{27}{4}$ b. $\frac{39}{12}$ c. $\frac{76}{8}$

d. $\frac{45}{8}$ e. $\frac{24}{16}$ f. $\frac{137}{24}$

8. Which of the following fractions may be named by symbols for whole numbers?

a. $\frac{300}{100}$ b. $\frac{76}{2}$ c. $\frac{84}{21}$

d. $\frac{33}{2}$ e. $\frac{192}{12}$ f. $\frac{5000}{1000}$

9.14. DECIMAL NUMBERS

Let us consider the subset, D, of fractional numbers which may be named by fractions whose denominators are powers of ten. There will be many fractional numbers in this set which have other names. For example,

$$\frac{5}{10} = \frac{1}{2},$$
$$\frac{25}{10^2} = \frac{25}{100} = \frac{1}{4},$$
$$\frac{125}{10^3} = \frac{125}{1000} = \frac{1}{8}.$$

We must now decide whether or not a fraction is a member of this set D. For example, is $\frac{1}{4}$ a member of this set? Notice that

$$\frac{1}{4} = \frac{1}{2^2} = \frac{1 \cdot 5^2}{2^2 \cdot 5^2} = \frac{25}{100} = \frac{25}{10^2}.$$

Hence, $\frac{1}{4}$ is a member of this set. Observe the following:

a. $\dfrac{25}{45} = \dfrac{5}{9} = \dfrac{5}{3^2}$ Does not belong to D

b. $\dfrac{110}{125} = \dfrac{22}{25} = \dfrac{22}{5^2} = \dfrac{22 \cdot 2^2}{5^2 \cdot 2^2} = \dfrac{88}{100}$ Belongs to D

c. $\dfrac{6}{98} = \dfrac{3}{49} = \dfrac{3}{7^2}$ Does not belong to D

d. $\dfrac{50}{90} = \dfrac{5}{9} = \dfrac{5}{3^2}$ Does not belong to D

e. $\dfrac{15}{24} = \dfrac{5}{8} = \dfrac{5}{2^3} = \dfrac{5 \cdot 5^3}{2^3 \cdot 5^3} = \dfrac{625}{1000}$ Belongs to D

The denominators of the simplest names of fractions b and e can be multiplied by a whole number to obtain a product which is a power of ten. The numerators and denominators of these fractions are then multiplied by these whole numbers to get the equivalent fractions whose denominators are powers of 10.

Notice that the denominators of b and e and, in fact, of all fractions that belong to D, have no prime factors other than 2 and 5. A fractional number is an element of D if and only if the denominator of its simplest name has no prime factors other than 2 and 5.

The set D contains 1 because $10^0 = 1$. In fact, the set D contains all the whole numbers. The elements of the set

$$D = \{0, 1, 2, \ldots, \tfrac{1}{10}, \tfrac{2}{10}, \ldots, \tfrac{1}{100}, \tfrac{2}{100}, \ldots\}$$

are called *Decimal Numbers*.

9.15.   DECIMAL FRACTIONS

There is another form of expressing decimal numbers that is simpler than their common fraction form. This form is called the *Decimal-Fraction Form*. It follows the same scheme used for expressing whole numbers which are themselves decimal numbers.

For example,

$$\frac{824}{1000} = \frac{(8 \cdot 100) + (2 \cdot 10) + (4 \cdot 1)}{1000}$$

$$= \frac{8 \cdot 100}{1000} + \frac{2 \cdot 10}{1000} + \frac{4 \cdot 1}{1000}$$

$$= \frac{8}{10} + \frac{2}{100} + \frac{4}{1000}$$

$$= \left(8 \cdot \frac{1}{10^1}\right) + \left(2 \cdot \frac{1}{10^2}\right) + \left(4 \cdot \frac{1}{10^3}\right).$$

If we agree that this sum should be abbreviated by the symbol 824, we will have an exact counterpart for the notation we developed for the whole numbers. Here we have assigned the place values $\dfrac{1}{10^1}, \dfrac{1}{10^2},$ and $\dfrac{1}{10^3}$

to the positions occupied by the "8," "2," and "4," respectively. The only difficulty is that we now have a symbol, 824, to represent both

$$(8 \cdot 10^2) + (2 \cdot 10^1) + (4 \cdot 10^0)$$

and

$$\left(8 \cdot \frac{1}{10^1}\right) + \left(2 \cdot \frac{1}{10^2}\right) + \left(4 \cdot \frac{1}{10^3}\right).$$

To alleviate this confusion we use a dot, called a *decimal point*. Thus, 824 will mean

$$(8 \cdot 10^2) + (2 \cdot 10^1) + (4 \cdot 10^0)$$

and .824 will mean

$$\left(8 \cdot \frac{1}{10^1}\right) + \left(2 \cdot \frac{1}{10^2}\right) + \left(4 \cdot \frac{1}{10^3}\right).$$

We have now extended our place value system as a means of recording not only the whole numbers, which are decimal numbers, but all of the decimal numbers.

For example,

$$(3 \cdot 10^3) + (5 \cdot 10^2) + (1 \cdot 10^1) + (7 \cdot 10^0) + \left(5 \cdot \frac{1}{10^1}\right) + \left(2 \cdot \frac{1}{10^2}\right)$$

may be written as 3517.52. The decimal point is placed to the right of the units place and separates the place values of the powers of 10 and the place values of reciprocals of powers of 10. Notice that the units' place is the point of reference, that is the place value of $10^0 = 1$. We read the places to the right of the decimal point according to their place value. Thus, $0.5 = 5 \cdot \frac{1}{10}$ is read "five tenths";

$$0.03 = \frac{3}{100} = 3 \cdot \frac{1}{10^2}$$

is read "three hundredths."

The decimal fraction 0.06 tells us that the 6 is in the $\dfrac{1}{10^2} = \dfrac{1}{100}$ place, hence is another name for $\dfrac{6}{100}$.

9.16. CHANGING COMMON FRACTIONS TO DECIMAL FRACTIONS

There is a set of fractional numbers each member of which, although not a decimal number, is equivalent to a decimal number. These are the fractional numbers named by fractions whose denominators contain only the numbers 2 and 5 as prime factors. Some examples are:

$$\tfrac{1}{2}, \tfrac{1}{4}, \tfrac{5}{8}, \tfrac{7}{25}, \tfrac{3}{40}, \tfrac{120}{80}, \quad \text{and} \quad \tfrac{6}{160}.$$

One method for expressing a decimal number as a decimal fraction is shown below.

$$\frac{7}{25} = \frac{7}{5^2} = \frac{7 \cdot 2^2}{5^2 \cdot 2^2} = \frac{28}{100}; \quad \text{thus} \quad \frac{7}{25} = 0.28.$$

$$\frac{3}{40} = \frac{3}{2^3 \cdot 5} = \frac{3 \cdot 5^2}{2^3 \cdot 5 \cdot 5^2} = \frac{75}{1000}; \quad \text{thus} \quad \frac{3}{40} = 0.075.$$

$$\frac{6}{160} = \frac{6}{2^5 \cdot 5} = \frac{6 \cdot 5^4}{2^5 \cdot 5 \cdot 5^4} = \frac{3750}{100,000}; \quad \text{thus} \quad \frac{6}{160} = 0.03750.$$

This method is to rename the number, if necessary, so that its denominator is a power of ten. There is a second method, that is, to use the process of division. Thus $\tfrac{3}{4}$ may be interpreted as $3 \div 4$. Consider the computational device for division of 3 by 4.

$$
\begin{array}{r}
0.75 \\
4{\overline{)3.00}} \\
\underline{2\ 8} \\
20 \\
\underline{20} \\
\end{array}
$$

Let us analyze and justify this algorithm.

$$\tfrac{3}{4} = \left(\tfrac{100}{100}\right)\left(\tfrac{3}{4}\right) = \left(\tfrac{1}{100}\right)\left(\tfrac{300}{4}\right) = \left(\tfrac{1}{100}\right)(75) = \tfrac{75}{100} = 0.75.$$

For any decimal number this division will be exact. We thus call decimal numbers *terminating decimals*.

Some fractions do not belong to the set of decimal numbers. That is, there are some fractions which may not be expressed as terminating decimals. We saw earlier that these fractions have denominators which have prime factors other than 2 and 5. For example, some fractions that may not be expressed as decimal fractions are $\frac{1}{3}, \frac{5}{6}, \frac{3}{7}, \frac{7}{12}, \frac{1}{22}$.

Although we cannot find a terminating decimal equivalent to these fractions, it is possible to find terminating decimals that approximate these fractions as closely as we desire. By "approximate" we mean that their numerals name decimal numbers that differ from the fractional number by an amount as small as we think desirable.

We must now consider the computational device for dividing 1 by 3.

$$
\begin{array}{r}
0.3 \\
3\overline{)1.0} \\
\underline{9} \\
1
\end{array}
\qquad
\begin{array}{r}
0.33 \\
3\overline{)1.00} \\
\underline{9} \\
10 \\
\underline{9} \\
1
\end{array}
\qquad
\begin{array}{r}
0.333 \\
3\overline{)1.000} \\
\underline{9} \\
10 \\
\underline{9} \\
10 \\
\underline{9} \\
1
\end{array}
$$

To justify the above divisions we note the following:

$$1 = 3\,(0.3) + .1. \qquad 1 = 3\,(0.33) + 0.01. \qquad 1 = 3\,(.333) + 0.001.$$

It is intuitively clear that the above process will not terminate. That is, $\frac{1}{3}$ cannot be represented by a terminating decimal. If we continue the divisions we see that $\frac{1}{3} = 0.333\cdots$. The three dots mean that when we divide 1 by 3 the division never terminates. Because of this, we call such a number a *non-terminating decimal*. Notice that $\frac{1}{3}$ is approximately 0.3, but that it is closer to 0.333, and so on. Thus, we can approximate $\frac{1}{3}$ as closely as we like by a decimal fraction.

EXERCISE 9.6

1. Which of the following name decimal numbers?

a. $\frac{7}{125}$ b. $\frac{1}{3}$ c. $\frac{26}{27}$
d. $\frac{62}{50}$ e. $\frac{3}{4}$ f. $\frac{9}{8}$

2. Change the following common fractions to decimal fractions.

a. $\frac{3}{4}$ b. $\frac{6}{25}$ c. $\frac{23}{125}$
d. $\frac{37}{500}$ e. $\frac{144}{240}$ f. $\frac{49}{2800}$

3. Write the following decimal fractions as common fractions in simplest form.

a. 0.042 b. 0.25 c. 1.64
d. 37.84 e. 2.013 f. 4.005

4. Write the following in expanded notation.

a. 176.82 b. 34.976 c. 0.842
d. 765.009 e. 0.032 f. 0.0007

5. Write the following as a common fraction with a power of 10 as the denominator and then as a decimal fraction.

a. $\frac{1}{4} = \frac{25}{100} = 0.25$ b. $\frac{3}{5}$ c. $\frac{7}{16}$
d. $\frac{12}{25}$ e. $\frac{123}{125}$ f. $\frac{17}{200}$

6. Which of the following are terminating decimals?

a. $\frac{1}{4}$ b. $\frac{2}{3}$ c. $\frac{5}{7}$
d. $\frac{3}{25}$ e. $\frac{7}{250}$ f. $\frac{7}{9}$

CHAPTER 10

The Non-negative Rational Numbers

10.1. A DIFFERENT VIEWPOINT

Up to this point we have considered fractional numbers as numbers associated with a physical process—the measurement of unit lengths or of unit regions divided into congruent subunits. Now we shall take a second look at these numbers from the point of view of a whole new system designed and created deliberately to have all the properties of the whole numbers, plus some additions. We are particularly interested in the closure property of division, except by zero. This new set contains *non-negative rational numbers*. In this chapter, however, we shall call them *rational numbers,* for until negative numbers are introduced (Chapter 12) it will be understood that whenever we mention rational numbers we will mean non-negative rational numbers.

Before we begin the study of rational numbers, let us recall the properties of the whole numbers. Each member in the set

$$W = \{0, 1, 2, 3, 4, \ldots\}$$

has an immediate successor—the next larger number. The successor of 1 is $1 + 1 = 2$; of 2, $2 + 1 = 3$; and so on. Thus the successor of n is $n + 1$. Every number, n, except 0, has an immediate predecessor, the next smaller number, $n - 1$. The set of whole numbers has a least element 0, but no greatest element. Considering this set and the operations of addition and multiplication, we have the following properties:

1. **Closure**   If a and b are any two whole numbers, then $a + b$ and ab are unique whole numbers.

2. **Commutative**   If a and b are any two whole numbers,

$$a + b = b + a \quad \text{and} \quad ab = ba.$$

3. **Associative**   If a, b, and c are whole numbers,

$$(a + b) + c = a + (b + c),$$

and

$$(ab)\,c = a(bc).$$

4. **Identity elements**   For any whole number a,

$$a + 0 = 0 + a = a \quad \text{and} \quad a \cdot 1 = 1 \cdot a = a.$$

Zero is called the *identity element for addition,* and one is called the *identity element for multiplication.*

5. **Distributive**   For any whole numbers a, b, and c,

$$a\,(b + c) = ab + ac \quad \text{and} \quad (b + c)\,a = ba + ca.$$

The set of whole numbers is not closed under the operations of subtraction and division. Multiplication is distributive over subtraction. That is, $a\,(b - c) = ab - ac$, when $b \geq c$.

6. **Cancellation properties**   If a, b, and c are whole numbers, $a + b = a + c$ implies $b = c$, and $ab = ac$ (with $a \neq 0$) implies $b = c$. These are called the cancellation properties of addition and multiplication.

10.2.   DEFINITIONS

We now want to create a system of numbers which is closed under the operation of division (except by zero), and possesses all the properties of the whole numbers. We recall that $a \div b = r$ (with $b \neq 0$) means $r \cdot b = a$. We would like a set of numbers in which it is always possible to find such a number, r. When we worked with the set of whole numbers this was not always possible; for example, there is no whole number r such that $6 \div 4 = r$.

When b divides a we define $a \div b = c$ where $a = bc$. When b does not divide a we create a new number, r, called a *rational number*, with the property that if $a \div b = r$, then $a = br$. We use the symbol $\frac{a}{b}$, and call it a *fraction*. The number, r, represented by this fraction, $\frac{a}{b}$, is a *rational number*.

According to this definition the fraction $\frac{a}{b}$ (where a and b are whole numbers and $b \neq 0$) represents a rational number r for which $a = b \cdot r$. Thus $\frac{7}{4}$ represents a rational number, r, such that $7 = 4 \cdot r$. Similarly,

$$\frac{2}{6} = r \quad \text{implies} \quad 6 \cdot r = 2.$$
$$\frac{1}{2} = r \quad \text{implies} \quad 2 \cdot r = 1.$$
$$\frac{5}{10} = r \quad \text{implies} \quad 10 \cdot r = 5.$$

In general, $\frac{a}{b}$ is a number such that $b \cdot \left(\frac{a}{b} \right) = a$.

Notice that $\frac{10}{5} = r$ implies $5 \cdot r = 10$, but $5 \cdot 2 = 10$, hence $\frac{10}{5}$ is another name for the whole number 2.

$$\frac{14}{7} = r \quad \text{implies} \quad 7 \cdot r = 14; \text{ thus, } \tfrac{14}{7} \text{ is another name for 2.}$$
$$\frac{24}{12} = r \quad \text{implies} \quad 12 \cdot r = 24; \text{ thus, } \tfrac{24}{12} \text{ is another name for 2.}$$
$$\frac{16}{8} = r \quad \text{implies} \quad 8 \cdot r = 16; \text{ thus, } \tfrac{16}{8} \text{ is another name for 2.}$$

These observations lead us to a crucial question: how can we tell when two different fractions are really names for the same rational number? Another question asks how the set of whole numbers is related to the set of rational numbers?

10.3. EQUALITY FOR RATIONAL NUMBERS

We defined the rational number r as the number that satisfies the sentence $b \cdot r = a$. We represent this number r by the fraction symbol $\frac{a}{b}$. We know that

$$c(br) = (cb)r = c \cdot a.$$

Since r is also named by the fraction $\left(\dfrac{c \cdot a}{c \cdot b}\right)$, where $c \neq 0$, we write

$$\frac{c \cdot a}{c \cdot b} = \frac{a}{b}, \; c \neq 0.$$

The equal sign here means that $\left(\dfrac{c \cdot a}{c \cdot b}\right)$ and $\left(\dfrac{a}{b}\right)$ are names for the same rational number.

There is another way to tell whether or not two fractions are names for the same rational number. Consider

$$\frac{a}{b} = \frac{a \cdot d}{b \cdot d} \text{ and } \frac{c}{d} = \frac{c \cdot b}{d \cdot b},$$

where $b \neq 0$ and $d \neq 0$. Since $\dfrac{ad}{bd}$ and $\dfrac{cb}{db}$ have the same denominators, they are equal if and only if their numerators are equal: that is, $a \cdot d = b \cdot c$. We may now state: the fractions $\dfrac{a}{b}$ and $\dfrac{c}{d}$ represent the same rational number if and only if $a \cdot d = b \cdot c$.

EXERCISE 10.1

1. Which of the following pairs of fractions name the same rational numbers?

a. $\frac{76}{152}, \frac{1216}{2432}$.　　b. $\frac{3}{8}, \frac{75}{200}$.

c. $\frac{1}{2}, \frac{39}{80}$.　　d. $\frac{15}{40}, \frac{45}{123}$.

e. $\frac{9}{7}, \frac{9}{9}$.　　f. $\frac{17}{84}, \frac{76}{125}$.

2. Give a rule for determining whether or not two fractions name the same rational number.

3. Is it possible to have two different fractions, both in simplest form, that name the same rational number?

4. Under what operations is the set of whole numbers closed?

5. What are the successors of the following whole numbers?

a. 3.　　b. 7.　　c. 0.

d. 1.　　e. 9.　　f. 87.

6. State the commutative properties for the set of whole numbers.

7. State the associative properties for the set of whole numbers.

8. What is the least element in the set of whole numbers? the greatest?

9. Define a rational number.

10. What rational numbers, r, make the following sentences true?

   a. $3r = 5$.   b. $7r = 10$.   c. $2r = 1$.

   d. $5r = 27$.   e. $6r = 9$.   f. $12r = 3$.

10.4. THE RATIONAL NUMBERS BETWEEN ZERO AND ONE

Let us try to visualize, on the number line, the set of points corresponding to all the rational numbers. On the number line there are no points between 0 and 1 which are graphs of whole numbers. Similarly, for any two successive whole numbers, n and $n + 1$, there are no points corresponding to whole numbers between the two points corresponding to n and $n + 1$. This means that on the number line there are wide gaps between the points which correspond to the whole numbers. Let us concentrate at present on just those rational numbers between 0 and 1.

Consider the rational numbers between 0 and 1 and the points on the number line that correspond to them. We shall call these points *rational points*. Figure 10.1 shows the rational points between 0 and 1 which may be named by fractions with denominators 2, 4, and 8.

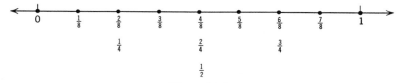

Figure 10.1

We now ask ourselves, how many rational points are there between the points corresponding to $\frac{1}{8}$ and $\frac{1}{4}$. We know that

$$\tfrac{1}{8} = \tfrac{2}{16} \quad \text{and} \quad \tfrac{1}{4} = \tfrac{4}{16};$$

hence there is a rational point between the points corresponding to $\frac{1}{8}$ and $\frac{1}{4}$. This point corresponds to $\frac{3}{16}$, but since

$$\tfrac{1}{8} = \tfrac{4}{32} \quad \text{and} \quad \tfrac{3}{16} = \tfrac{6}{32},$$

the point that corresponds to $\frac{5}{32}$ is between the points corresponding to $\frac{1}{8}$ and $\frac{3}{16}$. However,

$$\tfrac{1}{8} = \tfrac{8}{64} \quad \text{and} \quad \tfrac{5}{32} = \tfrac{10}{64}.$$

hence, the point corresponding to $\frac{9}{64}$ is between the points corresponding to $\frac{1}{8}$ and $\frac{5}{32}$.

Clearly this process could be carried on indefinitely, and would apply no matter what rational numbers were involved. Another way of expressing this is to say that between any two rational numbers, no matter how close together they are, there is always a third rational number. Accordingly, between any two rational numbers there must be infinitely many rational numbers. We describe this situation by saying that the set of rational numbers is *dense*.

One way to find a rational number between any two given rational numbers is to find the average of the two given numbers. For example, $\frac{1}{8}$ and $\frac{1}{4}$, their average is

$$\frac{\frac{1}{8} + \frac{1}{4}}{2} = \frac{\frac{3}{8}}{2} = \frac{3}{16}.$$

We know from the previous discussion that $\frac{3}{16}$ is between $\frac{1}{8}$ and $\frac{1}{4}$.

Let us now try to enumerate the rational numbers between 0 and 1. We wish to do this in a systematic way, taking a first one, then a second, and so on, in such a way that any given rational number ultimately will be chosen. We cannot take the set of rational numbers in their natural order since there is no next rational number after zero. Between zero and any rational number it is possible to find as many rational numbers as we please.

Let us take the rational number $\frac{1}{2}$, then let us take the rational numbers named by fractions with denominators 3 and numerators in increasing order ($\frac{1}{3}$, $\frac{2}{3}$), then those named by fractions with denominators 4 and numerators in increasing order ($\frac{1}{4}$, $\frac{2}{4}$, $\frac{3}{4}$), and so forth. We will omit $\frac{2}{4}$ because we already have included it under its simplest name $\frac{1}{2}$.

We now have a systematic method of putting the set of rational numbers between 0 and 1 into a one-to-one correspondence with the set of counting numbers.

$$
\begin{array}{ccccccccccc}
1 & 2 & 3 & 4 & 5 & 6 & 7 & 8 & 9 & 10 & 11 \\
\updownarrow & \updownarrow & \updownarrow & \updownarrow & \updownarrow & \updownarrow & \updownarrow & \updownarrow & \updownarrow & \updownarrow & \cdots \\
\frac{1}{2} & \frac{1}{3} & \frac{2}{3} & \frac{1}{4} & \frac{3}{4} & \frac{1}{5} & \frac{2}{5} & \frac{3}{5} & \frac{4}{5} & \frac{1}{6} & \frac{5}{6}
\end{array}
$$

Since we can put the set of rational numbers between 0 and 1 into a one-to-one correspondence with the counting numbers, we say there are just as many rational numbers between 0 and 1 as there are counting numbers.

10.5. THE WHOLE NUMBERS AND THE RATIONAL NUMBERS

We found earlier that there is a one-to-one correspondence between the set of whole numbers and the set of rational numbers represented by fractions with denominators 1.

$$0\ 1\ 2\ 3\ 4$$
$$\updownarrow \updownarrow \updownarrow \updownarrow \updownarrow \cdots.$$
$$\frac{0}{1}\ \frac{1}{1}\ \frac{2}{1}\ \frac{3}{1}\ \frac{4}{1}$$

To each whole number there corresponds exactly one rational number (of course, each number has many names), and to each rational number in this set there corresponds exactly one whole number.

We saw also that this correspondence preserves the order of the elements of the two sets and the operations performed on them. Thus,

$$3 \leftrightarrow \tfrac{3}{1}, 2 \leftrightarrow \tfrac{2}{1}, 5 \leftrightarrow \tfrac{5}{1}, 6 \leftrightarrow \tfrac{6}{1},$$
$$3 > 2 \quad \text{and} \quad \tfrac{3}{1} > \tfrac{2}{1},$$
$$3 + 2 = 5 \quad \text{and} \quad \tfrac{3}{1} + \tfrac{2}{1} = \tfrac{5}{1},$$
$$3 \cdot 2 = 6 \quad \text{and} \quad \tfrac{3}{1} \cdot \tfrac{2}{1} = \tfrac{6}{1}.$$

Because of this consistency of order relations and operations, we say that the *system of whole numbers is embedded in the system of rational numbers.*

Because of this relation between the whole numbers and the rational numbers we say that the *system of whole numbers is a subsystem of the system of rational numbers.*

10.6. SUMMARY

We shall now give the definitions of addition and multiplication of rational numbers and the properties of these operations. These properties were discussed in the unit on fractions.

Addition If $\frac{a}{b}$ and $\frac{c}{d}$ are any two rational numbers, then

$$\frac{a}{b} + \frac{c}{d} = \frac{ad + bc}{bd}.$$

Multiplication If $\frac{a}{b}$ and $\frac{c}{d}$ are any two rational numbers then

$$\frac{a}{b} \cdot \frac{c}{d} = \frac{ac}{bd}.$$

Properties of Addition and Multiplication

Closure   If $\frac{a}{b}$ and $\frac{c}{d}$ are rational numbers, then $\frac{a}{b} + \frac{c}{d}$ and $\frac{a}{b} \cdot \frac{c}{d}$ are rational numbers.

Commutative   If $\frac{a}{b}$ and $\frac{c}{d}$ are rational numbers, then

$$\frac{a}{b} + \frac{c}{d} = \frac{c}{d} + \frac{a}{b} \quad \text{and} \quad \frac{a}{b} \cdot \frac{c}{d} = \frac{c}{d} \cdot \frac{a}{b}.$$

Associative   If $\frac{a}{b}$ and $\frac{c}{d}$ and $\frac{e}{f}$ are rational numbers, then

$$\left(\frac{a}{b} + \frac{c}{d}\right) + \frac{e}{f} = \frac{a}{b} + \left(\frac{c}{d} + \frac{e}{f}\right) \text{and} \left(\frac{a}{b} \cdot \frac{c}{d}\right) \cdot \frac{e}{f} = \frac{a}{b} \cdot \left(\frac{c}{d} \cdot \frac{e}{f}\right).$$

Identity Elements   Since

$$\frac{a}{b} + \frac{0}{b} = \frac{0}{b} + \frac{a}{b} = \frac{a}{b},$$

we called $\frac{0}{b}$ the additive identity for addition. Since

$$\frac{a}{b} \cdot \frac{1}{1} = \frac{1}{1} \cdot \frac{a}{b} = \frac{a}{b},$$

we called $\frac{1}{1}$ the multiplicative identity for multiplication.

Distributive   If $\frac{a}{b}, \frac{c}{d}$, and $\frac{e}{f}$ are rational numbers,

$$\frac{a}{b}\left(\frac{c}{d} + \frac{e}{f}\right) = \frac{a}{b} \cdot \frac{c}{d} + \frac{a}{b} \cdot \frac{e}{f}.$$

Multiplicative Inverse   Every rational number $\frac{a}{b}$, with $a \neq 0$, has a multiplicative inverse, $\frac{b}{a}$, such that

$$\frac{a}{b} \cdot \frac{b}{a} = \frac{1}{1}.$$

EXERCISE 10.2

1. Name a rational number between each of the following pairs of rational numbers.

    a. $\frac{1}{3}, \frac{7}{8}$ b. $\frac{5}{4}, \frac{17}{9}$

    c. $\frac{2}{3}, \frac{9}{7}$ d. $\frac{1}{2}, \frac{5}{6}$

    e. $\frac{12}{16}, \frac{18}{14}$ f. $\frac{1}{16}, \frac{2}{3}$

2. List ten rational numbers between $\frac{1}{3}$ and $\frac{1}{8}$.

3. Order the following rational numbers from the least to the greatest.

$$\frac{3}{4}, \frac{5}{6}, \frac{1}{3}, \frac{7}{8}, \frac{1}{2}, \frac{5}{16}, \frac{7}{24}.$$

4. Name seven rational numbers that are less than $\frac{1}{3}$ and greater than $\frac{1}{5}$.

5. How many rational numbers are greater than $\frac{1}{2}$ and less than $\frac{7}{8}$?

6. What property of rational numbers do the following sentences illustrate?

    a. $\frac{2}{3} + \frac{5}{6} = \frac{5}{6} + \frac{2}{3}$,

    b. $\frac{1}{3} \times \frac{156}{6} = (\frac{1}{3} \times \frac{120}{6}) + (\frac{1}{3} \times \frac{36}{6})$,

    c. $(\frac{1}{2} \times \frac{1}{4}) \times \frac{2}{5} = \frac{1}{2} \times (\frac{1}{4} \times \frac{2}{5})$,

    d. $\frac{3}{4} \times \frac{4}{3} = 1$.

7. What is the product of a rational number and its reciprocal?

8. Explain the density property of the rational numbers.

9. What rational number does not have a multiplicative inverse?

10. Does the operation of addition of rational numbers have an identity element? What is it?

11. Is the set of whole numbers dense?

12. Under what operations is the set of rational numbers closed?

13. Is the set of rational numbers ordered?

14. What is the trichotomy principle? Does it hold for the set of rational numbers?

15. Construct some statements to show that subtraction and division of rational numbers are not commutative operations.

16. List ten fractions which name the rational number (a) zero; (b) one.

17. Is multiplication of rational numbers distributive over subtraction? Give some reasons to substantiate your answer.

18. The product of two rational numbers is the multiplicative identity. One of them is $\frac{9}{76}$. What is the other?

19. The product of two rational numbers is the additive identity. One of them is $\frac{14}{5}$. What is the other?

20. Construct some statements to show that subtraction and division of rational numbers are not associative operations.

CHAPTER **11**

The Integers

11.1. DEFINITION

The set of whole numbers and the set of non-negative fractional numbers (which we called the rational numbers) have their origin in counting situations. So does the set of integers. All of these numbers and the symbols which represent them are creations of the human mind. Integers meet the need to count and measure with respect to a point of reference when the direction relative to this point of reference is important. Examples of such situations are common in the physical world.

1. Measurement of temperature
2. Measurement of altitude
3. Measurement of profit and loss

A temperature might be 2 degrees above zero or 2 degrees below zero; an altitude may be 100 feet above sea level or 100 feet below sea level; a business may make a profit of 500 dollars or register a loss of 500 dollars. If integers are used, the temperatures are +2 degrees or −2 degrees; the altitudes are +100 feet or −100 feet; the profit and loss are +500 and −500 dollars, respectively.

The *integers* will be denoted by the symbols

$$\{\cdots -3, -2, -1, 0, +1, +2, +3, \cdots.\}$$

226

These symbols are read "negative three", "negative two", "negative one", "zero", "positive one", "positive two", "positive three", and so on. The superscripts $+$ and $-$ describe the relation of the integer to the point of reference, zero, and tell the direction of the integer from zero. The superscript is called the *sign* of the integer.

The set $\{+1, +2, +3, \cdots\}$ is called the set of *positive integers*. The set $\{\cdots, -3, -2, -1\}$ is called the set of *negative integers*.

Pairs of numbers such as $+2$ and -2 are called *opposites* or *additive inverses*. Thus, -2 is the opposite of $+2$, and $+2$ is the opposite of -2. Every integer has an opposite. Zero is its own opposite.

We represent the additive inverse or opposite of any integer a as $-a$. For example,

The additive inverse of $+9$ is $-(+9) = -9$,
The additive inverse of $+6$ is $-(+6) = -6$,
The additive inverse of -3 is $-(-3) = +3$,
The additive inverse of -5 is $-(-5) = +5$.

11.2. INTEGERS AND THE NUMBER LINE

On the number line we can locate points corresponding to the integers. In Figure 11.1 a line and a set of points, represented by equally spaced dots, is shown. These points are chosen to correspond to the integers. One centrally located point is labeled 0, as shown in Figure 11.2. The points to the right of 0 are labeled successively $+1, +2, +3, \cdots$. The points to the left of 0 are labeled $-1, -2, -3, \cdots$, successively. The labeling is continued indefinitely in both directions since the line extends indefinitely in both directions.

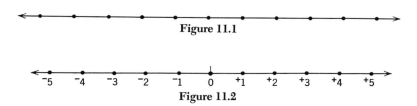

Figure 11.1

Figure 11.2

Notice that the point corresponding to the opposite of $+2$ (that is, the point corresponding to -2) is the same distance from the point corresponding to 0 as $+2$, but in the opposite direction. Thus, the points corresponding to $+4$ and -4 are each four units from the point corresponding to 0 but in opposite directions. When we are interested only in the magnitude of the distance and not in the direction we find it convenient to consider the concept of *absolute value*.

For absolute value we use a symbol such as $|+4|$ and read it "the absolute value of +4." The absolute value of a number is always non-negative and indicates the magnitude of the distance of the corresponding point from the origin. For example,

$$|+6| = 6,$$
$$|-2| = 2,$$
$$|-3| = 3.$$

The absolute value of zero is zero.

$$|0| = 0.$$

11.3. ORDERING THE INTEGERS

Figure 11.2 is a geometric representation of the integers and suggests the following generalizations.

1. Positive integers may be thought of as extending indefinitely to the right of zero.

2. Negative integers may be thought of extending indefinitely to the left of zero.

3. Opposites are represented by pairs of points appearing at the same distance from the point represented by zero but in opposite directions.

4. The points representing the integers are ordered from left to right. The integers are ordered in the same way. Thus

$$+5 > +2,$$
$$+2 > -3,$$
$$-2 > -5.$$

We see then that

$$\cdots < -3 < -2 < -1 < 0 < +1 < +2 < +3 < \cdots .$$

5. The integers separate themselves into three disjoint subsets:
   a. The set of positive integers.
   b. The set of negative integers.
   c. The set consisting of zero.

6. Zero is greater than every negative integer and less than every positive integer.

7. Every positive integer is greater than every negative integer.

Now that we have ordered the integers we may define absolute value in a more precise manner. If a is any integer, the *absolute value* of a, denoted by $|a|$, is defined as follows:

If $a > 0$,   then $|a| = a$.
If $a = 0$,   then $|a| = 0$.
If $a < 0$,   then $|a| = -a$.

EXERCISE 11.1

1. Write the following as integers.

    a. 78° above zero.
    b. 15° below zero.
    c. 5° above zero.
    d. The Fahrenheit temperature at which water boils.
    e. The Fahrenheit temperature at which water freezes.

2. Write the altitudes of the following places as integers.

    a. Mount Everest   29,028 ft. above sea level.
    b. Death Valley   1,286 ft. below sea level.
    c. Salton Sea   280 ft. below sea level.
    d. Mount Evans   14,210 ft. above sea level.

3. What is the opposite of each of the following?

    a. +6.   b. −14.   c. 0.
    d. −7.   e. +c.   f. +(m + n).
    g. +15.   h. +ab.   i. −p.

4. Write the absolute values of

    a. +3.   b. −7.   c. −18.
    d. 0.   e. +9.   f. +14.
    g. +94.   h. −17.   i. −42.

5. Write an integer that is

    a. 7 greater than +6.
    b. 9 less than −2.
    c. 14 greater than −6.
    d. 3 less than 0.
    e. 2 greater than −2.
    f. 5 greater than 0.

6. Fill in the blanks with "positive" or "negative".

a. A _____ integer is greater than its opposite.

b. The additive inverse of +2 is a _____ integer.

c. The absolute value of a negative integer is _____ .

d. Zero is less than every _____ integer.

e. Zero is greater than every _____ integer.

7. Using the symbols "$<$" and "$>$", compare the following pairs of integers:

a. +7, +15. b. −6, +9.

c. −8, −16. d. −16, +4.

e. 0, +7. f. +8, −6.

8. Order the following integers. List them from least to greatest.

$$-6, +9, 0, +18, -14, -3, +7, +8, -9, +72.$$

9. Which of the following statements are true?

a. Zero is its own opposite.

b. Zero is greater than every negative integer.

c. Zero is less than every negative integer.

d. The additive inverse of every positive integer is a positive integer.

10. What is the intersection of the set of negative integers and the set of positive integers?

11. What is the union of the set of negative integers, the set of positive integers and zero?

12. Name the integers with the absolute values listed below.

a. 4. b. 7. c. 6. d. 9.

e. 0. f. 2. g. 17. h. 24.

13. How many units from zero is the graph of the opposite of each integer below?

a. −6. b. +7. c. −12.

11.4. ADDITION OF INTEGERS

We must now define the operation of addition for the integers. Let us list the cases which we must consider:

a. The sum of two positive integers, as +3 + +2.

b. The sum of two negative integers, as −3 + −2.

c. The sum of an integer and its additive inverse, as +2 + −2.

d. The sum of a negative and a positive integer, as +3 + −4.

e. The sum of a negative integer and zero, as −3 + 0.

f. The sum of a positive integer and zero, as +3 + 0.

If we think of +3 as representing a profit of 3 dollars and +2 as representing a profit of 2 dollars, then +3 + +2 will represent a profit of 5 dollars which we represent as +5. Then

$$+3 + {}^+2 = {}^+5.$$

If we think of $^-3$ as representing a loss of 3 dollars and $^-2$ as representing a loss of 2 dollars, then $^-3 + {}^-2$ will represent a loss of 5 dollars which we represent as $^-5$. Then

$$^-3 + {}^-2 = {}^-5.$$

If we think of $^+2$ as representing a profit of 2 dollars and $^-2$ as representing a loss of 2 dollars, then $^+2 + {}^-2$ will represent neither a profit nor a loss, which we represent as 0. Then

$$^+2 + {}^-2 = 0.$$

If we think of $^+3$ as representing a profit of 3 dollars and $^-4$ as representing a loss of 4 dollars, then $^+3 + {}^-4$ will represent a loss of 1 dollar which we represent as $^-1$. Then

$$^+3 + {}^-4 = {}^-1.$$

If we think of $^-3$ as representing a loss of 3 dollars and 0 as representing neither a profit nor a loss, then $^-3 + 0$ will represent a loss of 3 dollars which we represent as $^-3$. Then

$$^-3 + 0 = {}^-3.$$

If we think of $^+3$ as representing a profit of 3 dollars and 0 as representing neither a profit nor a loss, then $^+3 + 0$ will represent a profit of 3 dollars which we represent by $^+3$. Then

$$^+3 + 0 = {}^+3.$$

The above examples and others like them lead us to the following generalizations:

1. If $a \geqslant 0$ and $b \geqslant 0$, then $a + b = {}^+(|a| + |b|)$.
For example,

$$^+3 + {}^+2 = {}^+(|{}^+3| + |{}^+2|) = {}^+(3 + 2) = {}^+5.$$

2. If $a < 0$ and $b < 0$, then $a + b = {}^-(|a| + |b|)$.
For example,

$$^-3 + {}^-2 = {}^-(|{}^-3| + |{}^-2|) = {}^-(3 + 2) = {}^-5.$$

3. If $a \geqslant 0$ and $b < 0$ and $|a| > |b|$, then $a + b = {}^+(|a| - |b|)$.
For example,

$$^+3 + {}^-2 = {}^+(|{}^+3| - |{}^-2|) = {}^+(3 - 2) = {}^+1.$$

4. If $a \geqslant 0$ and $b < 0$ and $|b| > |a|$, then $a + b = {}^-(|b| - |a|)$.
For example,

$$^+2 + {}^-3 = {}^-(|{}^-3| - |{}^+2|) = {}^-(3 - 2) = {}^-1.$$

5. The sum of an integer and its opposite is zero: $a + {}^-a = 0$.
For example,

$$^+2 + {}^-2 = 0.$$

6. The sum of an integer and zero is that integer: $a + 0 = a$.
For example,

$$^+2 + 0 = {}^+2, \; {}^-3 + 0 = {}^-3.$$

11.5. PROPERTIES OF ADDITION OF INTEGERS

Addition of integers has all the operational properties of the addition of whole numbers. For example, if we add two integers, the sum is always an integer; hence the *set of integers is closed under the operation of addition*. Notice that

$$
\begin{array}{ll}
^+3 + {}^+5 = {}^+8, & {}^+5 + {}^+3 = {}^+8, \\
^-7 + {}^-4 = {}^-11, & {}^-4 + {}^-7 = {}^-11, \\
^+3 + {}^-7 = {}^-4, & {}^-7 + {}^+3 = {}^-4.
\end{array}
$$

In general, if a and b are any two integers, then

$$a + b = b + a.$$

The operation of addition of integers is commutative. Observe that

$$
({}^+2 + {}^+3) + {}^+7 = {}^+5 + {}^+7 = {}^+12, \quad {}^+2 + ({}^+3 + {}^+7) = {}^+2 + {}^+10 = {}^+12,
$$
$$
({}^-3 + {}^+4) + {}^-5 = {}^+1 + {}^-5 = {}^-4, \quad {}^-3 + ({}^+4 + {}^-5) = {}^-3 + {}^-1 = {}^-4.
$$

In general, if a, b, and c are any integers, then

$$(a + b) + c = a + (b + c).$$

The addition of integers is associative. Notice that

$$
\begin{array}{l}
^+2 + 0 = 0 + {}^+2 = {}^+2, \\
^+3 + 0 = 0 + {}^+3 = {}^+3, \\
^+4 + 0 = 0 + {}^+4 = {}^+4, \\
^-7 + 0 = 0 + {}^-7 = {}^-7.
\end{array}
$$

In general, if a is any integer,

$$a + 0 = 0 + a = a.$$

Zero is the additive identity for the set of integers.

The operation of addition of integers has one property which the operation of addition of whole numbers does not possess. Notice that

$$^+2 + {}^-2 = 0$$
$$^+3 + {}^-3 = 0$$
$$^-7 + {}^+7 = 0$$

These examples illustrate the following property of the operation of addition of integers: For every integer a, there exists another integer ^-a such that $a + {}^-a = 0$.

This number, ^-a, is called the *additive inverse* of a. Thus the additive inverse of $^+2$ is its opposite, $^-2$; of $^-3$, its opposite, $^+3$.

11.6 SUBTRACTION OF INTEGERS

We define the operation of subtraction of integers as the inverse of the operation of addition of integers. Thus

$$^+3 - {}^+7 = n$$

means

$$n + {}^+7 = {}^+3.$$

In general, if a, b, and n are integers

$$a - b = n$$

means

$$n + b = a.$$

Let us examine the example, $^+3 - {}^+7 = n$. This means

$$n + {}^+7 = {}^+3.$$

But if we add $^-7$ to $(n + {}^+7)$ and to $^+3$ we get

$$+3 + {}^-7 = (n + {}^+7) + {}^-7$$
$$= n + ({}^+7 + {}^-7) \qquad \text{Associative property}$$
$$= n + 0 \qquad \text{Additive inverse}$$
$$= n \qquad \text{Additive identity}$$

Hence, $^+3 - {}^+7 = {}^+3 + {}^-7 = {}^-4$. Notice that subtracting $^+7$ from $^+3$ gives the same result as adding the opposite of $^+7$, that is, $^-7$, to $^+3$. This is true in general and we say that *the subtraction of any integer may be replaced by the addition of its opposite*. For example,

$$^+6 - {}^+2 = {}^+6 + {}^-2 = {}^+4,$$
$$^-7 - {}^-3 = {}^-7 + {}^+3 = {}^-4,$$
$$^+6 - {}^-2 = {}^+6 + {}^+2 = {}^+8.$$

Further, *the set of integers is closed under the operation of subtraction;* that is, if we subtract any two integers the result is always an integer.

In observing the subtraction examples above, we discover that subtraction may always be replaced by the addition of the additive inverse of the number subtracted. This closely parallels what happened when we studied the division of rational numbers. We found that division by any rational number, except zero, could be replaced by multiplication of the multiplicative inverse of that number. We should note at this point that the operations of addition and subtraction of integers have all the properties of the operations of both addition and subtraction of whole numbers, plus the closure property for subtraction and the additive inverse property.

EXERCISE 11.2

1. Add the following pairs of integers.

    a. $^+9, {}^-7$.   b. $^+7, {}^-3$.
    c. $^+18, {}^-6$.   d. $^-8, {}^+17$.
    e. $^+4, {}^+9$.   f. $^-4, {}^+9$.
    g. $^-9, {}^-3$.   h. $^+18, {}^-6$.
    i. $^-15, {}^-4$.   j. $^-2, {}^-15$.

2. Subtract the second integer from the first for each pair in problem 1.
3. Subtract the first integer from the second for each pair in problem 1.
4. Solve $^+7 - {}^-9 = n$ and $^+7 + {}^+9 = m$. Compare m and n. What can you say about $^+7 - {}^-9$ and $^+7 + {}^+9$?
5. If $a > b > 0$, is $a + {}^-b$ positive or negative?
6. If $0 < a < b$, is $a + {}^-b$ positive or negative?
7. If $a > b > 0$, is $b + {}^-a$ positive or negative?

8. If $0 < a < b$, is $b + {}^-a$ positive or negative?

9. Find the following sums:

    a. $^+19 + {}^+27 + {}^+18$.
    b. $^-16 + {}^+13 + {}^-74$.
    c. $^-21 + {}^-13 + {}^+19$.
    d. $^-4 + 0 + {}^-7$.
    e. $^+8 + {}^-9 + {}^-7$.

10. Express each of the following as sums of integers.

    a. $^+3 - {}^-7$.   b. $^-9 - {}^-4$.
    c. $^-16 - {}^+14$.   d. $^+13 - {}^-7$.

11. If the temperature at 7:00 A.M. is $^+36°$ and the temperature rises $20°$ between 7:00 A.M. and noon, what is the temperature at noon?

12. The temperature outdoors at 10:00 A.M. is $35°$ and $72°$ indoors. By noon the temperature has risen $10°$ outdoors and fallen $3°$ indoors. What is the difference at noon between the temperature outdoors and the temperature indoors?

13. On the hottest day of one summer the temperature was $102°$. On the coldest day that year the temperature was $^-10°$. What was the difference in temperature from the coldest day to the hottest day?

14. A player had scored 120 points. He was set 60 points each for four consecutive hands. What was his resulting score?

15. A man put $300 in his checking account when he opened it. During the month he wrote checks for $40, $25, $135, and $69. He made deposits of $20 and $34. What was his balance at the end of the month?

16. Use the triplets of integers below to show that addition of integers is associative.

    a. $^+9, {}^-7, {}^+6$.   b. $^-13, {}^+14, {}^-26$.
    c. $^+30, {}^-14, {}^+87$.   d. $^+44, {}^-69, {}^-72$.

17. Use the pairs of integers below to show that subtraction of integers is not commutative.

    a. $^-43, {}^+16$.   b. $^-84, {}^-36$.
    c. $^+69, {}^-14$.   d. $^-97, {}^+126$.

11.7. MULTIPLICATION OF INTEGERS

Suppose we think of the positive integers as measuring the minutes in the future and the negative integers as measuring the minutes in the past. The $^+2$ will represent two minutes in the future, $^-2$ will represent two minutes in the past, and 0 will represent the present moment. Suppose we are pouring gasoline into a tank at the rate of 5 gallons per minute. We can represent this flow as $^+5$ since the tank is filling. If we pump gasoline out of the tank at the rate of 5 gallons per minute, we may represent this flow as ⁻5 since the tank is emptying.

If we are filling the tank, three minutes from now (+3) there will be 15 gallons more (+15) in the tank. That is,

$$(+3) \cdot (+5) = {}^+15.$$

Three minutes ago (−3) there was 15 gallons less (−15) in the tank. That is,

$$(-3) \cdot (+5) = {}^-15.$$

If we are pumping gasoline from the tank, three minutes from now (+3) there will be 15 gallons less (−15) in the tank. That is,

$$(+3) \cdot (-5) = {}^-15.$$

Three minutes ago (−3) there was 15 more gallons (+15) in the tank than there is at this moment. That is,

$$(-3) \cdot (-5) = {}^+15.$$

The discussion above suggests defining the product of two integers as follows:

    a. If $a \geqslant 0$ and $b \geqslant 0$, then $ab = |a| \cdot |b|$.
    b. If $a < 0$ and $b < 0$, then $ab = |a| \cdot |b|$.
    c. If $a > 0$ and $b < 0$, then $ab = {}^-(|a| \cdot |b|)$.
    d. If $a < 0$ and $b > 0$, then $ab = {}^-(|a| \cdot |b|)$.

Using these definitions for the multiplication of integers, we can show that the operation of multiplication of integers has all the properties of the operation of multiplication of whole numbers. The closure property certainly holds, because the product of any two integers is an integer. Observe the following:

$$
\begin{array}{ll}
(+2) \cdot (+6) = {}^+12, & (+6) \cdot (+2) = {}^+12, \\
(-3) \cdot (-4) = {}^+12, & (-4) \cdot (-3) = {}^+12, \\
(-7) \cdot (-3) = {}^+21, & (-3) \cdot (-7) = {}^+21.
\end{array}
$$

In general, if a and b are integers, then $ab = ba$. That is, the operation of multiplication of integers is commutative.
Notice the following products:

$$[(+2)(+3)] \cdot (-4) = (+6) \cdot (-4) = -24,$$
$$(+2) \cdot [(+3) \cdot (-4)] = (+2) \cdot (-12) = -24,$$
$$[(-6)(-2)] \cdot (-5) = (+12) \cdot (-5) = -60,$$
$$(-6) \cdot [(-2) \cdot (-5)] = (-6) \cdot (+10) = -60,$$
$$[(+3)(-4)] \cdot (+7) = (-12) \cdot (+7) = -84,$$
$$(+3) \cdot [-4) \cdot (+7)] = (+3) \cdot (-28) = -84$$

These examples suggest that if a, b, and c, are integers, then

$$(ab)\,c = a(bc).$$

That is, the operation of multiplication of integers is associative.
We know that

$$(+1) \cdot (+5) = (+5) \cdot (+1) = +5,$$
$$(+1) \cdot (-6) = (-6) \cdot (+1) = -6,$$
$$(+1) \cdot (+3) = (+3) \cdot (+1) = +3,$$

and in general, if a is any integer, then

$$a \cdot (+1) = (+1) \cdot a = a;$$

and $+1$ is the multiplicative identity for the integers.
The distributive property also holds for the integers. Notice that

$$(+2) \cdot (+3 + {}^-4) = (+2) \cdot (-1) = -2$$

and

$$(+2) \cdot (+3) + (+2) \cdot (-4) = +6 + {}^-8 = -2.$$

Hence,

$$(+2) \cdot (+3 + {}^-4) = (+2) \cdot (+3) + (+2) \cdot (-4);$$
$$(-3) \cdot (-2 + {}^-3) = (-3) \cdot (-5) = +15$$

and

$$(-3) \cdot (-2) + (-3) \cdot (-3) = +6 + {}^+9 = +15;$$

hence,

$$(-3)\cdot(-2 + -3) = (-3)\cdot(-2) + (-3)\cdot(-3).$$

In general, if a, b, and c are integers,

$$a(b + c) = ab + ac.$$

11.8. DIVISION OF INTEGERS

Since the operation of multiplication of integers has all the properties of the operation of multiplication of whole numbers, division of integers may be defined as the inverse operation of multiplication. Hence,

$$(-2) \div (+3) = n \text{ means } (+3)\cdot(n) = -2,$$
$$(+6) \div (+2) = n \text{ means } (+2)\cdot(n) = +6,$$
$$(-9) \div (-4) = n \text{ means } (-4)\cdot(n) = -9.$$

It is evident from the above examples, that division of integers is not always possible. We see that

$$(+6) \div (+2) = +3 \text{ since } (+2)\cdot(+3) = +6.$$

However, there is no integer n, such that $(-4)\cdot(n) = (-9)$; therefore $(-9) \div (-4)$ cannot be represented by an integer.

The division $+18 \div +2$ requires that the missing factor n be found in the product $(n)\cdot(+2) = +18$. Since $+2$ is positive and $+18$ is positive it follows from the definition of the multiplication of integers that n is also positive. Since $(+9)\cdot(+2) = +18$, $n = +9$. The division $(+8) \div (-2)$ requires that the missing factor n be found in the product $(n)\cdot(-2) = +8$. Since -2 is negative and $+8$ is positive, the integer, n, must be negative. Since $(-4)\cdot(-2) = +8$, $n = -4$.

The division $(-15) \div (-3)$ requires that the missing factor n be found in the product $(n)\cdot(-3) = -15$. Since $(-3)\cdot(+5) = -15$, $n = +5$.

The foregoing examples illustrate that if $b \neq 0$, $a \div b$ is positive if both a and b are both positive or both negative, and negative otherwise. If $a = 0$ and $b \neq 0$, then $a \div b = 0$.

EXERCISE 11.3

1. Fill in the blanks with "positive" or "negative."

    a. The product of a positive integer and a negative integer is a _____ integer.
    b. The product of a negative integer and a negative integer is a _____ integer.

c. The product of a negative integer and a _____ integer is a negative integer.

d. The quotient of a negative integer and a _____ integer is a positive integer.

2. Find the products of the following pairs of integers.

a. $(-7)(+24)$.   b. $(-8)(-32)$.
c. $(+3)(+76)$.   d. $(+9)(-16)$.
e. $(-5)(-26)$.   f. $(+18)(-37)$.
g. $(-56)(-42)$.   h. $(+14)(+35)$.

3. Use the following triplets of integers to show that multiplication of integers is associative.

a. $+7, -3, +9$.   b. $-18, -3, -5$.
c. $+6, +4, -7$.   d. $-4, +3, -6$.

4. Indicate how the following blanks should be filled.

a. $(-18) \div (-2) = +9$ because $(-2) \times$ _____ $= -18$.
b. $(-24) \div (+4) = -6$ because $(+4) \times$ _____ $= -24$.
c. $(+36) \div (+3) = +12$ because $(+3) \times$ _____ $= +36$.
d. $(-81) \div (-9) = +9$ because $(-9) \times$ _____ $= -81$.

5. Find each of the following quotients.

a. $-18 \div -6$.   b. $+39 \div +3$.
c. $-69 \div +23$.   d. $+128 \div -2$.
e. $-168 \div -8$.   f. $+945 \div -27$.

11.9. THE INTEGERS AND THE WHOLE NUMBERS

The set of rational numbers has a subset

$$\{\tfrac{0}{1}, \tfrac{1}{1}, \tfrac{2}{1}, \tfrac{3}{1}, \cdots\}$$

which can be replaced by the whole numbers for all arithmetical purposes. We say that the whole numbers are a subsystem of the rational numbers. Another way of saying this is to say that the rational numbers are an extension of the whole numbers.

The set of integers is also an extension of the set of whole numbers. Let

$$P = \{0, +1, +2, +3, \cdots\}.$$

We can set up a one-to-one correspondence between the set of whole numbers and the elements of P:

$$0 \quad +1 \quad +2 \quad +3 \cdots$$
$$\updownarrow \quad \updownarrow \quad \updownarrow \quad \updownarrow$$
$$0 \quad 1 \quad 2 \quad 3 \cdots$$

Notice that

$$3 > 2 \quad \text{and } {}^{+}3 > {}^{+}2,$$
$$3 + 2 = 5 \text{ and } {}^{+}3 + {}^{+}2 = {}^{+}5,$$
$$3 \cdot 2 = 6 \text{ and } ({}^{+}3) \cdot ({}^{+}2) = {}^{+}6,$$
$$3 - 2 = 1 \text{ and } {}^{+}3 - {}^{+}2 = {}^{+}1,$$
$$8 \div 4 = 2 \text{ and } {}^{+}8 \div {}^{+}4 = {}^{+}2.$$

So far as their order and the performance of the operations are concerned, the set consisting of the positive integers and zero (called the non-negative integers) and the set of whole numbers behave exactly alike. Because of this similarity, it is customary to use the symbols $0, 1, 2, 3, \cdots$ to denote both the whole numbers and the non-negative integers.

EXERCISE 11.4

Solve the following number sentences. The domain is the set of integers.

1. ${}^{-}4 + n = {}^{+}6.$
2. ${}^{+}3 + n = {}^{-}6.$
3. ${}^{-}4 - n = {}^{-}5.$
4. $x > {}^{-}4.$
5. ${}^{-}4 < x \text{ and } x < {}^{+}3.$
6. $5 < n \text{ and } n < 19.$
7. ${}^{-}3 < y \text{ and } y < 0.$
8. $X \leqslant {}^{+}3.$
9. $\chi \geqslant {}^{-}5.$
10. $n + 3 < {}^{-}9.$
11. What is the union of the set of positive integers and zero?
12. Why can the symbol 6 be used for ${}^{+}6$?
13. Under what operations is the set of integers closed?
14. Which of the following statements are true?

   a. Another name for ${}^{+}9$ is 9.
   b. Zero is the additive identity for the set of integers.
   c. ${}^{-}1$ is the multiplicative identity for the set of integers.
   d. Between 0 and ${}^{-}7$ there are 7 integers.

CHAPTER **12**

The Rational Numbers

12.1. DEFINING THE RATIONAL NUMBERS

We have discussed the extension of the system of whole numbers to the system of non-negative rational numbers. We shall now create the system of rational numbers as an extension of the system of integers.

The set of integers is closed with respect to addition, subtraction, and multiplication but not with respect to division. We shall define the rational numbers and the operations on them in such a manner that they possess the same properties as the set of integers; however, the set of rational numbers will be closed under the operation of division, except by zero.

Let us define the rational number r as an ordered pair (a, b), where a and b are integers and $b \neq 0$. Two ordered pairs (a, b) and (c, d) can be said to name the same rational number if and only if $ad = bc$.

We use the symbol $\dfrac{a}{b}$ to represent the rational number defined by the ordered pair (a, b). Examples of rational numbers are

$$\frac{+1}{-2}, \frac{+3}{+4}, \frac{-4}{+5}, \frac{-8}{-4}.$$

Since two rational numbers (a, b) and (c, d) name the same number if and only if $ad = bc$, we see that

241

$$\frac{+1}{-2} = \frac{-2}{+4} \quad \text{because} \quad (+1)(+4) = (-2)(-2),$$

$$\frac{+3}{-4} = \frac{+9}{-12} \quad \text{because} \quad (+3)(-12) = (-4)(+9),$$

$$\frac{-3}{-6} = \frac{-4}{-8} \quad \text{because} \quad (-3)(-8) = (-6)(-4).$$

12.2. OPERATIONS WITH RATIONAL NUMBERS

We shall now define the operations of addition, subtraction, multiplication, and division of rational numbers.

For any two rational numbers (a, b) and (c, d) we define addition by

$$(a, b) + (c, d) = (ad + bc, bd).$$

Using the more familiar fraction symbol to name the rational numbers (a, b) and (c, d), we have

$$\frac{a}{b} + \frac{c}{d} = \frac{ad + bc}{bd}.$$

Notice that this is the same definition given for the addition of non-negative rational numbers. This, of course, is as it should be since the non-negative rationals are a subset of the rational numbers.

From the definition of addition we see that

$$\frac{+3}{+4} + \frac{+2}{+3} = \frac{(+3)(+3) + (+4)(+2)}{(+4)(+3)} = \frac{+9 + +8}{+12} = \frac{+17}{+12},$$

$$\frac{-4}{+5} + \frac{-6}{+2} = \frac{(-4)(+2) + (+5)(-6)}{(+5)(+2)} = \frac{-8 + -30}{+10} = \frac{-38}{+10},$$

$$\frac{-7}{+3} + \frac{+5}{+4} = \frac{(-7)(+4) + (+3)(+5)}{(+3)(+4)} = \frac{-28 + +15}{+12} = \frac{-13}{+12}.$$

Multiplication for any two rational numbers (a, b) and (c, d) is defined as

$$(a, b) \cdot (c, d) = (ac, bd).$$

Using the more familiar fraction symbol to record this multiplication we have

$$\frac{a}{b} \cdot \frac{c}{d} = \frac{ac}{bd}.$$

Thus

$$\frac{3}{4} \cdot \frac{2}{3} = \frac{(3)\,(2)}{(4)\,(3)} = \frac{6}{12},$$

$$\frac{-3}{7} \cdot \frac{2}{4} = \frac{(-3)\,(2)}{(7)\,(4)} = \frac{-6}{28},$$

$$\frac{-3}{5} \cdot \frac{-5}{3} = \frac{(-3)\,(-5)}{(5)\,(3)} = \frac{15}{15}.$$

EXERCISE 12.1

1. Which of the following pairs of rational numbers are equal?

   a. $(4, 5)$, $(-3, 7)$.
   b. $(2, -4)$, $(-6, 12)$.
   c. $(-1, 1)$, $(2, -2)$.
   d. $(3, 7)$, $(2, 5)$.
   e. $(-2, -3)$, $(4, 6)$.
   f. $(1, -5)$, $(1, -6)$.

2. Which of the following pairs of fractions name the same rational number.

   a. $\dfrac{3}{8}, \dfrac{48}{128}$. b. $\dfrac{5}{7}, \dfrac{-35}{-49}$.

   c. $\dfrac{27}{36}, \dfrac{45}{60}$. d. $\dfrac{-49}{56}, \dfrac{84}{-96}$.

3. Perform the following operations.

   a. $\dfrac{2}{3} + \dfrac{-3}{4}$. b. $\dfrac{5}{8} + \dfrac{-2}{4}$.

   c. $\left(\dfrac{2}{3}\right)\left(\dfrac{-7}{8}\right)$. d. $\left(\dfrac{5}{16}\right)\left(\dfrac{3}{-5}\right)$.

   e. $\dfrac{2}{3} + \dfrac{1}{2} + \dfrac{-1}{4}$. f. $\left(\dfrac{-1}{2}\right)\left(\dfrac{-7}{5}\right)\left(\dfrac{3}{14}\right)$.

4. Write the following rational numbers as fractions.

   a. $(-3, 8)$. b. $(7, 8)$. c. $(-5, -9)$.
   d. $(8, -9)$. e. $(12, 16)$. f. $(4, -7)$.

5. Write the following as ordered pairs.

   a. $\dfrac{-3}{8}$. b. $\dfrac{7}{16}$. c. $\dfrac{9}{15}$.

   d. $\dfrac{3}{-4}$. e. $\dfrac{5}{-14}$. f. $\dfrac{7}{-18}$.

12.3. PROPERTIES OF THE RATIONAL NUMBERS

Closure Property

Since $(a, b) + (c, d) = (ad + bc, bd)$ and $ad + bc$ and bd are integers because a, b, c, and d are integers, we see that the set of rational numbers is closed under the operation of addition.

Similarly, since $(a, b) \cdot (c, d) = (ac, bd)$ and ac and bd are integers, the set of rational numbers is closed under the operation of multiplication.

Commutative Property

$$(a, b) + (c, d) = (ad + bc, bd)$$
$$(c, d) + (a, b) = (cb + da, db)$$

But $$(ad + bc, bd) = (cb + da, db).$$
Hence

$$(a, b) + (c, d) = (c, d) + (a, b).$$
$$(a, b) \cdot (c, d) = (ac, bd),$$
$$(c, d) \cdot (a, b) = (ca, db).$$

Since $(ac, bd) = (ca, db)$ we have $(a, b) \cdot (c, d) = (c, d) \cdot (a, b)$.

Associative Property

It can be shown, that if $(a, b), (c, d)$ and (e, f) are any rational numbers, then

$$[(a, b) + (c, d)] + (e, f) = (a, b) + [(c, d) + (e, f)]$$

and

$$[(a, b) \cdot (c, d)] \cdot (e, f) = (a, b) \cdot [(c, d) \cdot (e, f) \cdot].$$

Additive Identity

Observe that

$$(a, b) + (0, b) = (ab + 0\,b, b^2) = (ab, b^2),$$

but

$$(a, b) = (ab, b^2),$$

since

$$ab^2 = b\,(ab),$$
$$= (ab)\,b,$$
$$= ab^2.$$

Hence $(0, b)$, which is called zero, is the additive identity for the set of rational numbers. Zero has many names, such as

$$(0, 1) = (0, 2) = (0, 3) = \cdots,$$

or, in fractional symbols,

$$\frac{0}{1} = \frac{0}{2} = \frac{0}{3} = \frac{0}{4} = \frac{0}{5} = \frac{0}{d} \qquad d \neq 0.$$

Multiplicative Identity

We see that

$$(a, b) \cdot (1, 1) = (a \cdot 1, b \cdot 1) = (a, b).$$

Hence $(1, 1)$, called one, is the multiplicative identity for the set of rational numbers. Remember that $(1, 1)$ has many names, including

$$(1, 1) = (2, 2) = (3, 3) = (4, 4) = \cdots.$$

Additive Inverses

Notice that

$$(a, b) + (^-a, b) = (ab + ^-ab, b^2) = (0, b^2) = (0, b)$$

and

$$(a, b) + (a, ^-b) = (a(^-b) + ab, ^-b^2) = (0, ^-b^2) = (0, b).$$

From this we see that the additive inverse of the rational number (a, b) may be written as either $(^-a, b)$ or $(a, ^-b)$. Following the notation used for integers, we could denote the additive inverse of (a, b) as $^-(a, b)$.

Using fractional symbols we see that

$$\frac{^-a}{b} = \frac{a}{^-b} = -\frac{a}{b}.$$

Distributive Property

It can be shown that if (a, b), (c, d), and (e, f) are any rational numbers, then

$$(a, b) \cdot [(c, d) + (e, f)] = [(a, b) \cdot (c, d)] + [(a, b) \cdot (e, f)].$$

Multiplicative Inverses

We see from the above that the set of rational numbers possesses all the properties of the set of integers. In addition, every rational number except the additive identity, zero, has a multiplicative inverse (reciprocal). Observe that if $a \neq 0$,

$$(a, b) \cdot (b, a) = (ab, ba) = (1, 1).$$

Hence the multiplicative inverse of (a, b), $a \neq 0$, is (b, a).

EXERCISE 12.2

1. What is the multiplicative inverse of each of the following?

   a. $\dfrac{-7}{8}$.   b. $\dfrac{-9}{16}$.   c. $\dfrac{3}{4}$.

   d. $\dfrac{18}{43}$.   e. $\dfrac{1}{-2}$.   f. $\dfrac{-3}{7}$.

2. What is the additive inverse of each of the following?

   a. $\dfrac{1}{2}$.   b. $\dfrac{-7}{16}$.   c. $\dfrac{3}{12}$.

   d. $\dfrac{-7}{15}$.   e. $\dfrac{5}{1}$.   f. $\dfrac{-3}{7}$.

   Which of the following statements (3–8) are true?
3. For every rational number x, $x = x$.
4. The symbol $\dfrac{-6}{0}$ names a rational number.
5. If a and b are rational numbers and $ab = 0, b \neq 0$, then $a = 0$.
6. If a, b, and c are rational numbers, then $ab + ac = a(b + c)$.
7. If a and b are rational numbers, then $ab \neq ba$.
8. If a and b are rational numbers, then $a + b = b + a$.
9. Write the additive inverse of a $\dfrac{a}{b}$ in three ways.
10. What is the multiplicative identity for the set of rational numbers?
11. What is the additive identity for the set of rational numbers?
12. Prove that if $(a, b), (c, d)$, and (e, f) are rational numbers, then $[(a, b) + (c, d)] + (e, f) = (a, b) + [(c, d) + (e, f)]$.
13. Prove that if $(a, b), (c, d)$, and (e, f) are rational numbers, then $(a, b) \cdot [(c, d) \cdot (e, f)] = [(a, b) \cdot (c, d)] \cdot (e, f)$.
14. Prove that if $(a, b), (c, d)$, and (e, f) are rational numbers, then $(a, b) \cdot [(c, d) + (e, f)] = (a, b) \cdot (c, d) + (a, b) \cdot (e, f)$.

12.4. ORDER OF THE RATIONAL NUMBERS

A rational number (a, b) is defined as *positive* if and only if ab is a positive integer. A rational number (a, b) is defined as *negative* if and only if ab is a negative integer. The rational number $(0, b)$, called zero, is neither positive nor negative. Notice that

$$\frac{+1}{+2}, \frac{-1}{-2}, \frac{3}{4}, \frac{-3}{-5}, \frac{-6}{-7}, \frac{3}{8}$$

all name positive rational numbers;

$$\frac{-1}{2}, \frac{3}{-2}, \frac{4}{-3}, \frac{7}{-1}, \frac{-3}{+2}$$

all name negative rational numbers;

$$\frac{0}{3}, \frac{0}{-1}, \frac{0}{5}, \frac{0}{-7}, \frac{0}{-9}, \frac{0}{6}$$

all name the rational number zero.

The set of rational numbers may be separated into three disjoint sub-sets:

1. The positive rational numbers
2. The negative rational numbers
3. Zero.

The rational number (a, b) is said to be *less than* the rational number (c, d) if and only if there exists a positive rational number (e, f), such that

$$(a, b) + (e, f) = (c, d).$$

Using the fractional symbol for the rational number, we see that

$$\frac{a}{b} < \frac{c}{d}$$

if and only if there exists a positive rational number named by $\frac{e}{f}$ such that

$$\frac{a}{b} + \frac{e}{f} = \frac{c}{d}.$$

Notice that

$$\frac{3}{5} < \frac{4}{5} \quad \text{because} \quad \frac{3}{5} + \frac{1}{5} = \frac{4}{5},$$

$$\frac{-2}{-5} < \frac{3}{5} \quad \text{because} \quad \frac{-2}{-5} + \frac{1}{5} = \frac{3}{5},$$

$$\frac{2}{3} < \frac{3}{4} \quad \text{because} \quad \frac{2}{3} + \frac{1}{12} = \frac{3}{4},$$

$$\frac{-7}{8} < 0 \quad \text{because} \quad \frac{-7}{8} + \frac{7}{8} = 0,$$

$$\frac{-1}{2} < \frac{-1}{3} \quad \text{because} \quad \frac{-1}{2} + \frac{1}{6} = \frac{-1}{3}.$$

Every rational number may be named by a fraction that has a positive denominator. Notice that

$$\frac{2}{-3} = \frac{-2}{3},$$

$$\frac{-2}{-3} = \frac{2}{3},$$

$$\frac{0}{-3} = \frac{0}{3}.$$

Since this is true we have another method for determining whether a given rational number is less than another rational number. If $\frac{a}{b}$ and $\frac{c}{d}$ are rational numbers named by fractions with positive denominators, then

1. $\frac{a}{b} > \frac{c}{d}$ if $ad > bc,$

2. $\frac{a}{b} = \frac{c}{d}$ if $ad = bc,$

3. $\frac{a}{b} < \frac{c}{d}$ if $ad < bc.$

For example,

$$\frac{2}{3} > \frac{3}{5} \quad \text{because} \quad 2 \cdot 5 > 3 \cdot 3,$$

$$\frac{-2}{7} < \frac{9}{3} \quad \text{because} \quad (-2)(3) < (9)(7).$$

We observe that every positive rational number is greater than zero.

$$\frac{+2}{+3} > \frac{0}{+3} \quad \text{because} \quad (+2)(+3) > (+3)(0) = 0$$

$$\frac{+9}{+7} > \frac{0}{+4} \quad \text{because} \quad (+9)(+4) > (+7)(0) = 0$$

$$\frac{+a}{+b} > \frac{0}{+b} \quad \text{because} \quad (+a)(+b) > (+b)(0) = 0$$

Every negative rational number is less than zero.

$$\frac{-3}{+4} < \frac{0}{+4} \quad \text{because} \quad (-3)(+4) < (+4)(0) = 0$$

$$\frac{-6}{+2} < \frac{0}{+3} \quad \text{because} \quad (+3)(-6) < (+2)(0) = 0$$

12.5. SUBTRACTION AND DIVISION OF RATIONAL NUMBERS

Since subtraction is the inverse of the operation of addition, we define $(a, b) - (c, d)$ to be the rational number (e, f) such that $(c, d) + (e, f) = (a, b)$. Since every rational number has an additive inverse, subtraction is always possible, as it was for the set of integers. In fact, subtracting a rational number is the same as adding its additive inverse (see Chapter 11). Thus

$$\frac{2}{3} - \frac{1}{3} = \frac{2}{3} + \frac{-1}{3} = \frac{1}{3},$$

$$\frac{3}{4} - \frac{-2}{4} = \frac{3}{4} + \frac{2}{4} = \frac{5}{4},$$

$$\frac{-1}{8} - \frac{-3}{8} = \frac{-1}{8} + \frac{3}{8} = \frac{2}{8}.$$

Division is the inverse operation of multiplication. We define $(a, b) \div (c, d), c \neq 0$, as the rational number (e, f), such that $(c, d) \cdot (e, f) = (a, b)$. Since every rational number except zero has a multiplicative inverse, it is always possible to divide one rational number by another, except, of course, that division by zero is impossible. In fact, dividing by a rational number is the same as multiplying by its multiplicative inverse (see Chapter 10). For example,

$$\frac{2}{3} \div \frac{1}{2} = \frac{2}{3} \cdot \frac{2}{1} = \frac{4}{3},$$

$$\frac{-3}{4} \div \frac{-1}{2} = \frac{-3}{4} \cdot \frac{-2}{1} = \frac{6}{4},$$

$$\frac{3}{8} \div \frac{-1}{3} = \frac{3}{8} \cdot \frac{-3}{1} = \frac{-9}{8}.$$

12.6. THE RATIONAL NUMBER LINE

The number line helps to clarify the meaning of rational numbers and exhibit their order relation.

Figure 12.1 shows a portion of the rational number line on which it is clearly indicated that both integers and fractional numbers correspond to rational numbers.

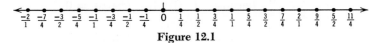

Figure 12.1

For example,

$$-1 \leftrightarrow \frac{-1}{1}$$

$$-2 \leftrightarrow \frac{-2}{1}$$

$$\frac{1}{4} \leftrightarrow \frac{+1}{+4}$$

It is apparent from the rational number line that every rational number has an opposite. That is, every rational number has an additive inverse. The additive inverse of $\frac{1}{4}$ is $\frac{-1}{4}$, the additive inverse of $\frac{-2}{3}$ is $\frac{2}{3}$. If $\frac{a}{b}$ is any rational number, its additive inverse is $\frac{-a}{b}$ or $\frac{a}{-b}$ or $-\frac{a}{b}$.

EXERCISE 12.3

1. Rewrite each of the following sets as ordered sets.

 a. $\left\{ \frac{-3}{4}, \frac{5}{6}, \frac{-4}{5}, \frac{9}{4} \right\}$

 b. $\left\{ \frac{-1}{8}, \frac{3}{4}, \frac{5}{6}, \frac{-7}{16}, \frac{-9}{2} \right\}$

2. Of the following pairs of rational numbers, which is the greater in each pair?

 a. $\frac{1}{2}, \frac{-3}{4}$ b. $\frac{5}{6}, \frac{-5}{8}$

 c. $\frac{-17}{9}, \frac{-18}{7}$ d. $\frac{-1}{3}, \frac{-5}{8}$

 e. $\frac{-3}{4}, \frac{-5}{9}$ f. $\frac{-1}{1}, \frac{-3}{1}$

3. If a and b are rational numbers with $a < 0$ and $b < 0$, is $ab > 0$, or is $ab < 0$?
4. If a and b are rational numbers with $a > b$ and $c < 0$, is $ca > cb$, or is $ca < cb$?
5. If a and b are rational numbers with $a < 0$ and $b > 0$, is $ab < 0$, or is $ab > 0$?
6. If r is a rational number and $r < 0$, is $r^2 > 0$, or is $r^2 < 0$?
7. Which of the following are true statements?
 a. For every rational number y, $y < 2y$.
 b. For all rational numbers a, b, and c, if $a > 0$ and $b = c + a$, then $b > c$.
 c. For every rational number a, $a^2 > 0$

    d. For every two rational numbers a and b, exactly one of the following statements is true: $a > b$, $a = b$, or $a < b$.

8. Find the solution sets of the following sentences.

    a. $n + \dfrac{1}{2} = \dfrac{1}{3}$ b. $n + \dfrac{5}{6} = \dfrac{3}{8}$

    c. $\dfrac{2}{3} - n = \dfrac{5}{8}$ d. $n - \dfrac{2}{5} = \dfrac{3}{4}$

    e. $\dfrac{-7}{8} \cdot n = \dfrac{2}{3}$ f. $\dfrac{-2}{3} \cdot n = \dfrac{7}{8}$

    g. $n \div \dfrac{-5}{3} = \dfrac{-3}{5}$ h. $\dfrac{3}{4} \div n = \dfrac{3}{16}$

12.7. THE PROPERTIES OF THE RATIONAL NUMBERS

We summarize the properties of the rational numbers in Table 12.1, with r, s, and t denoting rational numbers.

Table 12.1
Properties of Addition and Multiplication of Rational Numbers

Addition	Multiplication
1. Closure If r and s are rational numbers, then $r + s$ is a unique rational number.	If r and s are rational numbers, then rs is a unique rational number.
2. Commutativity If r and s are any rational numbers, then $$r + s = s + r.$$	If r and s are any rational numbers, then $$rs = sr.$$
3. Associativity If r, s, and t are any rational numbers, then $$(r + s) + t = r + (s + t)$$	If r, s, and t are any rational numbers, then $$(rs)\,t = r\,(st)$$
4. Additive and Multiplicative Identities An element 0 exists so that for any r $$r + 0 = 0 + r = r$$	An element 1 exists such that for any r $$r \cdot 1 = 1 \cdot r = r.$$
5. Additive and Multiplicative Inverses For every r there exists an element r such that $$r + {}^-r = {}^-r + r = 0$$	For every r, $r \neq 0$, there exists an element $\dfrac{1}{r}$ such that $$r \cdot \dfrac{1}{r} = \dfrac{1}{r} \cdot r = 1$$
6. Distributive Property: For every r, s, and t $r(s + t) = rs + rt$ and $(s + t)r = sr + tr$.	

12.8. SUBSYSTEMS OF THE RATIONAL NUMBERS

All the numbers of arithmetic may be studied from two different aspects, the first of which approaches numbers as mathematical ideas applicable to certain counting situations. We saw one illustration of this in our study of the whole numbers viewed as the cardinal numbers associated with the elements in a set. From the second aspect numbers may be examined as mathematical objects whose properties are studied independently of their origin or their use in counting. This is a more abstract approach and harder to understand. When we view numbers as mathematical objects their properties depend upon certain defined relations and operations that can be performed on them. These relations are the order properties, and the operations are addition, subtraction, multiplication and division. We viewed the rational numbers in this way.

When any set of numbers are observed as mathematical objects, they form a *number system*. So far we have considered three number systems: the whole numbers, the integers, and the rational numbers.

There are certain differences among these number systems, of which the most important concern the inverse operations of subtraction and division. The set of whole numbers is closed under the operations of addition and multiplication but not under the operations of subtraction and division. The set of integers is closed under addition, multiplication and subtraction but not division. Finally, the set of rational numbers is closed under addition, multiplication, subtraction, and, except for zero, division.

Both the set of rational numbers and the set of integers are extensions of the set of whole numbers. Hence they may be thought of as including the whole number system. In the case of integers, the whole numbers may be identified with the non-negative integers. In the case of rational numbers, they may be identified with the non-negative rational numbers with the denominator of one. The relationship of these three number systems is shown in Figure 12.2.

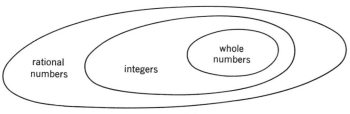

Figure 12.2

12.9. THE NUMBER FIELD

The set of rational numbers together with the operations of addition and multiplication and their properties is called by mathematicians, a *number field* or simply a *field*.

Any set of elements in which an addition and a multiplication is defined (it may be different from ordinary addition and multiplication) and having all the properties listed in Table 12.1 is a *field*. In Chapter 14, Mathematical Systems, we shall study other examples of fields. Of the many fields of mathematics, the field of rational numbers, called the rational field, is the most important in elementary arithmetic.

EXERCISE 12.4

1. Under what operations is the set of rational numbers closed?
2. Is the set of rational numbers dense?
3. Define a mathematical field.
4. Which of the following sets and the operations of addition and multiplication are mathematical fields?

    a. $\{0, 1, 2, \ldots\}$
    b. {rational numbers}
    c. $\{\cdots, -3, -2, -1, 0, 1, 2, 3, \cdots\}$

5. What is the additive identity for the set of rational numbers?
6. Which element in the set of rational numbers does not have a reciprocal?
7. Why is the operation of subtraction closed for the set of rational numbers?

CHAPTER 13

Real Numbers

13.1. FURTHER EXTENSION OF THE NUMBER SYSTEM

Although the rational number system is sufficient for most purposes of elementary arithmetic, in geometry and algebra and other branches of mathematics there is a need for another kind of number. We meet this need by an extension of the rational number system to one called the *real number system.*

The simplest examples of numbers which are not rational numbers are square roots such as $\sqrt{2}$, $\sqrt{5}$, $\sqrt{7}$, and $\sqrt{56}$. If $2^2 = 4$, then 2 is called the *square root* of 4. We use the radical sign, $\sqrt{}$, to show this relationship and write $\sqrt{4} = 2$. Some square roots are rational numbers, such as

$$\sqrt{9} = 3,$$
$$\sqrt{\tfrac{1}{4}} = \tfrac{1}{2},$$

but there are many numbers such as 2 which do not have a rational number as a square root. We can prove that $\sqrt{2}$ is not a rational number by the following:

THEOREM. There exists no rational number whose square is 2. That is, $\sqrt{2}$ is not a rational number.

To prove this theorem we shall use an indirect proof.

PROOF. Let $\dfrac{a}{b}$ represent a rational number expressed as a fraction in simplest form; that is, a and b are relatively prime.

Let us assume that

$$2 = \frac{a^2}{b^2}.$$

then $2b^2 = a^2$. Now since $2b^2 = a^2$, a^2 must be an even number, and therefore a must be an even number, because if it were odd, a^2 would be odd.

Since all even numbers may be written in the form $2n$, let $a = 2n$. If we agree that

$$a^2 = (2n)(2n) = 2(2n^2),$$

then,

$$2b^2 = 2(2n^2), \text{ or } b^2 = 2n^2 = 2m.$$

Hence b^2 is even, and b is even. Therefore we may conclude that a and b are both even and have a common factor 2.

However, this contradicts our assumption that $\frac{a}{b}$ is in simplest form and thus $\sqrt{2}$ cannot be represented as a rational number.

13.2. THE REAL NUMBER LINE

We have showed that the non-negative rational numbers are dense; that is, between any two of them there are infinitely many others. This is also true for all the rational numbers.

From this it follows that there are infinitely many rational numbers, and corresponding to them on the number line, infinitely many rational points. These points are spread throughout the number line. Any segment of the number line, no matter how small, contains infinitely many rational points. This might lead us to the conclusion that every point on the number line is a rational point. This is not so, for there are many points on the line that are not rational points. These points are called *irrational points* and correspond to numbers called *irrational numbers*.

We can show that there is at least one point on the number line that is not a rational point.

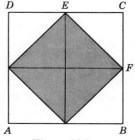

Figure 13.1

Figure 13.1 shows a square, *ABCD*, whose side is two units long. The area of this square region is four square units. The shaded square region is one half of the square region *ABCD*. Hence its area is two square units. Each of its sides is therefore $\sqrt{2}$ units in length.

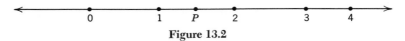

Figure 13.2

We lay off a segment congruent to $\overline{EF}$, the side of the shaded square, from 0 on the number line in Figure 13.2 to a point *P*. This point corresponds to $\sqrt{2}$. Since we know that $\sqrt{2}$ is not a rational number we see that there is at least one point on the number line which is not a graph of a rational point.

13.3. IRRATIONAL NUMBERS

The explanation of these so-called "holes" in the number line (that is, points that are not rational points) is not easy to understand. We have shown that at least one of the points on the number line which does not correspond to a rational number is the graph of the irrational number $\sqrt{2}$. We shall not attempt to show that all the others are graphs of other irrational numbers but simply state that the numbers represented by these gaps are called irrational numbers.

The irrational numbers have a misleading name; irrational in this case does not mean unreasonable but merely "not rational." Some irrational numbers are

$$\sqrt{2}, \sqrt{3}, 5 + \sqrt{7}, \pi.$$

All the points on the number line fall into two nonempty sets: the set of points that are rational points and the set of points that are irrational points.

13.4. THE REAL NUMBERS

The union of the set of rational numbers and the set of irrational numbers is called the set of *real numbers*. Every point on the number line is associated with either a rational number or an irrational number. Hence every point on the number line is associated with a real number and is called the *real number line*.

Having now filled all the gaps in the line, we say that the real number line is not only dense, but continuous. A geometric line may now be interpreted in terms of the real numbers. There is a one-to-one correspondance between the points on the line and the real numbers.

The real number system is an extension of the rational number system. It is used extensively in algebra, trigonometry, and in the calculus and its applications.

EXERCISE 13.1

1. What is the union of the set of rational numbers and the set of irrational numbers?

2. Which of the following are names for irrational numbers?

    a. 7.   b. $\sqrt{5}$.   c. π.   d. $3 + \sqrt{16}$.
    e. $\sqrt{9}$.   f. $5 + \sqrt{2}$.   g. $\sqrt{144}$.   h. 2π.

3. If n is any rational number, is n^2 always a rational number? Why?

4. If n is any irrational number, is n^2 always an irrational number?

5. Show that there is no rational number whose square is 3. That is, show that $\sqrt{3}$ is an irrational number.

   Which of the following are true?

6. The set of rational numbers and the set of irrational numbers are disjoint sets.

7. The intersection of the set of rational numbers and the set of irrational numbers is the set of real numbers.

8. If n is any whole number, then $\sqrt{n}$ is an irrational number.

9. The set of irrational numbers is a subset of the set of real numbers.

10. Every rational number is a real number.

11. Every real number is an irrational number.

   Write the converse of the following true implications. Is the converse true or false?

12. If r is a rational number, then it is a real number.

13. If r is an irrational number, then it is a real number.

14. If a is a rational number, then a^2 is a rational number.

15. If $\sqrt{2}$ were a rational number, then it could be represented by $\frac{a}{b}$ where a and b are integers and $b \neq 0$.

CHAPTER **14**

Mathematical Systems

14.1. FINITE SYSTEMS

A *mathematical system* is any nonempty set of elements together with one or more operations defined on the elements of the set. We have studied several mathematical systems: (1) the system of whole numbers and the operations of addition and multiplication; (2) the system of integers and their operations; (3) the system of rational numbers and their operations. All of these systems were infinite systems. We shall now study some mathematical systems that are *finite systems*; that is, the number of elements in the set of the system is finite.

A particular finite system, called a *modular system*, results from the use of a numeration system similar to that of the hours on a clock face.

For simplicity, let us examine such a system by using the five-hour clock shown in Figure 14.1. This clock resembles a timer; the numbers in its system are 0, 1, 2, 3, and 4. Counting in this system repeats these numbers over and over: 1, 2, 3, 4, 0, 1, 2, 3, 4, 0, 1, 2, 3, 4, $\cdots$. We shall now define the operations of this system.

Addition

The addition of $2 + 1$ is defined thus: the hand on the clock starts at 0; it travels two spaces in a clockwise direction, and then it travels one

258

Figure 14.1

more space in a clockwise direction. Thus $2 + 1 = 3$. Using this definition of addition we see that

$$2 + 3 = 0,$$
$$4 + 3 = 2,$$
$$3 + 3 = 1.$$

An addition chart for this system, called a *modulo-five system,* is shown in Table 14.1.

Table 14.1

+	0	1	2	3	4
0	0	1	2	3	4
1	1	2	3	4	0
2	2	3	4	0	1
3	3	4	0	1	2
4	4	0	1	2	3

From this addition table we can see the following: (1) the operation of addition in the modulo-five system is commutative since for any numbers a and b in the system, $a + b = b + a$; (2) there is an identity element, 0, for addition since for any number a, $a + 0 = 0 + a = a$; (3) the set of numbers is closed under addition. Every element a has an additive inverse since

$$0 + 0 = 0,$$
$$2 + 3 = 0,$$
$$4 + 1 = 0.$$

It is less obvious, but it can be proved, that addition is also associative.

Study the following statements to convince yourself of the associativity of addition:

$$(2 + 3) + 4 = 2 + (3 + 4)$$
$$0 + 4 = 2 + 2$$
$$4 = 4,$$
$$(3 + 4) + 4 = 3 + (4 + 4)$$
$$2 + 4 = 3 + 3$$
$$1 = 1.$$

Multiplication

For the modulo-five system we shall define 2×3 thus: the hand of the clock starts at 0 and travels three spaces in a clockwise direction, then it travels three more spaces. Thus $2 \times 3 = 1$; that is, 2×3 means two turns of three spaces on each turn. Thus

$2 \times 4 = 3,$ (two clockwise turns of four spaces each turn),
$3 \times 4 = 2,$ (three clockwise turns of four spaces each turn),
$4 \times 4 = 1,$ (four clockwise turns of four spaces each turn).

A multiplication chart for the modulo-five system is shown in Table 14.2.

Table 14.2

$\times$	0	1	2	3	4
0	0	0	0	0	0
1	0	1	2	3	4
2	0	2	4	1	3
3	0	3	1	4	2
4	0	4	3	2	1

Studying the multiplication chart for the modulo-five system we discover the following: (1) multiplication is commutative since for any numbers a and b, $a \times b = b \times a$; (2) there is an identity element, 1, since for any number a, $a \times 1 = 1 \times a = a$; (3) the set of elements is closed under multiplication. Every element, except the additive identity, 0, has a multiplicative inverse:

$$3 \times 2 = 1,$$
$$4 \times 4 = 1,$$
$$1 \times 1 = 1.$$

Again, it is less obvious, but it can be proved, that multiplication is associative. The following examples should help convince you of the associativity of multiplication:

$$(2 \times 3) \times 4 = 2 \times (3 \times 4)$$
$$1 \times 4 = 2 \times 2$$
$$4 = 4,$$
$$(3 \times 3) \times 4 = 3 \times (3 \times 4)$$
$$4 \times 4 = 3 \times 2$$
$$1 = 1.$$

That multiplication is also distributive over addition in this system is shown in the following examples:

$$2 \times (3 + 4) = (2 \times 3) + (2 \times 4)$$
$$2 \times 2 = 1 + 3$$
$$4 = 4,$$
$$3 \times (4 + 1) = (3 \times 4) + (3 \times 1)$$
$$3 \times 0 = 2 + 3$$
$$0 = 0,$$
$$4 \times (3 + 3) = (4 \times 3) + (4 \times 3)$$
$$4 \times 1 = 2 + 2$$
$$4 = 4.$$

Try some other examples to convince yourself that the distributive property holds for this system.

After the addition and multiplication charts have been constructed, we no longer need the clock, and can study the properties of this system by observing the operation tables.

Subtraction

Using the addition chart (Table 14.1) we can observe the properties of subtraction in this system. Defining subtraction as the inverse of a addition, that is $a - b = c$ means $b + c = a$, we know that $2 - 3 = n$ means $n + 3 = 2$. Since $4 + 3 = 2$, $2 - 3 = 4$. What is the additive inverse of 3? Since $3 + 2 = 0$, the additive inverse of 3 is 2. Notice that

$$2 - 3 = 4,$$

and

$$2 + 2 = 4.$$

Subtracting a number in this system is the same as adding its additive inverse. Since each element in the system has an additive inverse, we see that the modulo-five system is closed under subtraction.

Division

Defining division as the inverse of multiplication, that is, $a \div b = c$, $b \neq 0$, means $b \times c = a$, we know that

$$2 \div 3 = n \text{ means } n \times 3 = 2.$$

Since $4 \times 3 = 2$, $2 \div 3 = 4$. What is the multiplicative inverse of 3? Since $3 \times 2 = 1$, the multiplicative inverse of 3 is 2. Notice that

$$2 \div 3 = 4,$$
$$2 \times 2 = 4.$$

Dividing by any number, except zero, in this system is the same as multiplying by its multiplicative inverse. Since each element, except zero, has a multiplicative inverse, we see that the modulo-five system is closed under division except by zero.

EXERCISE 14.1

1. In the modulo-five system, what is the identity for multiplication; for addition?

2. Does every element in the modulo-five system have a multiplicative inverse? Which do? Which do not?

3. In the modulo-five system does each element have an additive inverse?

4. Using the modulo-five system find the solutions of the following sentences.

a. $n + 4 = 3$.   b. $2 + 3 = n$.
c. $2n - 3 = 4$.   d. $4n + 2 = 3$.
e. $4 + n = 2$.   f. $0 + n = 3$.

5. Using a seven-hour clock, construct an addition and a multiplication table for a modulo-seven system.

6. Is addition commutative in the modulo-seven system?

7. What is the additive identity in the modulo-seven system?

8. In the modulo-seven system what is the additive inverse of

a. 6?   b. 3?   c. 2?   d. 5?

9. Are the following statements true? Would you guess that the operation of multiplication is associative in the modulo-seven system?

a. $(3 \times 4) \times 5 = 3 \times (4 \times 5)$.
b. $(2 \times 5) \times 3 = 2 \times (5 \times 3)$.
c. $(5 \times 5) \times 6 = 5 \times (5 \times 6)$.

10. In the modulo-seven system which of the following statements are true?

a. $3 \times (4 + 5) = (3 \times 4) + (3 \times 5)$.
b. $6 \times (2 + 4) = (6 \times 2) + (6 \times 4)$.
c. $5 \times (2 + 6) = (5 \times 2) + (5 \times 6)$.

11. What do the answers in problem 10 suggest in regard to the distributive property for the modulo-seven system?

12. On a regular twelve-hour clock, what time is it?

a. Four hours after 10:00 P.M.
b. Eight hours after 5 A.M.
c. Ten hours after 11:00 P.M.
d. Nine hours after 7:00 A.M.

13. Using a four-hour clock, construct a multiplication table for the modulo-four system.

14. In the modulo-four system find

a. 2×2.   b. 3×2.   c. 1×3.

15. In the modulo-four system which of the elements in addition to zero do not have a multiplicative inverse?

14.2. SYSTEMS WITHOUT NUMBERS

It is possible to have a mathematical system in which the elements of the system are not numbers at all, nor are the usual symbols denoting the operations, $+$, $\times$, $-$, and $\div$ necessary. For example, we may use symbols such as $\triangle$, *, $\varnothing$, or $\odot$ to represent the operation. In fact, we may replace the ordinary symbol, $+$, by $\odot$ without changing the addition result, just as long as the definition of the operation denoted by the symbol remains unchanged. Thus if $+$ and $\odot$ were said to represent ordinary addition, both $6 + 9$ and $6 \odot 9$ would equal 15 for the set of counting numbers. Let

$$E = \{0, 2, 4, 6, \cdots\},$$

and

$$O = \{1, 3, 5, 7, \cdots\},$$

and the symbol * mean the addition of two elements from these sets; an operation table from this system is shown in Table 14.3. Notice that the elements of this system are E and O, where E and O are sets of numbers.

Table 14.3

*	E	O
E	E	O
O	O	E

We know that $E * E = E$ because the sum of two even numbers is an even number (see Chapter 8). Similarly, we know that $E * O = O$ because the sum of an even number and an odd number is an odd number. Also, $O * O = E$ because the sum of two odd numbers is an even number.

Is the operation, *, commutative over the set $\{E, O\}$? As we examine the operation table we see that $E * O = O * E$. Of course, $E * E = E * E$, and $O * O = O * O$. Since we have examined all the possibilities, we conclude that the operation is commutative.

Is there an identity element? We observe that

$$E * E = E,$$
$$O * E = O,$$
$$E * O = O.$$

Combining the element E with any element in the system always gives the element with which E was combined by the operation. Hence E is the identity element.

We can also test this operation for associativity. Since there are only two elements in the system, it is simple to try all the possibilities. Notice one example:

$$(E * O) * E = E * (O * E)$$
$$O * E = E * O$$
$$O = O.$$

Examining all possibilities we find that the operation is associative. Is there an inverse element for each element? Notice that

$$E * E = E,$$
$$O * O = E,$$

Hence every element is its own inverse.

Now let us consider a purely abstract system. Suppose the elements of our system are the elements of the set

$$S = \{ \ominus, \diamondsuit, \triangle, \square \}.$$

Let the operation $\odot$ be defined by Table 14.4.

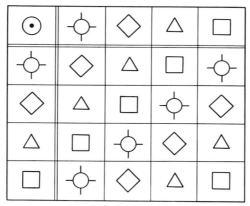

Table 14.4

Notice that this operation table is symmetric with respect to the diagonal from the upper left to the lower right. Perhaps you have already discovered that if an operation table is symmetric about this diagonal, then the operation is commutative. This is easily explained. Find $\triangle \odot \square$. We find $\triangle \odot \square$ in the third row and the fourth column. Now we find $\square \odot \triangle$ in the fourth row and the third column. We see that they are across the diagonal from each other. We say that they are *reflections* of each other. If this is true for each pair of elements, then the upper half of the table must be just like the lower half. If we folded the table along the diagonal the two halves would match. This is an easy way to tell whether or not an operation is commutative.

Study the table and discover whether the set is closed under the operation and whether there is an identity element. Obviously, the identity element is $\square$.

Check several examples to see whether or not the associative property holds.

Does every element have an inverse?

EXERCISE 14.2

Study the following operation tables. Then answer the questions below.

Table A

+	1	2	3	4	5
1	2	3	4	5	1
2	3	4	5	1	2
3	4	5	1	2	3
4	5	1	2	3	4
5	1	2	3	4	5

Table B

*	X	Y
X	X	Y
Y	X	Y

Table C

$\odot$	a	b	c	d
a	a	b	c	d
b	b	c	d	a
c	c	d	a	b
d	d	a	b	c

Table D

$\boxtimes$	R_0	R_1	R_2	R_3
R_0	R_2	R_3	R_0	R_1
R_1	R_3	R_2	R_1	R_0
R_2	R_0	R_1	R_2	R_3
R_3	R_1	R_0	R_3	R_2

1. Use the tables above to find

   a. $5 + 5$ b. $R_1 \boxtimes R_3$ c. $X * X$
   d. $b.c$ e. $2 + 4$ f. $a.d$
   g. $(5 + 2) + 3$ h. $(R_1 \boxtimes R_2) \boxtimes R_0$
   i. $(a.b).c$ j. $(Y * X) * Y$
   k. $R_1 \boxtimes (R_2 \boxtimes R_3)$ l. $a.(c.d)$

2. Which of the operations defined by the tables above are commutative?
3. Is the operation defined in Table B associative?
4. Is the operation defined in Table A associative?
5. What is the identity for the operation defined in

   a. Table A?   b. Table C?   c. Table D?

6. Given the set $S = \{\triangle, \square, \wedge, \vee\}$ and the operation $*$ defined by the table below, answer the following questions:

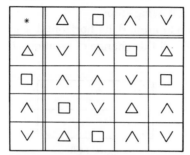

   a. Is the set closed under the operation?
   b. Is there an identity element? What is it?
   c. What is the inverse of $\square$?
   d. What is the inverse of $\wedge$?
   e. Does every element have an inverse?
   f. Is the operation commutative?

14.3. A MATHEMATICAL GROUP

The study of groups is a relatively new field of mathematics. A mathematical *group* is a mathematical system. It is defined as a set of elements with a given binary operation which has the following properties:

1. The set is closed under the operation.
2. There is an identity element.
3. The operation is associative.
4. There is an inverse element for each member of the set.

The modulo-five system and the operation of addition form a group. Since this system is also commutative, it is called a *commutative group*.

Some very interesting groups can be developed through movement of objects. Consider the rectangle in Figure 14.2.

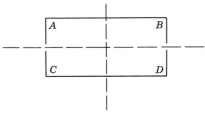

Figure 14.2

The elements of our set shall be the movements of the rectangle which are described in the following steps:

1. Turn the rectangle around its horizontal axis, so that it looks like Figure 14.3. We shall call this change of position "*H.*"

Figure 14.3

2. Put the rectangle back in its original position. Now turn it around its vertical axis; it will look like Figure 14.4. We shall call this movement "*V.*"

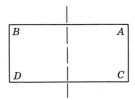

Figure 14.4

3. Put the rectangle back in its original position. Now rotate it half way around in a clockwise direction; it will look like Figure 14.5. We shall call this rotation "*R.*"

Figure 14.5

4. Put the rectangle back in its original position. Rotate it completely around to its original position; it will look like Figure 14.6. This rotation shall be called "*I*."

Figure 14.6

The four movements *H*, *V*, *R*, and *I* leave the rectangle just like it was at the beginning except that the letters in the corners have changed position. We now have a set of movements $\{I, R, H, V\}$ which will be the elements of our system.

We shall now define an operation * upon these elements. We define $H * V$ as meaning we perform movement *H* and follow it by movement *V*. (A good way to perform these operations is to use a cardboard rectangular region and do the actual movements with it. Be sure that you put the letters in the corners on both sides of the card.)

We are now ready to construct the operation table (Table 14.5).

Table 14.5
Second Movement

First Movement

*	I	R	V	H
I	I	R	V	H
R	R	I	H	V
V	V	H	I	R
H	H	V	R	I

The elements in the left column of the table represent the first movement of the operation; those in the top row represent the second movement.

We now ask ourselves, is this system a group? We see from examination of the table that there is closure; every result of an operation is a member of the set of elements of the system. There is an identity element, I, since

$$R * I = R, \quad I * R = R,$$
$$V * I = V, \quad I * V = V,$$
$$H * I = H, \quad I * H = H.$$

Let us check for associativity:

$$(R * V) * H = R * (V * H)$$
$$H * H = R * R$$
$$I = I,$$
$$(V * V) * H = V * (V * H)$$
$$I * H = V * R$$
$$H = H.$$

Although we have not checked all the possibilities, it can be proved that this operation is associative.

Does every element have an inverse? Since

$$I * I = I,$$
$$V * V = I,$$
$$H * H = I,$$
$$R * R = I,$$

we conclude that every element is its own inverse.

Since there are closure, associativity, identity element, and an inverse for every element, we conclude that this system is a group.

Since the operation table is symmetric about the diagonal, the operation is commutative and the system is a commutative group.

14.4. A NONCOMMUTATIVE GROUP

All of the groups that we have studied have been commutative groups. Now let us study a group that is noncommutative, using the following example:

A professor had three graduate assistants. He was anxious that each assistant should have experience teaching algebra, trigonometry and calculus. The three students, Ross, Smith, and Taggart, were each assigned to a particular class which was considered to be his own. Each was to teach his own class for one week. The next week Ross was to take Smith's class, Smith was to take Taggart's class, and Taggart was to take Ross's class. These changes were made by the professor by the following diagram which he placed on the bulletin board outside his office door.

$$\begin{bmatrix} R & S & T \\ T & R & S \end{bmatrix}$$

The top row of letters represented Ross (R), Smith (S), and Taggart (T). The letter under R was T; this meant that Taggart was to teach Ross's class. Similarly, the R under the S meant that Ross was to teach Smith's class, and the S under the T meant that Smith was to teach Taggart's class.

Each week the professor hung a similar diagram on the bulletin board. The rotating of classes was to continue all semester, and the three students soon began to guess which class each would be teaching the following week. It was not long before they found out that there were only six possibilities.

$$I = \begin{bmatrix} R & S & T \\ R & S & T \end{bmatrix} \qquad X = \begin{bmatrix} R & S & T \\ S & T & R \end{bmatrix} \qquad Y = \begin{bmatrix} R & S & T \\ S & R & T \end{bmatrix}$$

$$Z = \begin{bmatrix} R & S & T \\ T & S & R \end{bmatrix} \qquad W = \begin{bmatrix} R & S & T \\ R & T & S \end{bmatrix} \qquad V = \begin{bmatrix} R & S & T \\ T & R & S \end{bmatrix}$$

As the weeks passed the professor decided to have a little fun with the students and indicated their class assignments as follows: ZX. This meant that the students were to find the final result (called a product) by first performing arrangement Z, then arrangement X. Similarly WY meant teaching that class assignment which resulted from doing arrangement W, followed by arrangement Y. Thus, to figure the week's teaching assignment for ZX, the students reasoned as follows: ZX means

$$\begin{bmatrix} R & S & T \\ T & S & R \end{bmatrix} \quad \cdot \quad \begin{bmatrix} R & S & T \\ S & T & R \end{bmatrix}$$

(perform Z, then perform X). In assignment Z, T replaces R, R replaces T and S keeps the same assignment. The result of this assignment would be charted as

$$R \quad S \quad T$$
$$T \quad S \quad R \ .$$

Now X must be performed. In X, S replaces R, T replaces S, and R replaces R. Thus ZX would mean performing Z, then performing X. The steps in this product are the following:

1. $ZX = \begin{bmatrix} R & S & T \\ T & S & R \end{bmatrix} \ \cdot \ \begin{bmatrix} R & S & T \\ S & T & R \end{bmatrix} \ .$

2. Performing Z: $\begin{bmatrix} R & S & T \\ T & S & R \end{bmatrix} \ .$

3. Performing X, we must replace in the result of Z, R by S, S by T, and T by R; hence we could make a diagram

$$R \quad S \quad T$$
$$T \quad S \quad R$$
$$R \quad T \quad S$$

4. The final result is

$$\begin{bmatrix} R & S & T \\ R & T & S \end{bmatrix} \ .$$

But this is assignment W. Hence $ZX = W$.

The students decided that they could save a lot of time, which they could certainly use for study, by constructing an operation table for their teaching assignments. This operation table is shown in Table 14.6.

Table 14.6

Second Assignment

		I	X	Y	Z	W	V
First Assignment	I	I	X	Y	Z	W	V
	X	X	V	W	Y	Z	I
	Y	Y	Z	I	X	V	W
	Z	Z	W	V	I	X	Y
	W	W	Y	X	V	I	Z
	V	V	I	Z	W	Y	X

The set of elements, $\{I, X, Y, Z, W, V\}$ and the operation defined by Table 14.6 give us a mathematical system. We now ask ourselves the following questions:

1. Is the set closed under the operation?
2. Is there an identity element: What is it?
3. Is the operation associative?
4. Does every element have an inverse?

To check the associative property we must examine all possibilities of the product of three elements of the system. For example,

$$(WY)Z = W(YZ),$$
$$XZ = WX,$$
$$Y = Y,$$
$$(VW)X = V(WX),$$
$$YX = VY,$$
$$Z = Z.$$

After studying other possibilities would you guess that the operation is associative?

For every two elements of the set there is one and only one result which is also an element of the set. Since this is true, the set is closed under the operation.

Is there an identity element? Observe that

$$IX = X, \qquad XI = X,$$
$$IY = Y, \qquad YI = Y,$$
$$IZ = Z, \qquad ZI = Z,$$
$$IW = W, \qquad WI = W.$$

We see therefore that I is the identity element.

Does every element in the system have an inverse? Notice that

$$VX = XV = I,$$
$$YY = I,$$
$$ZZ = I,$$
$$WW = I.$$

Hence we see that every element has an inverse.

We can now conclude that this system is a group. Is it a commutative group? Notice that

$$XZ = Y \quad \text{and} \quad ZX = W.$$

Since $Y \neq W$, this is not a commutative group.

EXERCISE 14.3

1. Construct a mathematical system for the movements of an isosceles triangle. There will be two movements: (1) a turn around the vertical axis (call it V), and (2) no turn at all (call it I). What properties does this system have?

2. Construct a mathematical system for the movements of an equilateral triangle. Make a triangle and label the vertices as shown in the figure. There will be six movements. There will be three rotations about the axes (dotted lines in the figure) and three rotations in a clockwise direction, one of 120°, one of 240°, and one of 360°. List the properties of this system.

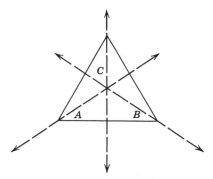

3. Make an operation table for the eight movements of the square. Four of them will be rotations (clockwise) of 90°, 180°, 270°, and 360°. The other four will be rotations around the vertical axis, the horizontal axis, and the two diagonals. Is this system a group? Is it a commutative group?

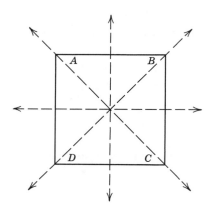

4. Is the system defined by the operation table below a group? Give reasons for your answer.

$*$	a	b	c	d
a	a	b	c	d
b	b	a	d	c
c	c	b	d	c
d	d	c	b	b

5. Use Table 14.6, section 14.4, and compute

   a. $(XY)Z$ b. $(YX)V$ g. $(ZX)(WV)$

6. A finite mathematical system can be created involving the rotation of the four tires on an automobile. Let the symbol of the operation in this system be "o". The set of elements in the system will be

$$\{I, R, S, T\}.$$

The rotations are illustrated below.

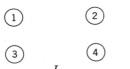

I

Tires remain unchanged

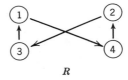

R

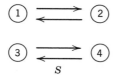

S

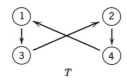

T

   a. Make an operation table for this system.
   b. Which rotation is the identity element?

7. Verify the associative law for the system in Problem 6 by giving the truth value of the following statements:

   a. $Ro(SoT) = (RoS)oT$,
   b. $To(ToS) = (ToT)oS$,
   c. $To(RoI) = (ToR)oI$,
   d. $So(RoT) = (SoR)oT$,
   e. $So(SoT) = (SoS)oT$.

8. In the system in Problem 6 what is the inverse of

    a. *R*?   b. *T*?   c. *S*?

9. Consider the checkerboard in the following figure.

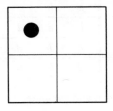

Call a move of the checker across or back, "*H*", a move up or down, "*V*", a diagonal move, "*D*", and no move, "*N*". Complete the table below.

	N	H	V	D
N				D
H		N		V
V		D		
D			H	

Is the operation commutative? Is there an identity element; what is it? Does every element have an inverse; what is it? Is the operation associative? Is the system a group?

ANSWERS TO SELECTED EXERCISES

EXERCISE 1.1

1. {April, August}. 3. {Nevada, New Hampshire, New Jersey, New Mexico, New York, North Carolina, North Dakota}. 5. {Arizona, California, New Mexico, Texas}. 7. {Sunday, Monday, Tuesday, Wednesday, Thursday, Friday, Saturday}. 11. {Maine, New Hampshire, Mass., Rhode Island, Conn., New York, New Jersey, Delaware, Maryland, Virginia, N. Carolina, S. Carolina, Georgia, Florida}. 13. {Washington, Idaho, Montana, N. Dakota, Minnesota, Michigan, New York, Vermont, N. Hampshire, Maine, Alaska}. 15. Set of states that border Pacific Ocean. 17. Set of months of the year with exactly 31 days. 20. a, d. 23. There are six possible answers. One is

$$\begin{array}{ccc} \star & \triangle & \square \\ \updownarrow & \updownarrow & \updownarrow \\ \triangledown & \phi & \ominus \end{array}$$

27. $A = D$; $E = F$. 29. $A \sim C \sim F$; $B \sim D \sim E$. 31. a. $=$; b $\neq$; c. $\sim$ and $\neq$; d. $\neq$; e. $\neq$. 32. No. 33. $A \sim C$.

EXERCISE 1.2

1. There are 8 possible subsets; three are: {11}, {12}, {13}. 5. a. $\emptyset$; b. {6, 12}; c. {8, 10, 12, 14}. 8. a. 2^2; b. 2^4; c. 2^5; d. 2^{300}. 9. b; c; d. 10. a; b; c; d.

EXERCISE 1.3

1. There are many possible answers. Examples include the following: a. {animals}; b. {plants}.
3.

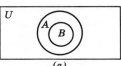

(a)

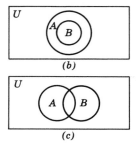

5. There are many possible answers. Examples include the following: a. {students at San Diego State College}; b. {automobiles}; c. {cups}; d. {sweaters}.

7.

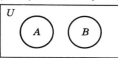

9.

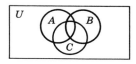

EXERCISE 1.4

1. a. 4; b. 5; c. 8.
2. **Finite:** a, c, d, e, f, g, h. **Infinite:** b, i.
3. 1   2   3   ·   ·   ·   *n*

   ↕   ↕   ↕   ↕

   1   3   5   ·   ·   · $(2n - 1)$

where $n = \{1, 2, 3, \cdots\}$.

5. a. There are many possible answers, one is {1, 2, 3}. b. {"1", "2", "3", "4", "5", "6", "7"}. c. There are many possible answers. One is {1, 2, 3, 4, 5}.

EXERCISE 1.5

1. a. 4; b. 9; c. 0; d. 6; e. 2.   2. a. {1, 2, 3, 4, 6, 8, 10}; b. {1, 2, 3, 4, 5, 6, 9, 12}; c. {2, 3, 4, 6, 8, 9, 10, 12}; d. {2, 4, 6}; e. {3, 6}; f. {6}; g. {1, 2, 3, 4, 5, 6, 8, 9, 10, 12}; h. {1, 2, 3, 4, 5, 6, 8, 9, 10, 12}; i. {1, 2, 3, 4, 5, 6}. 3. a. ∅; b. P; c. $P \cap Q$; d. $P \cap Q$ or $P \cap R$. 4. a. {b, c, d, e}; b. {d} or {e}; c. {c, d}. 5. a. A set consisting of all the elements of sets A and B. b. B. c. A set consisting of all the elements in set A or in set B or in both sets A and B. d. A or B. 7. a. Set of all elementary school teachers who have visited either Mexico or Canada or both countries. b. Set of all elementary school teachers who have visited both Mexico and Canada. 9. a. U; b. U; c. A; d. A; e. A; f. ∅; g. ∅; h. B. 11. a. {all males}; b. {all human beings 21 years of age or older}; c. {all single persons}; d. {all married persons}. 13. a, d, e, g.

EXERCISE 1.6

1. (d, d), (d, o), (d, g), (o, d), (o, o), (o, g), (g, d), (g, o), (g, g). 3. b, d. 4. {$(x, 1)$, $(x, 2)$, $(y, 1)$, $(y, 2)$, $(z, 1)$, $(z, 2)$, $(w, 1)$, $(w, 2)$}. 7. 6. 8. $5 \times n$. 9. $n \times m$. 10. no. 11. yes.

EXERCISE 1.7

2. a. $\{1,2,3,4,5,6,7\}$; b. $\{1,2,3,4,5,6,7,8\}$; c. $\{1,3,5,7\}$. 3. a. $\{1,3,5,7,9\}$; b. $\{0,1,2,3,4,5,7,8,9\}$; c. $\{0,2,3,4,6,9\}$; d. $\{6\}$; e. $\{(3,4),(3,8),(3,12),(3,16),$ $(6,4),(6,8),(6,12),(6,16),(9,4),(9,8),(9,12),(9,16)\}$; f. $\{4,8\}$; g. $\emptyset$.

EXERCISE 2.1

1. Statement; true. 3. Not a statement. 5. Statement, false. 7. Not a statement. 9. Statement, false. 11. **Conjunction:** The sky is blue and the grass is green. **Disjunction:** The sky is blue or the grass is green. 17. Dogs do not have four legs. 19. Water is not wet. 21. **Hypotheses:** I go skiing; **Conclusion:** I shall have fun. 27. a. $\sim p$; b. $p \vee \sim q$; c. $q \rightarrow \sim p$; d. $q \wedge p$.

EXERCISE 2.2

1. Tautology. 3. Tautology. 5. Not a tautology. 7. Tautology. 9. Not a tautology. 11. We shall have a test on Friday. 13. Reflexive; symmetric; transitive; equivalence relation. 15. Transitive. 17. Transitive. 18. a. $\sim [p \wedge (\sim p)]$; b. $[p \wedge (p \rightarrow q)] \rightarrow q$; c. $[(p \rightarrow q) \wedge (q \rightarrow r)] \rightarrow (p \rightarrow r)$.

EXERCISE 2.3

1. **Converse:** If Peggy and Patty have the same birthday, then they are twins. **Inverse:** If Peggy and Patty are not twins, then they do not have the same birthday. **Contrapositive:** If Peggy and Patty do not have the same birthday, then they are not twins.

9.

p	q	$p \wedge q$	$\sim (p \wedge q)$	$(\sim p) \vee (\sim q)$
T	T	T	F	F
T	F	F	T	T
F	T	F	T	T
F	F	F	T	T

12. Yes.

EXERCISE 2.4

1. $q \rightarrow \sim s$, is true; q, is true; therefore $\sim s$, is true by the law of detachment; since $\sim s$ is true, s is false. 3. $p \vee q$ is true; $\sim p$ is true; therefore p is false and q is true because $p \vee q$ is true and p is false. 5. $p \rightarrow r$ is true by hypotheses; p is true by hypotheses; therefore r is true by the law of detachment. 7. Let: p: *ABCD* is a square; q: *ABCD* is a rectangle; r: *ABCD* is a rhombus. It is given that $p \rightarrow q$, $q \vee r$, and $\sim r$ are true. We are to prove that q is true. q is true because $q \vee r$ is true and r is false, hence q must be true. 9. Let: p: *ABCD* is a rectangle; q: *ABCD* is a parallelogram; r: *ABCD* is a quadrilateral. $p \wedge q$, $p \rightarrow q$ and $q \rightarrow r$ are given true. We are to prove that $q \vee r$ is true. Since $p \wedge q$ is given true, p and q are both true. Therefore $q \vee r$ is true because a disjunction is true if one of its components are true.

EXERCISE 3.1

1. a. $\{1,2,3,4,8\}$; b. $\{a,b,c,g\}$; c. $\{2,4,6,8,10\}$; d. $\{1,3,5,7,9\}$; e. $\{a,c,h,m,$

r}; f. {a, c, e, l, p}. 3. Zero; there is no greatest element. 6. Addition, subtraction, multiplication and division. 7. Addition and multiplication. 9. Natural numbers. 10. a. 10; b. none; c. 54; d. 17. 13. a. 10; b. 13; c. 15; d. 20.

EXERCISE 3.2

1. Commutative property of addition. 2. Additive identity. 3. Associative property of addition. 4. Additive identity. 5. Commutative property of addition. 6. Cancellation property of addition. 9. Zero. 10. $2 + n < 6 + n$. 11. a, b. 12. a, b, c, d. 13. a. Identity for addition; b. Associative property of addition; c. Associative and commutative properties of addition. 16. Associative and commutative properties of addition. 17. a, b. 20. a is justified; b and c are not.

EXERCISE 3.3

6. a. Commutative property of multiplication; b. Associative property of multiplication; c. Commutative property of multiplication; d. Multiplicative identity; e. Cancellation property of multiplication. 7. a. $(2 \times 5) + (2 \times 8)$; b. $(7 \times 16) + (7 \times 34)$; c. $(14 \times 5) + (14 \times 9)$; d. $(28 \times 7) + (28 \times 16)$. 9. $2 \times n < 6 \times n$. 10. a, b, d. 12. $5 \times 0 = 0$; $7 \times 0 = 0$; $9 \times 0 = 0$; no. 15. Although at first glance one would say $51 \times 51 = 2601$ different combinations, this is not so unless you consider, for example, a cone with a chocolate and a strawberry dip as different from a cone with a strawberry and a chocolate dip. If you consider these cones as the same, there are $51 + 50 + \cdots + 1 = 1326$ different combinations.

EXERCISE 3.4

1. a. Walking five blocks north; b. taking off a sweater; c. erasing "4"; d. picking up the cards; e. lowering the left hand; f. opening the door. 2. b, c, d. 3. Subtraction. 4. Division.

5. $(a + b) + c = a + (b + c)$ Associative property of addition.
           $= a + (c + b)$ Commutative property of addition.
           $= (c + b) + a$ Commutative property of addition.

7. $ac + cb$ $= ca + cb$ Commutative property of multiplication.
           $= c(a + b)$ Distributive property.
           $= c(b + a)$ Commutative proprty of addition.

9. a $= b$ Given true.
   $a + c$ $= a + c$ Reflexive property of equality.
           $= b + c$ Substitution principle.
           $= b + d$ Substitution principle.

EXERCISE 3.5

1. a, c, d, g, i. 2. a. Distributive property of multiplication over addition; b. Distributive property of multiplication over subtraction; c. Distributive property of division over substraction; d. Distributive property of division over addition; e. Distributive property of multiplication over addition; f. Distributive property of multiplication over subtraction; g. Distributive property of multiplication over addition. 3. a, c, e. 5. a. $101 - 84 = 17$, $101 - 17 = 84$; b. $90 - 54 = 36$, $90 - 36 = 54$; c. $39 - 20 = 19$, $39 - 19 = 20$; d. $83 - 36 = 47$, $83 - 47 = 36$.

EXERCISE 4.1

3. a. 1956; b. 1510; c. 1776; d. 1969.
4. a. MDCCLXXVI; b. MCMLII; c. MCMLXIX; d. MCMXIX.

EXERCISE 4.2

2. Ten. 3. a. $(4 \times 10^2) + (8 \times 10^1) + (6 \times 10^0)$. 4. a. 2^4; b. 5^3; c. 3^5; d. 7^6. 5. a.
1; b. 1; c. 1; d. 1; e. 1; f. 1. 6. a. 4×1; b. 4×10^3; c. 4×10^6; d. 4×10; e. $4 \times$
10^2; f. 4×10^5. 7. a. 10,000,000; b. 10,000; c. 100,000,000; d. 1000; e. 1,000,000;
f. 100. 8. a. 321,760; b. 40,201; c. 530,000; d. 7010; e. 800,000. 10. a. 10^2; b. 10^6;
c. 10^7; d. 10^4; e. 10^9.

EXERCISE 4.3

5. 16. 6. 24. 7. a. 10; b. 12; c. 20. 9. a. 18; b. 57; c. 92; d. 455; e. 1049; f. 820.
10. a. 42; b. 114; c. 131; d. 105; e. 176; f. 1233. (all base eight) 11. a. 7777; b.
4444; c. 6666. 12. a. $>$; b. $<$; c. $<$. 13. a. 17; b. 59; c. 25; d. 224. 14. a. 12; b.
14; c. 31; d. 43; e. 100; f. 244; g. 1021; h. 2020; i. 10312. (all base five) 15. a. 19; b.
28; c. 24; d. 148; e. 82; f. 40; g. 7; h. 34; i. 1140. 17. a. 2χ; b. 12ε; c. $1\varepsilon 9$; d. $1\chi\varepsilon$.
(all base twelve) 18. a. $<$; b. $=$; c. $<$; d. $<$. 19. a. 4×10^2; b. 4×1; c. 4×1;
d. $4 \times$ eight; e. $4 \times$ twelve; f. $4 \times$ six^2.

EXERCISE 4.4

3. a. 47; b. 15; c. 428; d. 3069. 5. a. $54_{(eight)}$; b. $412_{(eight)}$; c. $777_{(eight)}$; d.
$531_{(eight)}$. 6. a. $111,011_{(two)}$; b. $110,100_{(eight)}$; c. $1,000,000_{(two)}$; d. $11,100,110_{(two)}$.
7. a. $=$; b. $<$; c. $>$; d. $<$. 9. $10_{(two)}$; $10_{(eight)}$.

EXERCISE 5.1

1. a. Associative property of addition; b. Commutative property of addition; c.
Commutative property of addition. 2. $140_{(eight)}$. 3. $162_{(eight)}$. 4. $1004_{(five)}$. 5.
$11,111_{(two)}$. 6. $1092_{(twelve)}$. 7. $1321_{(six)}$. 8. $230_{(eight)}$. 9. $262_{(eight)}$. 10. $535_{(twelve)}$.
11. $11_{(two)}$.

EXERCISE 5.2

1. $2104_{(eight)}$; $3276_{(twelve)}$; $11336_{(eight)}$; $36287_{(twelve)}$. 2. a. Multiplicative identity;
b. Distributive property of multiplication over addition; c. Basic sums; d. Com-
mutative property of multiplication. 3. a. Multiplicative identity; b. Distributive
property; c. Basic sums; d. Multiplicative identity; e. Distributive property; f.
Basic sums; g. Commutative property of multiplication. 4. a. Commutative property of multiplication; b. Associative property of multiplication; c. Commutative
property of multiplication. 5. $60 \times 64 = 3840$. 8. Quotient: $63_{(eight)}$; remainder:
$1_{(eight)}$. 9. Quotient: $108_{(twelve)}$; remainder: $4_{(twelve)}$. 10. Quotient: $30_{(five)}$; remainder; $22_{(five)}$. 11. Quotient: $10_{(two)}$; remainder: $1_{(two)}$.

EXERCISE 6.1

1. a. **Y**; b. **L**; c. **U**; d. **R**; e. **D**; f. **J**; g. **C**. 2. a. *L*; b. *C*; d. *R*; d. *L*. 4. True: a; False:
b, c, d. 5. c. 6. Line. 7. 6. 8. a. one; b. one. 9. a. infinitely many; b. one. 11. c. 12. b.

13. line. 15. line or a point. 16. One. 17. 3. 19. b. c. f. 23. a. *A, B, C, D;* b. *S, P, Q,*
R; c. *O;* d. ∅.

EXERCISE 6.2

2. a. 3. a. *A;* b. interior; c. interior except for point *A.* 4. a. $\overrightarrow{PS}$; b. $\overline{PS}$; c. $\overleftrightarrow{PS}$. 5. a, d,
e. 13. a. *J, L, N;* b. *Z, H;* c. *R, H, P, Q, Z;* d. *A, Y, J, N, C, L, B;* e. *S, T, V, K, W, X.*
15.

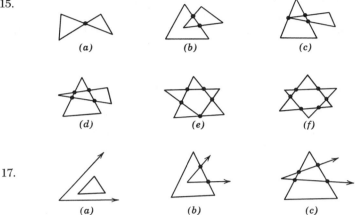

(a)　　　　　　(b)　　　　　　(c)

(d)　　　　　　(e)　　　　　　(f)

17.

(a)　　　　　　(b)　　　　　　(c)

EXERCISE 6.3

1. a, f, g, h. 5. 0. 8. None possible. 10. *a, b, e.* 11. *a, b, e, g, h.* 12. *b, e.* 13. *a, c, e,*
f, g.

EXERCISE 6.4

1. $\overline{AB} \cong \overline{EF}$; $\overline{KL} \cong \overline{GH}$. 4. a. $\overline{CD} \cong \overline{PQ}$; b. $\overline{AB} \cong \overline{EF}$. 5. 2 6. Center

EXERCISE 6.5

1. a. 2. None. 3. $\overline{AB}$ and $\overline{ZY}$; $\overline{AC}$ and $\overline{ZX}$; $\overline{BC}$ and $\overline{YX}$; ∠ *ABC* and ∠ *ZYX;* ∠
ACB and ∠ *ZXY;* ∠ *BAC* and ∠ *YZX.*

EXERCISE 7.1

1. a, c. 2. a. $7 + n = 16$; b. $9 + n = 14$; c. $n - 20 = 60$; d. $n + 12 > 46$; e. $7 +$
$5n < 69$. 3. a. {91}; b. {4, 5, 6, . . .}; c. {24, 25, . . .}; d. {4}; e. {4, 5, 6, . . ., 18}
(0, 1, 2, and 3 are not solutions because if $K = 0$, 1, 2, or 3, then $k - 4$ is not the
name of a whole number; f. {0, 1, . . ., 17}; g. {7, 8, . . ., 17}; h. {13, 14, . . .}.
7. a. 8. One. 14. Truth set.

EXERCISE 7.2

1. {5, 6, 7, . . .}. 3. {0, 1, 2, 3, 4, 5, 6}. 5. {10, 11, 12, . . ., 26}. 7. {19, 20, . . ., 47}.
9. {0, 1, 2, . . .}.

10.

```
  ←——•—•—•—•—•—•⎯•—•—•—•—•——→
     0  1  2  3  4  5  6  7  8  9  10
```

12.

23. The boy weighs less than 120 pounds. 24. $4750.

EXERCISE 7.3

2. $\{(4,5),(5,4)\}$. 3. $\{(5,2),(4,1)\}$. 4. $\{(1,5),(2,4),(2,5),(3,4),(3,5),(4,2),(4,3),$
$(4,4),(4,5),(5,1),(5,2),(5,3),(5,4),(5,5)\}$. 6. $\{(1,3),(1,4),(1,5),(2,5)\}$. 12. $\{(0,$
$9),(1,8),(2,7),(3,6),(4,5),(5,4),(6,3),(7,2),(8,1),(9,0)\}$.

13. $\left\{\begin{array}{l}(0,0),(0,1),\ldots,(0,11),\\(1,0),(1,1),\ldots,(1,9),\\(2,0),(2,1),\ldots,(2,7),\\(3,0),(3,1),\ldots,(3,5),\\(4,0),(4,1),\ldots,(4,3),\\(5,0),(5,1)\end{array}\right\}$

EXERCISE 8.1

3. a. $4^2 = 16$; b. $7^2 = 49$; c. $12^2 = 144$; d. $39^2 = 1521$. 4. a. 120; b. 666; c. 5050;
d. 378; e. 1485; f. 20100. 8. a. *E;* b. *O;* c. *E;* d. *E.* 9. Let the two odd numbers be
represented by $2k + 1$ and $2n + 1$. Then
$$(2k + 1) \times (2n + 1) = (2k \times 2n) + 2k + 2n + 1$$
$$= 4kn + 2k + 2n + 1$$
$$= 2(2kn + k + n) + 1.$$
But this is of the form $2m + 1$, an odd number.
13. Because it has an even factor. 14. Odd. 15. Odd. 16. a, c, e, f, g. 17. 1. 18. 1.
19. The even numbers are closed under multiplication and addition. The odd
numbers are closed under multiplication.

EXERCISE 8.2

2. 2. 3. $\{2, 3, 4, \ldots\}$. 6. a, c. e. 10. b, c, d, f. 11. a. 1, 2, 3, 4, 6, 12; b. 1, 17; c. 1,
3, 5, 9, 15, 45; d. 1, 2, 3, 4, 6, 9, 12, 18, 36; e. 1, 29; f. 1, 2, 3, 6, 9, 18. 13. a. $8^2 +$
3^2; b. $8^2 + 5^2$; c. $9^2 + 4^2$; d. $6^2 + 5^2$.

EXERCISE 8.3.

1. a. 2, 3; b. 5, 73; c. 2, 3; d. 2, 101. 2. a. 2^2; b. $2^2 \times 11^2$; c. 5×7^2; d. $3 \times 11 \times$
101; e. $7 \times 11 \times 13$; f. $2^2 \times 7 \times 5^2 \times 31$. 5. a, b, i. 6. b, c, d, f, h, i. 7. none. 8. b, i.
11. 1, 2, 3, 5, 6, 9, 10, 15, 18, 25, 27, 30, 45, 50, 54, 75, 90, 135, 150, 225, 270,
450, 625, 1350. 15. a. 421; b. 23; c. 11; d. 11; e. 61; f. 337. 16. a, b. 17. a. 1; b. 1;
c. 1; d. $>$; e. $>$. 19. 7^2.

EXERCISE 8.4

2. 1, 2, 4, 7, 14, 28. 3. 1, 2, 3, 4, 6, 12. 4. a. 15; b. 7; c. 6; d. 1; e. 36; f. 4. 7. a. 6;
b. 8; c. 18; d. *n.* 9. 1. 11. a. 36; b. 78; c. 252; d. 108; e. 3333; f. 375. 12. Their product. 13. a. 144; b. 108; c. 672; d. 36; e. 504; f. 1890.

EXERCISE 9.1

1. a. $(1,4)$; b. $(10,14)$; c. $(4,8)$. 2. a. $(3,4)$; b. $(4,14)$; c. $(4,8)$. 11. a. $\frac{2}{3}$; b. $\frac{1}{3}$; c. $\frac{3}{13}$;
d. $\frac{9}{37}$; e. $\frac{3}{8}$; f. $\frac{13}{10}$. 12. b, d, e. 14. a, c. 15. a. 75; b. 120; c. 1152; d. 16; e. 192; f. 75.

EXERCISE 9.2

2. a. $>$; b. $<$; c. $>$. 5. a. $=$; b. $<$; c. $>$; d. $<$; e. $=$; f. $>$.

EXERCISE 9.3.

1. a. $\frac{11}{15}$; b. $\frac{5}{2}$; c. $\frac{11}{9}$; d. $\frac{23}{23}$; e. $\frac{23}{12}$; f. $\frac{37}{24}$; g. $\frac{53}{24}$; h. $\frac{29}{16}$. 2. a. $\frac{1}{4}$; b. $\frac{1}{16}$; c. $\frac{5}{8}$; d. $\frac{19}{24}$; e. $\frac{1}{5}$; f. $\frac{1}{4}$. 9. a. $\frac{5}{3}$; b. $\frac{1}{3}$; c. $\frac{1}{8}$; d. $\frac{0}{12}$. 10. a. $\frac{7}{12}$; b. $\frac{11}{24}$; c. $\frac{15}{16}$; d. $\frac{30}{6}$.

EXERCISE 9.4

1. a. $\frac{1}{3}$; b. $\frac{2}{5}$; c. $\frac{1}{15}$; d. $\frac{9}{4}$; e. $\frac{1}{8}$; f. $\frac{7}{20}$. 5. a. $\frac{6}{5}$; b. $\frac{8}{3}$; c. $\frac{7}{8}$; d. $\frac{1}{3}$; e. $\frac{4}{3}$; f. $\frac{27}{19}$; g. $\frac{5}{2}$; h. $\frac{7}{12}$. 7. a. $\frac{8}{5}$; b. $\frac{1}{4}$; c. $\frac{3}{2}$; d. $\frac{8}{3}$; e. $\frac{16}{17}$; f. $\frac{1}{4}$. 8. a. Multiplicative inverses; b. Distributive property; c. Associative property of multiplication; d. Distributive property. 10. Definition of division. 11. Closure for multiplication. 12. Associative property of multiplication. 13. Multiplicative inverses and multiplicative identity.

EXERCISE 9.5

3. a. $\frac{7}{8}$; b. $\frac{3}{5}$; c. $\frac{17}{24}$; d. $\frac{18}{3}$; e. $\frac{242}{15}$; f. $\frac{4 \cdot 2}{9}$. 4. a. $5 \div 12$; b. $7 \div 16$; c. $9 \div 2$; d. $342 \div 12$; e. $216 \div 512$; f. $42 \div 7$. 6. a. $\frac{4}{3}$; b. $\frac{5}{6}$; c. $\frac{203}{450}$; d. $\frac{27}{20}$. 7. a. $6\frac{3}{4}$; b. $3\frac{1}{4}$; c. $9\frac{1}{2}$; d. $5\frac{5}{8}$; e. $1\frac{1}{2}$; f. $5\frac{17}{24}$. 8. a, b, c, e, f.

EXERCISE 9.6.

1. a, d, e, f. 2. a. 0.75; b. 0.24; c. 0.184; d. 0.074; e. 0.6; f. 0.0175. 3. a. $\frac{21}{500}$; b. $\frac{1}{4}$; c. $\frac{41}{25}$; d. $\frac{946}{25}$; e. $\frac{2013}{1000}$; f. $\frac{801}{200}$. 5. b. 0.6; c. 0.4375; d. 0.48; e. 0.984; f. 0.085. 6. a, d, e.

EXERCISE 10.1

1. a, b, e. 4. Addition, Multiplication. 5. a. 4; b. 8; c. 1; d. 2; e. 10; f. 88. 10. a. $\frac{5}{3}$; b. $\frac{19}{7}$; c. $\frac{1}{2}$; d. $\frac{27}{3}$; e. $\frac{9}{6}$; f. $\frac{3}{12}$.

EXERCISE 10.2

6. a. Commutative property of addition; b. Distributive property; c. Associative property of multiplication; d. Multiplicative inverses. 7. 1. 9. 0. 10. 0. 11. No. 12. Addition, multiplication, and division, except by zero. 13. Yes. 18. $\frac{76}{8}$. 19. 0.

EXERCISE 11.1

1. a. $+78$; b. -15; c. $+5$; d. $+212$; e. $+32$. 2. a. $+29,028$; b. -1286; c. -280; d. $+14,210$. 3. a. -6; b. $+14$; c. 0; d. $+7$; e. $-c$; f. $-(m+n)$; g. -15; h. $-ab$; i. $+p$. 4. a. 3; b. 7; c. 18; d. 0; e. 9; f. 14; g. 94; h. 17; i. 42. 5. a. $+13$; b. -11; c. $+8$; d. -3; e. 0; f. $+5$. 7. a. $<$; b. $<$; c. $>$; d. $<$; e. $<$; f. $>$. 12. a. $+4$, -4; b. $+7$, -7; c. $+6$, -6; d. $+9$, -9; e, 0; f. $+2$, -2; g. $+17$, -17; h. $+24$, -24. 13. a. 6; b. 7; c. 12.

EXERCISE 11.2

1. a. $+2$; b. $+4$; c. $+12$; d. $+9$; e. $+13$; f. $+5$; g. -12; h. $^+12$; i. -19; j. -17. 2. a. $^+16$; b. $+10$; c. -24; d. -25; e. -5; f. -13; g. -6; h. $+24$; i. -11; j. $+13$. 5. Positive. 6. Negative. 7. Negative. 8. Positive. 10. a. $^+3 + {}^+7$; b. $-9 + {}^+4$; c. $-16 + {}^-14$; d. $+13 + {}^+7$. 11. $+56°$. 12. $24°$. 13. $112°$. 14. -120. 15. $\$85$.

EXERCISE 11.3

1. a. negative; b. positive; c. positive; d. negative. 2. a. -168; b. $+256$; c. $+228$; d.

−144; e. +130; f. −666; g. +2352; h. +490. 4. a. +9; b. −6; c. +12; d. +9. 5. a. +3; b. +13; c. −3; d. −64; e. +21; f. −35.

EXERCISE 11.4

1. +10. 2. −9. 3. +1. 4. $\{-3, -2, -1, 0, 1, \ldots\}$. 5. $\{-3, -2, -1, 0, +1, +2\}$. 6. $\{6, 7, 8, \ldots, 18\}$. 7. $\{-2, -1\}$. 8. $\{\ldots, -1, 0, 1, 2, 3\}$. 9. $\{-5, -4, -3, \ldots\}$. 10. $\{\ldots, -14, -13\}$.

EXERCISE 12.1

1. b, c, e. 2. a, b, c, d. 3. a. $\frac{-1}{12}$; b. $\frac{1}{8}$; c. $\frac{-7}{12}$; d. $\frac{-3}{16}$; e. $\frac{11}{12}$; f. $\frac{3}{20}$.

EXERCISE 12.2

1. a. $\frac{-8}{9}$; b. $\frac{-16}{9}$; c. $\frac{4}{3}$; d. $\frac{43}{18}$; e. $\frac{-2}{7}$; f. $\frac{-9}{7}$. 2. a. $\frac{-1}{2}$; b. $\frac{+7}{16}$; c. $\frac{-3}{12}$; d. $\frac{7}{-15}$; e. $\frac{-5}{1}$; f. $\frac{3}{7}$. 3. True. 4. False. 5. True. 6. True 7. False. 8. True. 9. $\frac{-a}{b}, \frac{a}{-b}, -\frac{+a}{b}$. 10. 1. 11. 0.

EXERCISE 12.3

3. $ab > O$. 4. $ca < cb$. 5. $ab < O$. 6. $r^2 > O$. 8. a. $\frac{-1}{6}$; b. $\frac{-11}{24}$; c. $\frac{1}{24}$; d. $\frac{23}{20}$; e. $\frac{-16}{21}$; f. $\frac{-21}{16}$; g. 1; h. 4.

EXERCISE 12.4

1. Addition, subtraction, multiplication, and division, except by zero. 2. Yes. 4. b. 5. 0. 6. 0.

EXERCISE 13.1

2. b, c, d, f, h. 3. Yes. Closure property for multiplication. 4. No. 5. Let $\frac{a}{b}$ represent a rational number expressed as a fraction in simplest form; that is, a and b are relatively prime. Let us assume that

$$3 = \frac{a^2}{b^2}.$$

Then $3b^2 = a^2$. Now, since $3b^2 = a^2$, a^2 is a multiple of 3, and hence a is a multiple of 3. Let $a = 3n$. Then $a^2 = 9n^2$, and

$$3b^2 = 9n^2, \text{ or } b^2 = 3n^2.$$

Hence b^2 is a multiple of 3, and b is a multiple of 3. However, this contradicts our assumption that $\frac{a}{b}$ is in simplest form, and thus $\sqrt{3}$ cannot be represented as a rational number.

EXERCISE 14.1

1. 1; 0. 2. All except zero. 3. Yes. 4. a. 4; b. O; c. 1; d. 4; e. 3; f. 3. 6. Yes. 7. 0. 8. a. 1; b. 4; c. 5; d. 2. 12. a. 2 P.M.; b. 1 P.M.; c. 9 A.M.; d. 4 P.M. 14. a. O; b. 2; c. 3. 15. 2.

EXERCISE 14.2

1. a. 5; b. R_0; c. X; d. d; e. 1; f. d; g. 5; h. R_3; i. d; j. Y; k. R_0; l. b. 5. a. 5; b. a; c. R_2.

EXERCISE 14.3

1.

*	I	V
I	I	V
V	V	I

Properties: Closure; commutative; Associative; Identity; Inverses.

2.

*	R_0	R_1	R_2	V_1	V_2	V_3
R_0	R_0	R_1	R_2	V_1	V_2	V_3
R_1	R_1	R_2	R_0	V_2	V_3	V_1
R_2	R_2	R_0	R_1	V_3	V_1	V_2
V_1	V_1	V_3	V_2	R_0	R_2	R_1
V_2	V_2	V_1	V_3	R_1	R_0	R_2
V_3	V_3	V_2	V_1	R_2	R_1	R_0

R_0, R_1, R_2, V_1, V_2, and V_3 are defined as shown below:

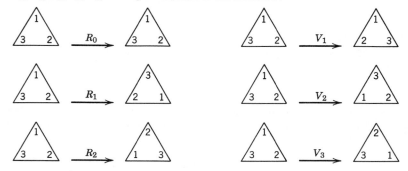

This system is a group, but not a commutative group.

3. R_0, R_1, R_2, R_3, H, V, D', and D are defined as shown below:

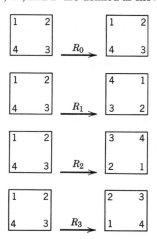

$$\begin{array}{cc} 1 & 2 \\ 4 & 3 \end{array} \quad \xrightarrow{H} \quad \begin{array}{cc} 4 & 3 \\ 1 & 2 \end{array}$$

$$\begin{array}{cc} 1 & 2 \\ 4 & 3 \end{array} \quad \xrightarrow{V} \quad \begin{array}{cc} 2 & 1 \\ 3 & 4 \end{array}$$

$$\begin{array}{cc} 1 & 2 \\ 4 & 3 \end{array} \quad \xrightarrow{D} \quad \begin{array}{cc} 3 & 2 \\ 4 & 1 \end{array}$$

$$\begin{array}{cc} 1 & 2 \\ 4 & 3 \end{array} \quad \xrightarrow{D'} \quad \begin{array}{cc} 1 & 4 \\ 2 & 3 \end{array}$$

$*$	R_0	R_1	R_2	R_3	H	V	D	D'
R_0	R_0	R_1	R_2	R_3	H	V	D	D'
R_1	R_1	R_2	R_3	R_0	D	D'	V	H
R_2	R_2	R_3	R_0	R_1	V	H	D'	D
R_3	R_3	R_0	R_1	R_2	D'	D	H	V
H	H	D'	V	D	R_0	R_2	R_3	R_1
V	V	D	H	D'	R_2	R_0	R_1	R_3
D	D	H	D'	V	R_1	R_3	R_0	R_2
D'	D'	V	D	H	R_3	R_1	R_2	R_0

This system is a group, but not a commutative group. 4. No. d and c do not have inverses. 5. a. V; b. Y; c. V.

6. a.

$\bigcirc$	I	R	S	T
I	I	R	S	T
R	R	S	T	I
S	S	T	I	R
T	T	I	R	S

b. I.

8. a. T; b. R; c. S.

9.

·	N	H	V	D
N	N	H	V	D
H	H	N	D	V
V	V	D	N	H
D	D	V	H	N

This operation is commutative; the identity is N; each element has an inverse; the operation is associative. This system is a commutative group.

Some Common Mathematical Symbols and their Meanings

SET SYMBOLS

$\{\ldots\}$	The set whose elements are $\cdots$.
$\{\ \}$ or ϕ	Empty or null set.
ε	Is an element of.
$\subseteq$	Is a subset of.
$\subset$	Is a proper subset of.
$\cup$	Union.
$\cap$	Intersection.
$N(A)$	Cardinal number of set A.
$\ldots$	And so on.
$\sim$	Equivalent.
X	Cartesian product

RELATION SYMBOLS

$=$	Is equal to or equals.
$\neq$	Is not equal to.
$<$	Is less than.
$\not<$	Is not less than.
$>$	Is greater than.
$\not>$	Is not greater than.
$\cong$	Is congruent to.
$/\!/$	Is parallel to.

LOGIC SYMBOLS

$p \wedge q$	p and q (conjunction).
$p \vee q$	p or q (disjunction).
$p \rightarrow q$	p implies q, or if p then q.
$\sim p$	not p.

GEOMETRIC SYMBOLS

$\overleftrightarrow{AB}$	Line AB.
$\overline{AB}$	Line segment AB.
$\overrightarrow{AB}$	Ray AB.
$\angle ABC$	Angle ABC.
$\overarc{AB}$	Arc AB.
$\triangle ABC$	Triangle ABC.
$\overset{\circ\!\longrightarrow}{AB}$	Half-line AB.

OPERATION SYMBOLS

$+$	Addition.
$-$	Subtraction.
$\times$ or $\cdot$	Multiplication.
$\div$	Division.

Index

Absolute value, 228, 229
Abstract system, 265
Addends, 50
Addition, addends of, 50
    additive inverse, 227, 233, 245, 250, 251, 259
    algorithm, 94–97
    associative property, 52, 196–197, 218, 224, 232, 244, 251, 259–260
    binary operation of, 50, 51
    cancellation property, 52–53, 218
    closure property, 51, 196, 218, 224, 232, 244, 251, 259
    commutative property, 51, 196, 218, 224, 232, 244, 251, 259
    identity element of, 52, 197, 218, 224, 233, 244–245, 251, 259
    in modular systems, 258–260
    of fractional numbers, 192–197
    of integers, 230–233
    of rational numbers, 223–224, 242
    of whole numbers, 50–53
    repeated, 55
    sign, 50
    sum, 50
Additive identity, 52, 197, 218, 224, 233, 244–245, 251, 259
Additive inverse, 227, 233, 245, 250, 251, 259

Algorithms, 93–107
    addition, 94–97
    definition, 93
    division, 102–106, 175
    Euclid's, 174–176
    multiplication, 99–102
    subtraction, 97–98
Angle, 120–122
    congruent, 131
    exterior of, 121
    interior of, 121–122
    naming, 120–121
    right, 131–132, 138
    vertex, 120
Arc, 133
Array, 25, 55, 198
Associative property, of addition, 52, 196–197, 218, 224, 232, 244, 251, 259–260
    of intersection of sets, 20–21
    of multiplication, 57–58, 203, 218, 224, 237, 244, 251, 261
    of union of sets, 18–19
Axes, 151–152
    first, 152
    second, 152
    x-axis, 152
    y-axis, 152
Axioms, 30, 108

291

Base, 73–74, 75
Base eight, *see* octal system
Base ten, *see* decimal system of numeration
Base twelve, *see* duodecimal system
Base two, *see* binary system
Bases other than ten, 78–91
    computation in, 96–97, 98, 101–102, 105–
        106
    conversion between, 80–81, 84, 87–89
    number names in, 83, 87, 91
Binary–octal relation, 88–89
Binary operation, 17, 50, 51
Binary relation, 35
Binary system, 86–89, 91
Boundary, 114, 116, 127
Braces, 2

Cancellation property, of addition, 52–53,
        218
    of multiplication, 59, 218
Cardinal number, 15, 47
Cardinality, 15
Carrying, 94–95
Cartesian product, 24–26, 54
Center of a circle, 132
Chain rule, 38
Changing fractions to decimals, 214–215
Circle, 132–133
Circular reasoning, 108–109
Classification of, quadrilaterals, 138–139
    triangles, 138
Closed region, 127
Closure property, of addition, 51, 196, 218,
        224, 232, 244, 251, 259, 267
    of division, 218, 249, 262
    of multiplication, 56, 202, 218, 224, 236,
        244, 251, 260
    of subtraction, 234, 249, 262
    of union of sets, 17
Collinear points, 112
Common denominator, 177, 194
Common factor, 173–174
Common fraction, 183
Common multiple, 177–178
Commutative group, 267, 270
Commutative operation, 18
Commutative property, of addition, 51, 196,
        218, 224, 232, 244, 251, 259
    of intersection of sets, 20
    of multiplication, 56–57, 202, 224, 237,
        244, 251, 260

Commutative property, of union of sets, 18
Complete factorization, 165, 166–167, 171–
        172
Complex fraction, 209
Components, 31
Composite numbers, 161–163
Compound open sentences, 146–148
Compound statements, 30–32
Conclusion of implication, 32
Congruent, 130–131
    angles, 131
    constructing congruent angles, 135–136
    constructing congruent triangles, 136–138
    line segments, 130–131
    triangles, 134–135, 136–138
Conjunction, 30–31, 147–148
    truth table of, 31
Constructing, congruent angles, 135–136
    congruent triangles, 136–138
Contrapositive, 40–42
Converse, 40–42
Coordinate, 48
Counting numbers, 46
Curves, 110, 126–127
    closed, 127
    open, 127
    simple closed, 126–127, 132–133

Dec (χ), 82
Decimal, changing fractions to, 214–215
    fractions, 212–215
    non-terminating, 215
    numbers, 211–212
    terminating, 215
Decimal fractions, 212, 215
Decimal numbers, 211–212
Decimal point, 213
Decimal system of numeration, 74, 76
Deductive system, 43, 108
Denominator, 183
Dense, 222
Described, members of set, 2
Diameter, 132
Difference, 21
Digits, 74, 90
Disjoint sets, 10
Disjunction, 30, 31–32, 147–148
    exclusive, 32
    inclusive, 32
    truth table of, 32
Distributive property, 27

Distributive property, of division over addition, 67–68
of division over subtraction, 68
of multiplication over addition, 59–60, 204, 218, 224, 237–238, 245, 251, 261
of multiplication over subtraction, 67, 218
Dividend, 103
Divisibility property of a sum, 168
Divisibility tests, 168–170
by 2, 168
by 3, 169–170
by 5, 169
by 9, 169–170
by 10, 169
Divisible, 103
Division, algorithm, 102–106, 175
and zero, 65–66
as repeated subtraction, 102
closure, 218, 249, 262
distributive property, 67–68
dividend, 103
divisor, 103
in modular systems, 262
inverse of multiplication, 63, 102, 204, 238, 249, 262
of fractional numbers, 204–206
of integers, 238
of rational numbers, 249
of whole numbers, 64–68
properties of, 66–68
quotient, 103
remainder, 103
Divisor, 103
Domain, 142, 144
Duodecimal system, 82–84

Egyptian system of numeration, 70–73
El (ε), 82
Element, of ordered pair, 23–24
of set, 1
Empty set, 2, 15
Endpoints, of line segment, 110
of ray, 120
Equal sets, 3
Equality, 3, 24, 142, 186–187, 219–220
Equation, 142
Equiangular triangle, 138
Equilateral triangle, 138
Equivalence relation, 35–36
Equivalent open sentences, 144–145
Equivalent sets, 4

Eratosthenes, Sieve of, 162–163
Euclid's algorithm, 174–176
Euler diagrams, 10
Even numbers, 16, 158–160, 176, 263–265
Exclusive, 32
Expanded notation, 76–77, 80–82, 213
Exponents, 75–76
Exterior of an angle, 121

Factor, 54, 103, 163–165
common, 173–174
expression, 163
tree, 164–165
Factorization, complete, 165, 166–167, 171–172
prime, 166–167
Field, 253
Figurate numbers, 155–158
hexagonal, 156
pentagonal, 155–156
square, 155–156
triangular, 155–158
Finite, set, 15–16
system, 258
Formal geometry, 108
Fractions, 180–216
addition, 192–197
and whole numbers, 207, 208
as symbols for division, 208–209
changing to decimals, 214–215
common, 183
complex, 209
decimal, 212–215
definitions, 180–187
denominator, 183
division of, 204–206
equality of, 186–187
improper, 210
multiplication of, 198–204
number line and, 188–190
numerator, 183
ordering, 190–192
proper, 209
properties of, 184–187, 190–192, 196–197, 202, 204
simplest name, 184–185
subtraction of, 194–196
symbol, 181–183, 219
the word, 180; *see also* Non-negative rational numbers; Rational numbers
Frames, 142

Fundamental theorem of arithmetic, 166–167
Geometric space, 109
Geometry, 108–140
  formal, 108
  informal, 108–140
  intuitive, 108
Goldbach, 165
Graph, 48, 148
Graphing, ordered pairs, 151–153
  solution sets, 148–149
Greatest common divisor, 174–176
Greatest common factor, 173–174
Group, 267–274

Half-line, 116
Half-plane, 116
Half-space, 114
Heptagon, 127
Hexagon, 127
Hindu-Arabic system of numeration, 73–75, 79
Hypotheses of implication, 32

Identity element, of addition, 52, 197, 218, 224, 233, 244–245, 251, 259
  of multiplication, 58–59, 201–202, 203–204, 218, 224, 237, 245, 251, 260
Implications, 30, 32–33
  conclusion of, 32
  derived, 40–42
  hypotheses of, 32
  truth table of, 33
Improper fractions, 210
Improper subset, 7
Inclusive, 32
Inequality, 142
Infinite set, 15–16, 46
Informal geometry, 108–140
Integers, 226–240
  absolute value, 228, 229
  addition, 230–233
  additive inverses, 227, 233
  and number line, 227–228
  and whole numbers, 239–240
  division, 238
  multiplication, 235–238
  negative, 227
  opposites, 227, 233
  ordering, 228–229
  positive, 227

Integers, properties, 228–229, 232–233, 234, 236–238
  sign, 227
  subtraction, 233–234
Interior of an angle, 121–122
Intersecting, lines, 112
  planes, 114
Intersection set, 19–21
Intuitive geometry, 108
Inverse, 40–42
Inverse operation, 62–63
Irrational numbers, 255, 256–257
Irrational points, 255
Isosceles triangle, 138

Lattice, 25, 152
Lattice plane, 152
Lattice point, 152
Law of detachment, 39
Law of excluded middle, 37
Law of syllogism, 37
Least common multiple, 176–178
Line(s), 109–110
  intersecting, 112
  parallel, 112
  properties of lines and planes, 111–114
  segment, 110
  skew, 114
Line segment, 110
Listed, 2
Logic, 29–45
Logical reasoning, 30
Logical system, 43
Logically equivalent, 41–42

Mathematical group, 267–274
Mathematical sentences, 141–142
Mathematical systems, 258–276
Member of a set, 1
Mixed numerals, 209–210
Modular systems, 258–263
Multiple, 103, 176
Multiplication, algorithm, 99–102
  and cartesian products, 54–55
  arrays, 55–56
  as repeated addition, 55
  associative property, 57–58, 203, 218, 224, 237, 244, 251, 261
  binary operation, 57
  by ten, 99
  cancellation property, 59, 218

Multiplication, closure property, 56, 202, 218, 224, 236, 244, 251, 260
  commutative property, 56–57, 202, 224, 237, 244, 251, 260
  distributive property, 59–60, 67, 204, 218, 224, 237–238, 245, 251, 261
  factor, 54
  identity element, 58–59, 201–202, 203–204, 218, 224, 237, 245, 251, 260
  in modular systems, 260–261
  multiplicative identity, 58–59, 201–202, 203–204, 218, 224, 237, 245, 251, 260
  multiplicative inverse, 202, 204, 205, 224, 245–246, 251, 260–261
  of fractional numbers, 198–204
  of integers, 235–238
  of rational numbers, 223–224, 242–243, 244–246
  of whole numbers, 54–60
  product, 54
  sign, 57–58
Multiplicative identity, 58–59, 201–202, 203–204, 218, 224, 237, 245, 251, 260
Multiplicative inverse, 202, 204, 205, 224, 245–246, 251, 260–261; *see also* Reciprocal

Natural numbers, 46
Negation, 30, 33
Negative integers, 227
Negative rational numbers, 246
Non-collinear points, 112
Non-commutative groups, 270–274
Non-negative rational numbers, 217–225; *see also* Fractions
Non-terminating decimals, 215
Null set, 2
Number, 13–14
  cardinal, 15, 47
  composite, 161–163
  counting, 46
  decimal, 211–212
  even, 16, 158–160, 176, 263–265
  figurate, 155–158
  irrational, 255, 256
  natural, 46
  negative, 227
  odd, 16, 158–160, 263–265
  pentagonal, 155–156
  positive, 227
  prime, 161–163

Numbers, rational, 217–225, 241–253, 255
  real, 254–257
  square, 155–156
  triangular, 155–158
  whole, 46–69
Number field, 253
Numeration systems, *see* Systems of numeration
Number line, 48
Number line, real, 255–257
Number line and fractions, 188–190
Number line and integers, 227–228
Number of subsets, 7–8
Number sentences, 141–154
Number systems, 252
Number theory, 155–179
Numeral, 13–14
Numerator, 183

Octagon, 127
Octal system, 79–82, 88–89, 91, 96–97, 98, 101–102, 105–106
Odd numbers, 16, 158–160, 263–265
One-to-one correspondence, 3–4, 16, 207–208, 222, 223, 239–240, 257
Open curves, 127
Open sentences, 141, 142, 144–145, 146–148
  compound, 146–148
  equivalent, 144–145
Operation, 17, 48
  addition, 48, 50
  basic, 48
  binary, 17, 50, 51
  commutative, 18, 20, 265
  division, 48, 64–68, 204–206, 238, 249, 262
  intersection, 19–21
  inverse, 62–63
  multiplication, 48, 54–60, 67, 198–202, 235–238, 244–245, 260–261
  primary, 48
  secondary, 48
  subtraction, 48, 63, 64, 194–196, 233–234, 249, 261–262
  union, 17–19
Opposites, 227, 233
Order property, 46–47, 190–192, 228–229, 246–249
Ordered pairs, 23–24, 25, 181–182, 241
  element of, 23–24
  equality of, 24
  graphing of, 151–153

Ordered set, 13
Overlapping sets, 10

Parallel, 112
  lines, 112
  planes, 114–115
Parallelogram, 139
Pentagon, 127
Pentagonal numbers, 155–156
Place value, 74–75, 76, 80, 90, 96
Plane, 111
Point, 109
Polygons, 127
Positive rational numbers, 246
Postulates, 30, 108
Powers of ten, 75–76, 211
Prime factorization, 166–167
Prime numbers, 161–163
  of form 4n + 1, 166
  twin, 166
Product, 54, 163
Product set, 25
Proof, 43–45
  direct, 43–44
  indirect, 44–45
Proper fraction, 209
Proper subset, 7
Properties of lines and planes, 111–114
Properties, associative, of addition, 52, 196–
      197, 218, 224, 232, 244, 251, 259–
      260
  of intersection of sets, 20–21
  of multiplication, 57–58, 203, 218, 224,
      237, 244, 251, 261
  of union of sets, 18–19
  closure, under addition, 51, 196, 218, 224,
      232, 244, 251, 259
    under division, 218, 249, 262
    under multiplication, 56, 202, 218, 224,
      236, 244, 251, 260
    under subtraction, 234, 249, 262
    under union of sets, 17
  commutative, of addition, 51, 196, 218,
      224, 232, 244, 251, 259
    of intersection of sets, 20
    of multiplication, 56–57, 202, 218, 224,
      237, 244, 251, 260
    of union of sets, 18
  distributive, of division over addition, 67–
      68
    of division over subtraction, 68

Properties, of multiplication over addition,
      59–60, 204, 218, 224, 237–238, 245,
      251, 261
  of multiplication over subtraction, 67,
      218

Quadrilateral, 127, 138–139
  classification of, 138–139
  parallelogram, 139
  rectangle, 139
  scalene, 139
  square, 139
  trapezoid, 139
Quotient, 103

Radius, 132
Rational number line, 249–250
Rational numbers, 217–226, 241–253, 255
  addition of, 223–224, 242
  and the whole numbers, 223
  between 0 and 1, 221–222
  comparison of, 246–249
  definitions of, 218–219, 241–242
  division of, 249
  equality of, 219–220
  multiplication of, 223–224, 242–243, 244–
      246
  negative, 246
  non-negative, 217–225
  number line and, 249–250
  operations with, 223–224, 242–243
  ordering, 246–249
  positive, 246
  properties of, 244–246, 251
  subsystems of, 252
  subtraction of, 249; *see also* Fractions
Rational points, 221, 255–256
Ray, 120
Real number line, 255–257
Real number system, 254–257
Real numbers, 254–257
Reciprocal, 202, 204; *see also* Multiplicative
  inverse
Rectangle, 139
Reflexive property, 35
Region, 127
Relations, 35
  binary, 35
  equivalence, 4, 35
Relative complement, 21
Relatively prime, 174

Remainder, 103
Renaming in subtraction, 97–98
Replacement set, 142
Right angle, 131–132, 138
Right triangle, 138
Roman system of numeration, 70–73

Scalene, quadrilateral, 139
   triangle, 138
Sentences, number, 141–154
   open, 141, 142, 144–145, 146–148
   with two variables, 150–151
Separation, of a line, 116
   of a plane, 116
   of space, 114–116
Sets, 1–28
   belongs to, 1, 2
   cardinality of, 15
   cartesian product of, 24
   disjoint, 10
   element of, 1
   empty, 2, 15
   equal, 3
   equality of, 3
   equivalent, 4
   finite, 15–16
   graphs of, 148–149, 151–153
   infinite, 15–16, 46
   intersection, 19–21
   matching, 3–4
   member of, 1
   members described, 2
   members listed, 2
   null, 2
   of counting numbers, 46
   of natural numbers, 46
   of whole numbers, 46
   operations on, 17–22, 24–27
   ordered, 13
   overlapping, 10
   product, 25
   relative complement, 21
   replacement, 142
   solution, 142–144
   standard, 14
   subset of, 6–8
   symbol for, 1–2
   truth, 143
   union, 17–19
   universal, 9
   well-defined, 1

Sign of integer, 227
Simple closed curves, 126–127, 132–133
Simplest name for a fraction, 184–185
Skew lines, 114
Solution, 143
Solution set, 142–144
   graphing, 148–149
Space, 109
Square, 139
Square numbers, 155–156
Square root, 163, 254
Standard set, 14
Statement, 30, 141
   compound, 30–32
Subset, 6–8
   improper, 7
   number of, 7–8
   proper, 7
Substitution principle, 36
Subtraction, algorithm, 97–98
   closure under, 234, 249, 262
   inverse of addition, 63, 97, 249, 261
   of fractional numbers, 194–196
   of integers, 233–234
   of rational numbers, 249
   of whole numbers, 64–68
   principle in Roman numerals, 72
   property, 97
   properties of, 66–68
   renaming in, 97–98
   repeated, 102
Sum, 50
Symbols, absolute value, 228
   addition, 50
   angle, 120
   belongs to a set, 2
   cardinality of set, 15
   cartesian product, 25
   congruent, 131
   conjunction, 31
   disjunction, 31
   empty set, 2
   equals or is equal to, 142
   equivalent sets, 4
   fraction, 182–183, 219, 241
   greatest common divisor, 174
   half-line, 116
   implication, 33
   improper subset, 7
   intersection, 19
   is greater than, 47, 142

Symbols, is greater than or equal to, 64
  is less than, 42, 142
  is member of, 2
  is not a member of, 6
  is not equal to, 142
  line, 110
  line segment, 110
  multiplication, 57–58
  negation, 33
  null set, 2
  ordered pair, 23
  proper subset, 7
  point, 109
  ray, 120
  relation, 35
  relative complement, 21
  set, 2
  subset, 7
    improper, 7
    proper, 7
  triangle, 122
  union, 17
Symmetric property, 35
Systems of numeration, 70–92
  accidentals of, 70
  ancient, 70–73
  bases other than ten, 78–91
  binary, 86–90
  duodecimal, 82–84
  Egyptian, 70–73
  Hindu-Arabic, 73–75, 90
  octal, 78–82, 88–90
  principles of, 70, 71, 72, 75
  Roman, 70–73

Tautology, 36–39
Ten, base of decimal system, 73
  multiples of, 99
  powers of, 75–76, 211
Terminating decimals, 215
Theorems, 30, 62, 108, 166–167, 254–255
Transitive property, 35
Trapezoid, 139
Triangle, 122–123, 127
  angles of, 122
  classification of, 138
  congruent, 134–135, 136–138
  equiangular, 138
  equilateral, 138
  exterior of, 123

Triangle, interior of, 123
  isosceles, 138
  naming, 122
  right, 138
  scalene, 138
  vertex, 122
Triangular numbers, 155–158
Trichotomy principle, 47
Truth set, 143
Truth table, 31
  conjunction, 31
  disjunction, 32
  implication, 33
Truth value, 30

Undefined words, 29–30, 108–109
Union of sets, 17–19
Universal set, 9
Universe, 9

Variable, 142
  domain of, 142
Venn diagram, 10–11, 27
Vertex, of angle, 120
  of triangle, 122

Well-defined, 1
Whole numbers, 46–69
  addition of, 50–53
  and fractions, 207–208
  and rational numbers, 223
  division, 64–66
  multiplication, 54–56
  number line and, 48
  operations of, 48
  order property, 46–47
  properties of addition, 50–53, 218
  properties of division, 66–68
  properties of multiplication, 54–56, 218
  properties of subtraction, 66–68, 218
  proving theorems, 62
  subsystem of rationals, 223
  trichotomy principle, 47

Zero, absolute value of, 228–229
  additive inverse of, 227
  and division, 65–66
  and empty set, 15, 47
  properties of, 48, 62, 177, 229

24935

24995

Willerding

Elementary mathematics